D0914650

JAMES FURMAN KEMP

A.B. Amherst 1881; E.M. Columbia School of Mines 1883; Sc.D. Amherst 1906;
LL.D. McGill 1913.

GEOLOGIST, ENGINEER, EDUCATOR, SPECIALIST IN GEOLOGY AS AN APPLIED SCIENCE, AND ADVISER OF
WIDE EXPERIENCE.

552
K

A
HANDBOOK OF ROCKS

FOR USE WITHOUT THE PETROGRAPHIC MICROSCOPE

By

JAMES FURMAN KEMP

Late Professor of Geology, Columbia University, New York, 1891–1926

SIXTH EDITION

COMPLETELY REVISED AND EDITED

By FRANK F. GROUT

Professor of Geology and Mineralogy,
University of Minnesota

TENTH PRINTING

D. VAN NOSTRAND COMPANY, Inc.

PRINCETON, NEW JERSEY

TORONTO   NEW YORK   LONDON

Wingate College Library

D. VAN NOSTRAND COMPANY, INC.
120 Alexander St., Princeton, New Jersey (*Principal office*)
257 Fourth Avenue, New York 10, New York

D. VAN NOSTRAND COMPANY, LTD.
358, Kensington High Street, London, W.14, England

D. VAN NOSTRAND COMPANY (Canada), LTD.
25 Hollinger Road, Toronto 16, Canada

COPYRIGHT 1896, 1900, 1904, 1908, 1911, 1918
BY J. F. KEMP

———

COPYRIGHT 1927
BY JAMES TAYLOR KEMP

———

SIXTH EDITION

COPYRIGHT © 1940 BY

James Furman Kemp
MEMORIAL FUND

———

All rights in this book are reserved. Without written authorization from D. Van Nostrand Company, Inc., 120 Alexander Street, Princeton, New Jersey, it may not be reproduced in any form in whole or in part (except for quotation in critical articles or reviews), nor may it be used for dramatic, motion-, talking-picture, radio, television or any other similar purpose.

———

*Reprinted June 1942, June 1946
September 1947, January 1949, January 1950
May 1952, December 1954, May 1956, January 1958*

PRINTED IN THE UNITED STATES OF AMERICA
BY LANCASTER PRESS, INC., LANCASTER, PA.

JAMES FURMAN KEMP

FROM Adelphi Academy in Brooklyn to Amherst College, and from Amherst to Columbia School of Mines, encompasses the formative period in the early training of the late Professor James Furman Kemp. In these several institutions a keen appreciation of the serious interests of life was developed, and he came under the inspiring guidance of two of the most distinguished teachers of geologic science in that generation, — Professor B. K. Emerson of Amherst, and Dr. John S. Newberry of Columbia. At Amherst his rare gift for science was soon discovered and a friendship with Emerson began which grew only stronger with time. It was undoubtedly this experience that led to his decision to become a mining engineer. At Columbia, where this purpose was pursued, he soon attracted the attention of Dr. Newberry, who made him his personal assistant, and ultimately, after an additional short period of teaching at Cornell, nominated him as his own successor.

Thus he became head of the Department of Geology at Columbia, a position filled with great distinction over a period of forty years. This was an eminently fortunate turn of affairs both for him and for the University, for it falls to the lot of few men to fit so perfectly into the complex duties of such a position.

It was in these early years of his teaching, while he was giving his whole effort to this service, that he wrote the textbook entitled *The Ore Deposits of the United States and Canada,* first issued in 1893, a pioneer in the field of economic geology. Three years later the very helpful guide known as the *Handbook of Rocks* was published. It was probably the most widely used book of its kind for a generation — useful alike to the student in the laboratory and the searcher in the field, to both trained and untrained men. Under his treatment, rocks became more than mere stones or lists of names. One soon came to appreciate that rocks came into existence under

iii

9586

the control of understandable laws, that they are all related in understandable ways, and that each one has a life history that anyone who knows how may read.

These two books together spread Professor Kemp's fame as a teacher. But his reputation for enthusiastic research in his chosen field had attracted even more attention. Probably no American geologist was more favorably known abroad. His contributions were largely in the field of economic geology, and it was the still more specialistic field of ore deposits that claimed his best effort throughout his life.

There was a time, following upon the appearance of certain important contributions to geological principles believed then to dominate in the relation of meteoric waters to the origin of ores of the metals, when confidence in igneous sources was at a low ebb, and there was much live discussion. In this controversy Professor Kemp took an active part, and his discrimination and keen insight showed to fine advantage. His defense of volcanism in this connection soon gained formidable support.

He did more than any other man of his time to win a responsible place for geology in the varied needs of a great city. For many years he was an advisory consultant for the City of New York, and in later years his services were in great demand on large public works. Thus, by force of circumstances, unsought but well earned, he came to be generally regarded as the outstanding representative of geology as an applied science.

Professor Kemp was born with a gift of ready speech and an unusually keen sense of humor, which together contributed materially to a successful life. His ability was outstanding, and to this background was added broad knowledge and live interest in many fields. He was an ideal teacher. He was himself an inspiration. He was loyal and absolutely fair, and his genius for friendliness and generosity was supreme. He believed in the Golden Rule and practised it. He believed in Christian principles and leaned on them. To him they were as sound and dependable as the rock foundations of the Earth.

CHARLES P. BERKEY

NOTE TO SIXTH EDITION

Several developments in rock study since the death of Professor Kemp in 1926 make it desirable to offer a sixth edition of his *Handbook of Rocks*. The book is intended as a text for work without a polarizing microscope, but some knowledge of general geology and mineralogy is prerequisite. These subjects are only briefly reviewed here, and if the student or reader is not prepared by work in the class room, he should undertake those courses by correspondence or by independent reading and study before he tries to classify rocks.

The main arrangement of chapters of the book is largely preserved in this edition, but all chapters have been rewritten, and some changes in emphasis have been made. The work of Professor Kemp himself has been used at several places, where it should be known by all students of rocks. The chapter on calculations in rock study has been much revised and extended. Although the beginning student is not commonly able to make rock analyses, he should know something of the results of analyses, just as students in mineralogy know the compositions of minerals, and he should be able to make certain calculations and diagrams of rock compositions, textures, and other features.

Foremost among the teachers of Rock Study to whom the revisor owes much is Doctor Charles P. Berkey, who suggested the revision and who contributes the memorial to Professor Kemp. His suggestions and assistance have added materially to the quality of the work. These are gratefully acknowledged.

The revisor has made some use of the text and illustrations from his *Petrography and Petrology* and here expresses thanks to the publishers, McGraw-Hill Book Company, Incorporated, for kind permission to make excerpts and use a number of cuts.

The sections of the book on the origin of rocks are larger than in previous editions because, as Doctor Berkey writes, it is probably "impossible to get a feeling of mastery in the handling of rocks without making acquaintance with origins in enough detail to cover every important probability." In the infinite variety of rocks which confuse the student, "the differences that give trouble are easily understood as expectable variations if one has an adequate working picture of how such formations are made."

A glossary of terms used in advanced petrology based on microscopic and chemical work is not needed for a student working on rocks without a microscope. Nevertheless, in reading about rocks he may encounter the names and lose the sense unless he can find what class of rocks is indicated. An abbreviated list of many such rock names is given before the index.

Two determinative tables are given in the book, one for common minerals and one for igneous rocks. These may be helpful for beginners, but the best way to know rocks is to have seen them before. Laboratory work should be based on good collections of labelled specimens.

As a laboratory exercise, it is well to require students to record on paper what structures, textures, and minerals can be seen in a series of specimens, by the eye and by use of a pocket lens. After page 46 has been studied and used, the rock name can be added, but the fundamental training in observation is a first requirement. Such exercises should be given early and repeated in the study of each of the three main classes of rocks, and if time permits, repeated again on field trips to outcrops or gravel pits and on cores and cuttings from drill holes.

CONTENTS

CHAPTER I

INTRODUCTION

Laboratory Methods, Rock-forming Minerals, Principles of Classification, Criteria for the Main Classes

A *rock* may be defined as anything that forms an essential part of the earth. Most rocks are composed of aggregates of minerals, but there are two prominent exceptions, coal which is largely of organic materials that are not minerals, and the natural glasses which cooled from lava so fast that no minerals formed. In instances a single mineral forms a rock, but this is exceptional. By far the greater number of masses of single minerals are in such small amounts that they cannot properly be considered rocks. Rock-salt, ice, calcite, serpentine, cemented fragments of quartz, kaolinite and a few others are in sufficient quantity, but the vast majority of rocks consist of two or more minerals.

The condition that a rock should form an essential part of the earth is introduced to bar out those minerals or aggregates, which, though important in themselves, are insignificant as entering into the mass of the globe. Thus the sulphide ores, while locally in considerable quantity, when broadly viewed are practically negligible. Yet there are minerals and aggregates that may properly give rise to differences of opinion. The following pages err, if at all, on the side of demanding that the amount should be large.

A rock must also have an individual character, sufficient to establish its identity with satisfactory sharpness. The species cannot be marked off with the same definition as in plants, animals, or minerals, and there is here again reasonable opportunity for differences of opinion as to the limits which should be set, some admitting of finer distinctions and greater multiplicity of species than others. Too great refinements and too minute subdivisions ought to be avoided.

1

The determining conditions of species will be taken up at greater length, when the preliminaries of classification have been set forth, but it must be appreciated that the point of view is also a most important factor. Thus if one is studying the geology of a district with close accuracy, and is tracing the history of its rocks with microscopic determinations, finer distinctions will naturally be drawn than those that suggest themselves to one who is engaged in ordinary mining or engineering enterprises. It is primarily for the latter class that these pages are prepared and throughout the descriptions and classifications here given, the necessary limitations and the practical needs of such observers are always kept in mind. Textural and mineralogical distinctions are used where easily visible on a specimen, although never made contradictory of principles of origin and classification which could be carried to greater length and subdivision.

Rocks embrace matter in a great variety of structures and conditions. While in general we picture them to ourselves as solid, yet under the terms of our definition, we have no logical right to bar out liquids or even gases. The physical condition may vary with ordinary temperatures. Thus we cannot reject ice as an extremely abundant and important rock, and yet its solid condition results from water with a moderate loss of heat, and at ordinary temperatures the same molecules may be in a liquid or gaseous state. All that we know of volcanoes indicates that liquid, molten magmas exist for long periods deep in the earth. In general, however, we think of rocks as solid, and therefore gases and liquids will receive no further attention.

In texture rocks may be loose and incoherent as in sand, gravel, volcanic dust and the like, or they may be extremely dense, hard and solid, as in countless familiar examples. This solidity has its limitations, for all observation and experience show that what are apparently solid masses are really broken up by multitudes of cracks into pieces of various sizes. All quarries and mines have these cracks, and they may aid or annoy the operators according to the purposes of excavation. They will again be referred to at length. Unless too deep within the earth, all rocks are also permeated with minute pores and spaces that admit of the penetration of water and other fluids. These are important factors in terrestrial circulations.

The student should note that the terminology of the several sciences is somewhat overlapping, but in any one subject the terms are fairly definite. The substance of a pure *sandstone* (rock study) is quartz (mineralogy), and silica or silicon dioxide, SiO_2 (chemistry). It is wholly improper to call such a rock silica, because several other rocks besides sandstone are made up of silica.

General Geology of Rocks

The study of general geology should normally precede a careful study of rocks. Even to those who have not had this general training, however, the formation of rocks is a matter of everyday observation. The rain washes mud into lakes or into rivers, which carry it toward the sea. The waves and currents of the sea sort and deposit the sands. The forests and swamps deposit immense quantities of organic remains. Glaciers scour out great valleys and deposit moraines of the debris. Volcanoes pour out lava and scatter the fragments from their explosions. All these visible and familiar activities of geologic agents result in the formation of rocks.

Nevertheless, when we study in detail the rocks produced by these visible processes, we find that they do not represent all the kinds of rocks found in the crust of the earth. The rocks that differ from them probably originated deep in the earth, where no human eye could watch their development. The details of the process in particular cases can be estimated by long and careful study of the history of the associated formations and by laboratory work producing artificial rocks; but it should be clearly understood that the processes are inferred and not observed. A large portion of the rocks now visible at or near the surface of the earth acquired their present general nature at great depths and came to light only after a long geologic time of uplift and erosion. The proof that many igneous masses have once been liquid is found in the manner of their occurrence, penetrating fractures and enclosing blocks of their walls.

A statistical study of the rocks exposed at the surface indicates that much of the bedrock nearest the surface has originated by transportation in water and deposition from suspension. Almost three-fourths of the rock exposures at the surface are such sediments. The rocks formed by the action of water, therefore, deserve a prominent place in rock study.

A different point of view, however, is obtained from a study of the structure of the earth's crust—the "crust" being defined as an outer layer of the earth approximately 10 miles thick. This crust has at most places only a thin layer of sediments, if any, and the underlying rocks are largely those formed by the cooling of a hot liquid, the "magma," such as the deep-seated liquid supplying the lava for volcanoes. It is estimated that the proportions of rocks in the crust are very close to the following:

	Per cent
From magma	95
From sedimentary mud	4
From sedimentary sand	0.75
From the calcareous hard parts of organisms	0.25

Some rocks of each of these groups may be altered so that they are best classified as metamorphic. All the other rocks together constitute an insignificant fraction of the whole crust, and so the dominance of the first group justifies the emphasis usually placed upon it. The magmatic products should logically be taken up first, also, because other rocks are largely derived from them, and because many ore deposits are related to the magmas from which these rocks form.

FIELD AND LABORATORY METHODS ON ROCKS

Field and laboratory work on rocks commonly emphasizes structures and textures more than minerals and classification. A course in rock study cannot be extended to cover all the structures, but a few notes are needed. Some rock outcrops are massive, with no plane or linear features, but these are more rare than has been supposed. Most rocks have internal structural features which can be mapped in the field and which have proved of great value in interpretation. No student of rocks should be satisfied until able to map a variety of field structures. Nearly all who have had any instruction in geology are familiar with the *dip* and *strike* of rocks, and the common methods of mapping them. The symbols used should differ for primary structures and those seen in *metamorphic* rocks. Some method should be used also to distinguish the plane structures of *bedding, flow layers, joints, faults,* and *dikes.*

To these should be added a record of linear features in a rock. These had not been recorded for very many rock exposures until some work by Hans Cloos resulted in very interesting conclusions.[1] If the arrow is omitted from the symbol for dip (as it can be without loss of clarity) the position of linear features may well be shown by an arrow, either with the dip and strike, or separately. The direction of the arrow should show the linear feature projected to the horizontal plane, and the head of the arrow may be marked with a figure to show the angle of the linear feature from the horizontal. It should be noted that linear features commonly lie in the plane of foliation, but that at only a few places do the lines coincide with the direction of dip of the foliation. See Fig. 1.

In igneous rocks the linear structures commonly indicate the direction of maximum lengthening of the mass during solidification. In metamorphic rocks, the interpretation is still a subject of discussion. (See page 218.)

When field work does not suffice for the recognition of a rock, or when the field is to be represented by a display of materials, the geologist commonly collects specimens. The first requirement of a specimen is that it should show the nature of the material in the outcrop as well as possible. Ordinarily it is possible to do this and also to trim the specimen to a neat size, about $3 \times 4 \times 1$ inches. The student should practise with the trimming hammer

[1] Hans Cloos: *Einführung in die Geologie; ein Lehrbuch der innern Dynamik.* Gebrüder Borntraeger, 1936.

J. F. Kemp: *New Methods in the Study of Granitic Intrusives.* Economic Geology, volume 20, pages 597–601, 1925.

Robert Balk: *Structural Behavior of Igneous Rocks.* Geological Society of America, Memoir 6, 1937.

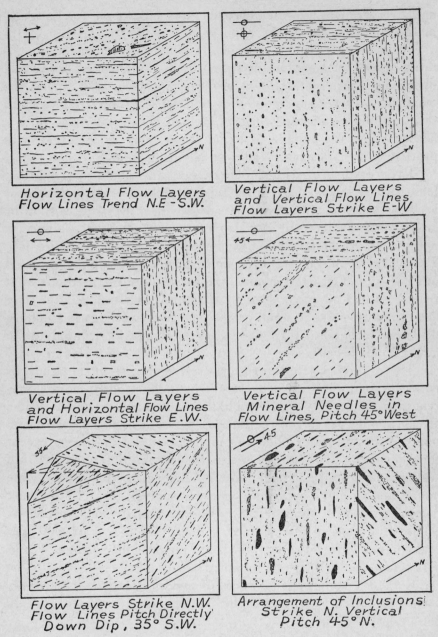

FIG. 1.— Diagram of foliation and lineation. (Modified from Balk.)

until his specimens have clean broken faces and are not too irregular or too much bruised by the hammer.

If, as distinct from a specimen, a sample is needed for quantitative work, the sampling may well be done by cutting a channel or taking a series of chips at arbitrary distances and mixing the material.[2] Here also a good deal of practise with a hammer helps the student to do good work at sampling; perhaps most skill is needed when the sample is to be taken from drill core,—with practice many cores can be split in half lengthwise.

Every student of rocks should carry and constantly use a pocket lens, because many of the identifying or characteristic features of rocks are very small and are best seen with a lens. If a shop or laboratory is available, it may also be recommended that a binocular microscope be added to the equipment for routine examination. The lens and binocular simply show details that might be missed otherwise, and do not involve the use of optical methods that require special microscopes and training in their use. After very brief practice, rocks in small grains such as the cuttings from churn drills are recognized through the lenses almost as definitely as in larger hand specimens.

There are few laboratory observations in use in the study of rocks, beyond those already familiar to the student in the pre-requisite mineralogy (determination of hardness, color, luster, streak, specific gravity, forms, cleavage, fracture, magnetism, taste, odor, effects of water and reagents, and effects of heat), except those involving use of the polarizing microscope. To make a thin section and examine it under a polarizing microscope takes some hours, and to make a chemical analysis several days. This book is concerned with more rapid methods, though some problems require the more detailed study. There are a few of the mineralogic methods, however, which are modified in rock study and a few new methods are to be noted.

Rocks are commonly mixtures of minerals, and their hardness cannot be tested satisfactorily by Moh's scale from 1 to 10. A

[2] F. F. Grout: *Rock Sampling for Chemical Analysis.* American Journal of Science, volume 24, pages 394–404, 1932.

mixture of biotite $(H = 2)$ and quartz $(H = 7)$ cannot be said to have a hardness of 2 or of 7. Most descriptions note the coherence with about five grades in general terms, such as; *friable, loosely cemented, medium, coherent, firmly cemented.* The character of the rock is related to brittleness and toughness, perhaps as much as to hardness. Careful tests can be made of "resistance to wear" by laboratory apparatus such as that used for testing road materials, but most geologists can estimate the five grades above noted by the use of a hammer and knife.

It is very important to distinguish clearly the hardness of a rock from the hardness of the minerals in it. A sandstone made up of quartz grains may be so loosely cemented that it is much more friable than a dolomite with grains of the same size. Experienced mineralogists use correct methods in testing such granular minerals and the student of rocks should acquaint himself with them. The rule is to identify the minerals by testing the hardness of the grains, not that of the rock. This is done by scratching standard test minerals with the rock, not by scratching the rock with the control or standard. A knife blade $(H = 6)$, a coin $(H = 3)$, and the thumb nail $(H = 2\frac{1}{2})$ are good substitutes and ordinarily sufficient. In the example just cited, soft sandstone pressed against a knife blade will scratch the steel, whereas the more coherent dolomite will not.

Magnetic minerals are detected in rocks by use of a permanent magnet, conveniently the knife used in testing hardness.

In specific gravity tests, the few rare notably heavy or notably light rocks can be distinguished by tossing the specimens in the hand. In the common range from 2.6 to 3.2, the differences are detected by that method only by those who have had experience and acquired skill. A balance is rarely used, partly because most rock specimens are too large to fit the common mineralogical balance. In well equipped laboratories special rock balances are available.

Colors of rocks are perhaps less constant and characteristic than well known variable colors of minerals. Colors may be accurately described by reference to Ridgway's Color Chart or an abstract of it [3] prepared especially for use of students of sediments. The streak is obtained chiefly by scratching with a knife.

Blowpipe tests are only rarely used in the study of rocks and rock minerals. Fusibility may help to identify some particular minerals, and may serve to determine whether a clay is refractory or easily melted. Heat tests may also affect the color, and give off characteristic odors from sediments.

The reagents most often applied in testing rocks for identification and description are water and hydrochloric acid. In water, salt will dissolve and can be detected by tasting; many clays slake and become plastic; and *bentonite* swells (page 155) and forms a milky suspension. Water is also used in panning out heavy minerals, and sorting clay, silt, and sand by washing. Dilute cold hydrochloric acid causes calcite to effervesce, but dolomite effervesces in dilute acid only when heated. The student should be warned, however, that acid tests are rarely needed, and that acid injures a specimen by forming soluble salts that give a salty taste the next time the specimen is studied. In *calcareous* rocks it is important not only to know the fact of effervescence but, after effervescence ceases, to estimate how much of the original is left undissolved and something of its character.

Several silicates give a silica jelly when evaporated in acid, and in the case of *nepheline*, this is one of the best laboratory tests (page 72).

A polished surface very often gives information about a rock not so easily found in any other way. On the polished surface, etching and staining by chemical reagents may help in mineral identification; [4] but such work is most often done in connection with more elaborate microscopic study.

THE CHEMICAL ELEMENTS IMPORTANT IN ROCKS

The chemical elements really important in rocks are comparatively few, and are those which are most widespread in nature.

[3] M. I. Goldman and H. E. Merwin: *Color Chart for Field Description of Sedimentary Rocks.* Div. of Geology and Geography, National Research Council, 1928.

[4] Gussow, W. C.: Trans. Royal Society of Canada, 1937, IV, page 133.

One of the most reliable estimates is that of F. W. Clarke and
H. S. Washington in Professional Paper 127 of the U. S. Geological Survey, p. 34, 1924.   Analyses of all the accessible terrestrial
matter, including the air and the ocean, have been used.   The average composition of the igneous rocks has first been determined;
next that of the sedimentary rocks.   Since the metamorphic rocks
represent either igneous or sedimentary originals, they do not call
for special treatment.   The average composition of the ocean and
that of the atmosphere have been computed.   In the final average
the rocky crust is credited with 93 per cent; and the waters with
7 per cent; both in round numbers since the atmosphere is but
0.03 per cent of the total.

Oxygen............ 49.52	Magnesium.......... 1.94	Sulphur............ 0.05
Silicon............. 25.75	Hydrogen........... 0.88	Barium............. 0.05
Aluminum.......... 7.51	Titanium............ 0.58	Fluorine............ 0.03
Iron............... 4.70	Chlorine............ 0.19	Nitrogen........... 0.03
Calcium............ 3.39	Phosphorus.......... 0.12	Chromium.......... 0.03
Sodium............. 2.64	Carbon.............. 0.09	Zirconium 0.02
Potassium.......... 2.40	Manganese.......... 0.08	Total............. 100.00

It is of interest to remark that of all the common metals,
useful in the arts, only aluminum, iron, manganese, and chromium
appear in the table.

There is good ground for believing that toward the center of
the earth the metallic elements become much more abundant and
that near the center some are in excess, but these inferences, however well-based, concern materials far beyond actual experience,
and of no great moment in this handbook.

Rock-forming Minerals

The chemical elements above cited are combined, except perhaps
in volcanic glasses and certain colloids, in the definite compounds
which form mineral species.   These compounds change, more or
less, in the course of time, under the action of various natural
agents, chief of which are water, carbonic acid and oxygen, but at
any particular stage, however complex the rock may be, it is made
up of definite chemical compounds, though we may not be able to
recognize them all.

Elements—graphite, sulphur, copper.

Sulphides—pyrite, pyrrhotite.

Haloid—halite.

Oxides—quartz, chalcedony, corundum, hematite, ilmenite, magnetite.

Hydrous oxides—limonite.

Carbonates—calcite, dolomite, siderite.

Sulphates—gypsum, anhydrite.

Silicates—Feldspar group, orthoclase, plagioclases.

    Feldspathoids, nepheline, leucite.

    Pyroxene group, augite, hypersthene.

    Amphibole group, actinolite, hornblende.

    Mica group, muscovite, biotite.

    Olivine, garnet, tourmaline, epidote, andalusite, staurolite, chlorite, talc, kaolinite, serpentine, zeolites.

In igneous rocks which are taken up first because they are the sources of others the groups of silicates are of first importance. The following discussion by groups is intended not as a textbook in mineralogy, but as a review, emphasizing the composition and relative importance.

The Feldspars[5] are silicates of aluminum and an alkali or alkaline earth metal or both. All have similar physical properties and their distinction is a matter of close observation. They are divided for hand specimen study into two groups, the *orthoclase* group (including *microcline*) and the *plagioclase* group from albite to anorthite. Intermediate between these two groups are relatively few feldspars, but much of the orthoclase and microcline has an intergrowth of albite forming *perthite*. This is rarely detected without the microscope but may be seen ·in the feldspar of coarse *pegmatites* as irregular wavy streaks. Perthite may be included with the orthoclase group.

The orthoclase group is chiefly $KAlSi_3O_8$. Several per cent of Na_2O may enter without visible effects in hand specimens. The clear orthoclase with glassy luster, in the later volcanic rocks is called *sanidine*. Green *amazonstone,* microcline, can rarely be

[5] Spelled felspar in England.

seen in rocks except in coarse pegmatites, and when microcline is not green, it so resembles orthoclase that no distinction is commonly made without the microscope.

The plagioclase feldspars embrace a practically unbroken series from pure sodium-aluminum silicate in *albite*, $NaAlSi_3O_8$, to pure calcium-aluminum silicate, *anorthite*, $CaAl_2Si_2O_8$. Various mixtures of these two molecules give the intermediate species. Practically in ordinary work we are forced to the distinctions of orthoclase and plagioclase, leaving the details to microscopic, chemical,

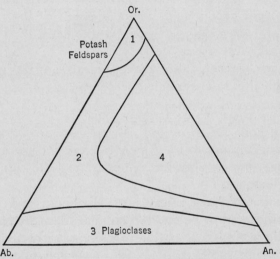

Fig. 2.— Diagram of the range in composition of the common feldspars, in terms of the orthoclase, albite, and anorthite molecules. Orthoclase and microcline fall in field 1, and plagioclase in field 3. The much less common anorthoclase and perthite lie in field 2, and very few lie in field 4. (After Alling and Winchell.)

or careful specific gravity determinations, but of course experience and familiarity with the general characters and associations of minerals in rocks often enables one to determine very closely the minor varieties. We would naturally look for orthoclase, albite, and oligoclase in acidic rocks or those high in silica, while in basic rocks we would expect labradorite and bytownite.

All the feldspars have very similar crystal forms when these are developed, as they occasionally are in rocks. If they are small and irregularly bounded, cleavage faces should be sought out and examined with a pocket lens. It is interesting to note that it is chiefly in igneous rocks that we obtain crystals uniformly developed on all sides, for in a fused magma they grow without a fixed support.

TABLE OF FELDSPAR MOLECULES OF COMMON ROCKS

	Monoclinic	Triclinic	Symbol
$KAlSi_3O_8$	orthoclase	microcline	Or.
$NaAlSi_3O_8$	(rare)	albite	Ab.
$CaAl_2Si_2O_8$		anorthite	An.

The plagioclases include intermediate members, distinguished by chemical or optical work, which may be given formulas as if the symbols were for chemical elements. Oligoclase $Ab_{90}An_{10}$ to $Ab_{70}An_{30}$; Andesine $Ab_{70}An_{80}$ to $Ab_{50}An_{50}$; Labradorite $Ab_{50}An_{50}$ to $Ab_{30}An_{70}$; Bytownite $Ab_{30}An_{70}$ to $Ab_{10}An_{90}$.

Advanced work may find other methods of grouping feldspars. Orthoclase and albite are silicic or acidic or alkalic feldspars in contrast with labradorite and bytownite, which are basic or calcic. With this contrast the andesine is medium. No such refinement is attempted without microscopic or chemical work, but since it is common practice the student should know the meaning of the terms, and realize that many petrographers feel that albite and orthoclase are not very different; one has sodium and the other potassium, but they have about the same silicon and aluminum. On the other hand the basic plagioclases are not only low in silicon but high in calcium, which is very different from sodium and potassium.

Distinction of

Orthoclase	*from*	Plagioclase

1. Not striated — Striated on basal cleavage faces
2. Stubby crystals — Lath like or platy
3. Flesh colored — White to gray
4. Pearly to chalky luster, rarely vitreous (sanidine) — Vitreous to pearly luster
5. With quartz and biotite in light colored rocks — With augite and olivine in dark rocks

These distinctions are arranged in order of importance or dependability. If the *striation* appears, no peculiarity of form,

Wingate College Library

color, or luster should be sufficient to cast doubt on the fact that the feldspar is plagioclase.   In the absence of striations the form is more dependable than the color, luster, or association, but all should be considered.

It is especially noteworthy that if two feldspars side by side show different colors, one is likely to be plagioclase, the other orthoclase; also that quartz rocks commonly have associated orthoclase and plagioclase, but dark rocks may have gray plagioclase without any orthoclase.

The feldspars are the most important minerals in the classification of igneous rocks (page 46), but the several ferromagnesian minerals closely follow them, and give a roughly parallel series (page 38).

The Feldspathoids are a group of minerals containing the same elements as feldspars, but analyses show a smaller percentage of silica.   Their physical properties are not very different from those of feldspar, but they are perhaps more soluble, and crystallize in more symmetrical forms.   *Nepheline* and *leucite* are the chief members, and they appear in only about one-tenth per cent of the igneous rocks.   Nepheline commonly forms blocky hexagonal prisms, with basal pinacoid terminations, so that vertical cross sections are rectangular.   It is a sodium aluminum silicate $(Na, K) AlSiO_4$, in which some of the sodium is "proxied" by potassium.   It may be recognized in some rocks by its form, but the identification is helped by its greasy luster, by its weathering more rapidly than the feldspars which are usually associated, and by its gelatinization on evaporation in acid.   Nepheline in older rocks was formerly known as elaeolite.

Leucite is an isometric silicate, $KAlSi_2O_6$, with a little sodium replacing part of the potassium.   It is a salt of metasilicic acid, H_2SiO_3, like the pyroxenes and amphiboles.   It appears as rock-making mineral in the igneous rocks of several localities.   *Melilite* is an extremely basic, calcium-aluminum silicate, $Ca_{12}Al_4Si_9O_{36}$, and appears in a few rare basalts.   Reference may also be made to *sodalite, noselite,* and *hauynite* which are occasionally met, but which are seen chiefly by work with a microscope.

Each of the common *ferromagnesian minerals* embraces a series in isomorphous relations. Their distinctions are commonly easy except that *hornblende* and *augite* are much alike. Most *olivine* is in yellow green, glassy grains about a sixteenth of an inch across and when scattered in dark rocks, is not easily recognized without a lens and good light. If weathered brown, it may be more readily identified. *Biotite* has commonly a brownish black color and is much softer than the rest of the group,—a pin point easily digs into the tiny grains. This leaves the two black, hard, cleavable minerals for further study.

Pyroxenes and Amphiboles may be described together. Each embraces a series of compounds of similar chemical composition, differing a little in physical and optical properties. As the table shows, they range from magnesium silicate through a series of calcium-magnesium silicates, which may hold some iron and aluminum, to an extreme that is a sodium-iron silicate.

Pyroxene	*Amphibole*
ORTHORHOMBIC GROUP	
Enstatite, $MgSiO_3$	Anthophyllite, $(Mg, Fe)_7(OH)_2Si_8O_{22}$
Bronzite	
Hypersthene, $(Mg, Fe)SiO_3$	
MONOCLINIC GROUP	
Diopside, $CaMgSi_2O_6$	Tremolite, $Ca_2Mg_5(OH)_2Si_8O_{22}$
	Actinolite, $Ca_2(Mg, Fe)_5(OH)_2Si_8O_{22}$
Augite $\begin{cases} Ca(Mg, Fe)Si_2O_6 \\ Ca(Mg, Fe)(Al, Fe)AlSiO_6 \end{cases}$	Hornblende, $\begin{cases} Ca_2(Mg, Fe)_4Al(OH)_2AlSi_7O_{22} \\ NaCa_2(Mg, Fe)_4Al(OH)_2Al_2Si_6O_{22} \end{cases}$
Acmite, $NaFeSi_2O_6$	$\begin{cases} Arfvedsonite \\ Glaucophane \end{cases}$ (approaching acmite)

Among the orthorhombic pyroxenes *enstatite* has least of the the molecule $FeSiO_3$, i.e., FeO less than 5 per cent; *bronzite* has more than 5 and less than 14 per cent; hypersthene has still higher percentages of FeO, giving it a darker color. The orthorhombic pyroxenes are much less common than the monoclinic, and are not easily distinguished without microscopic work, except that the bronzite may have a characteristic brown color.

The light-colored monoclinic pyroxenes are almost pure calcium-magnesium silicates, and are called *diopside*. They are common in crystalline limestones, and less common in the trachyte and andesite clans. The chief rock-making pyroxenes are the dark aluminous, ferruginous ones, which are called *augite,* and these are among the most important of all dark minerals. When pinacoidal cleavages appear in addition to the prismatic ones in pyroxenes, they are called *diallage.* The nepheline rocks rich in soda contain *acmite,* the soda-pyroxene.

The monoclinic *amphiboles* are closely parallel in their occurrence and relations to the pyroxenes. *Tremolite* is met in crystalline limestones. *Actinolite* may form *schistose* rocks by itself, but much the most important variety is *hornblende,* the black aluminous mineral corresponding to augite. The sodic amphiboles, arfvedsonite and glaucophane, are rare.

Distinction of

Augite	*from*	Hornblende
1. Crystals stubby, 8 sided		Crystals in needles, 6 sided
2. Cleavage angle near 90°		Cleavage angle near 60°
3. Dull, submetallic		"Silky" luster
4. Black to brown		Black to green
5. With plagioclase and olivine in dark rocks		With orthoclase and quartz in light-colored rocks

The pyroxenes and amphiboles are often collectively referred to as *metasilicates* (page 18). It is noteworthy that many blast furnace slags are calculated on the basis of the formulas for pyroxene.

Olivine is a silicate of magnesium and iron $(Mg, Fe)_2SiO_4$, and occurs in few rocks except basic igneous rocks.

The Mica Group embraces isomorphous series of some complexity. *Biotite,* the dark mica, is much the commonest in rocks, and enters into the classification in an important way. It grades from the light colored extreme, *phlogopite* with magnesium and little iron, to the very dark, iron-rich *lepidomelane.* *Muscovite* is a potassium mica with very little iron and magnesium. It has the same constituents as orthoclase with water added. It is widespread in granites, pegmatites, and schists.

This completes the list of silicates which are of the first order of importance in igneous rocks. *Zircon* and *sphene* are microscopic accessories of wide occurrence but are seldom visible to the naked eye. *Tourmaline* and others are fairly common in pegmatites.

Along the contacts of intrusions of heated igneous rocks, and in regions where the original sediments have undergone strong dynamic disturbances, with oftentimes attendant circulation of waters more or less heated, a series of characteristic silicates is developed,—*garnet, tourmaline, topaz, andalusite, scapolite, kyanite, sillimanite, staurolite, biotite, muscovite,* and *cordierite.* Some details of the development and associations of these are given in the discussion of metamorphic rocks. *Epidote* results when hot waters attack feldspars and ferro-magnesian silicates in proximity, so that the solutions may react on one another.

The hydrated silicates of chief importance include a magnesian series, embracing *talc* and *serpentine*, which result from the ferro-magnesian minerals; a ferruginous aluminous series, with much iron oxide, usually collectively called *chlorite,* and finally *kaolinite,* the hydrated silicate of alumina that is yielded chiefly by feldspars. *Zeolites* also are common, but rather as vein fillings and in amygdaloidal cavities than as important rock makers.

The oxides include quartz and its related minerals, *chalcedony* and *opal* (and *tridymite* and *cristobalite* determined by microscope and X-ray), and the oxides of iron—*magnetite* and *hematite,* and the hydrated oxides in a mixture called *limonite.* Magnetite and hematite are at places abundant enough to constitute rocks themselves. Magnetite is the most widespread of all the rock-making minerals. Limonite is an alteration product. *Chromite* is practically limited to the basic igneous rocks and their serpentinous derivatives. *Ilmenite* is a common accessory in many igneous rocks.

The carbonates, *calcite, dolomite,* and *siderite* are common in sediments. The sulphates of moment are *anhydrite* and *gypsum,* the latter the hydrous, the former the anhydrous salt of calcium.

The one chloride is the sodium chloride, rock salt or *halite*, and the one phosphate is *apatite*, which is a calcium phosphate and halide, rarely in grains large enough to be seen without a microscope. The two sulphides of iron, *pyrite* and *pyrrhotite* are the only ones sufficiently widespread to deserve mention. *Graphite* is the chief representative of the elementary substances, although native sulphur and native copper might perhaps with propriety be added.

Groupings of Minerals

We speak of minerals as *essential* and *accessory*, meaning by the former term those that constitute a large part of the rock, and that must be mentioned in the definition; by the latter those that are in small amounts or that are more or less fortuitous.

Primary minerals are those that date back to the origin of the rock as magma solidifies; *secondary* minerals are formed by the alteration of the primary after the magma has solidified. Feldspars, pyroxene and hornblende are good illustrations of the former; zeolites and kaolinite of the latter.

The common rock-forming silicates have been considered salts of three hypothetical silicic acids, named:

Orthosilicic acid . . . . H_4SiO_4
Metasilicic acid . . . . $H_4Si_2O_6$ or H_2SiO_3
Trisilicic acid . . . . $H_4Si_3O_8$

It is noteworthy that for a given amount of hydrogen (or in the case of salts, for a given amount of metal) the ortho-silicates have the least silica and trisilicates the most silica. These are much modified by isomorphous substitutions, but the general idea is an aid to the memory.

Trisilicates with about 65% silica: Orthoclase, Albite.

Metasilicates with about 55% silica: Leucite, Amphiboles, Pyroxenes.

Orthosilicates with about 45% silica: Nepheline, Olivine, Garnets, Anorthite, Micas.

	Trisilicates		Orthosilicates		Metasilicates		
	Or Ortho- clase $KAlSi_3O_8$	Ab Albite $NaAlSi_3O_8$	An Anorthite $CaAl_2Si_2O_8$	Nepheline $NaAlSiO_4$	Leucite $KAlSi_2O_6$	Bronzite (Pyroxene)	Antho- phyllite (Amphibole)
SiO_2	64.7	68.6	43.1	45.0	55.0	58.0	57.7
Al_2O_3	18.4	19.6	36.8	34.3	23.5	(FeO) 11.0	15.2
K_2O	16.9	—	—	—	21.5	(MgO) 29.7	24.7
Na_2O	—	11.8	—	20.7	—	(Al_2O_3) 1.3	(H_2O) 2.4

It is also apparent from the table that in an igneous rock rich in silica one might expect quartz, but in a melt low in silica all the silica would combine with metals. If nepheline, leucite, or olivine were melted with silica, it should be expected to react by simple addition to form feldspar, or pyroxene.

Nepheline........$NaAlSiO_4$ Leucite..........$KAlSi_2O_6$ Olivine...........Mg_2SiO_4
Quartz.............SiO_2 Quartz...............SiO_2 Quartz..............SiO_2
Quartz.............SiO_2

Albite..........$NaAlSi_3O_8$ Orthoclase........$KAlSi_3O_8$ Enstatite.........$2MgSiO_3$

Nepheline, olivine and a few other minerals are rarely found in rocks which contain quartz. The minerals not found with quartz may be said to be *unsaturated* with silica, while those which are capable of growing from magma in the presence of an excess of silica may be said to be *saturated* with silica. Thus quartz and unsaturated minerals are incompatible in igneous rocks.

Saturated Minerals
Feldspars
Pyroxenes
Amphiboles
Micas
Magnetite
Sphene
Tourmaline
Fayalite
Spessartite
Almandite

Unsaturated Minerals
Nepheline
Leucite
Olivine (except fayalite)
Analcime
Sodalite group
Cancrinite
Pyrope
Melilite
Corundum

TABLE I

Common Rock Minerals

Nonmetallic light-colored

- **Hard**
  - **Show cleavage**
    - Flesh colored, stubby . . . . Orthoclase
    - Gray white lath-like striated . . . . . . Plagioclase
    - Green columnar . . . . Actinolite
    - Gray or red, greasy luster, sol . . . . . . Nepheline
  - **Fracture only**
    - Isometric crystals in dark rocks . . . . Leucite
    - Green glassy granular . . . . Olivine
    - Fine-grained, yellowish green . . . . . . Epidote
    - Glassy, variously colored . . . . Quartz, chert
- **Soft**
  - **Cleavage**
    - Cubic, salty taste . . . . Halite
    - Rhombohedral cleavage, H = 3 . . . . Calcite and dolomite
    - Flexible plates, etc., H = 2 . . . . Gypsum
    - Rectangular cleavage, H = 3.5 . . . . . Anhydrite
    - Soapy feel, H = 1 . . . . Talc
    - Elastic mica . . . . Muscovite
    - Fibrous, brittle, H = 2–4 . . . . Zeolites
    - Fibrous, flexible, H = 2–4 . . . . Asbestos
  - **Fracture**
    - Yellow, burns with blue flame . . . . . . Sulphur
    - Earthy . . . . Kaolinite
    - Waxy look, H = 4 . . . . Serpentine
    - Soapy feel, H = 1 . . . . Talc

Nonmetallic dark-colored

- **Hard**
  - **Cleavage**
    - Black
      - cleavage about 90° . . . . Augite
      - cleavage about 60° . . . . Hornblende
    - Green, poor cleavage . . . . Epidote
  - **Fracture**
    - Dirty green . . . . Epidote
    - Brown, orthorhombic . . . . Staurolite
    - Red, isometric, glassy . . . . Garnet
    - Black, hexagonal columns fluted . . . . Tourmaline
    - Variously colored, waxy . . . . Jasper, quartz
    - Black to red, conchoidal . . . . (Obsidian)
- **Soft**
  - **Cleavage**
    - Brown to black, elastic mica . . . . . . Biotite
    - Green to dark blue gray, H = 1 . . . . Chlorite
    - Brown rhombohedrons . . . . Siderite
  - **Fracture**
    - Earthy . . . . Clay
    - Green to dark blue gray, H = 1 . . . . Chlorite
    - Green, waxy, H = 4 . . . . Serpentine
    - Green, dark, sandy grains . . . . Glauconite

Metallic colors

- **Black**
  - **Streak black**
    - Hardness = 6
      - strongly magnetic . . Magnetite
      - weakly magnetic . . . Ilmenite
    - Hardness = 1 to 3 . . . . Graphite (and coal)
  - Streak red . . . . Hematite
  - Streak yellow . . . . Limonite
- **Red**
  - Metallic . . . . Copper
  - Earthy . . . . Hematite
- **Yellow**
  - Metallic, black streak, H = 6 . . . . Pyrite
  - Earthy, yellow streak . . . . Limonite

An igneous rock that contains only saturated minerals is a saturated rock. With free quartz the rock is oversaturated, and with some unsaturated minerals, it is an undersaturated rock.

Certain melts of saturated minerals like pyroxene may yield early crystals of unsaturated minerals, which leave the liquid enriched in silica; so that, if the early crystals do not react with the late liquid, quartz may grow from it. There are a few well known examples of diabases with early olivine and late quartz.

A final grouping or division of minerals is based largely on color and composition. The light colored minerals are chiefly feldspars, feldspathoids and quartz, which are compounds of silicon and aluminum. These are called *felsic* (*fe* for feldspar, *l* for lenads or feldspathoids, and *s* for silica). In contrast to these, the dark minerals are colored by iron compounds, commonly associated with magnesia. These are the ferromagnesian group, called *mafic* for short (*ma* for magnesia and *f* for iron).

Principles Underlying the Classification of Rocks

Rocks are classified in order to place them in their natural relations so far as possible and to allow of their systematic study. At the same time they are so diverse in their nature and origin

---

Notes on Table:

Calcite and dolomite are not easily distinguished in the field or hand specimen except by tests with acid (page 9).

Gypsum is perhaps recognized by field geologists mostly by the odd feeling of lack of grit between the teeth; this is especially needed in the identification of fine-grained rock gypsum. *Anhydrite* is a little harder than gypsum, but the two minerals may occur together and cause confusion if they are fine-grained. To distinguish fine anhydrite from limestones, the effervescence of limestones in acid is the best test.

The crystal forms appear so commonly in garnet and staurolite that other tests are less used.

Other minerals recognizable in hand specimens are so rare that they are omitted in this table and discussion. If rocks show prominent grains that do not fit those of the table, consider as of probable occurrence; analcime, andalusite, apatite, bronzite, cassiterite, chalcopyrite, cordierite, corundum, fluorite, glaucophane, kyanite, opal, prehnite, pyrrhotite, rutile, the sodalite group, sphene, topaz, tremolite, wollastonite, zircon.

that the subject is not an easy one. They must however be grouped on the basis of their structures and textures; or of their mineralogical composition; or of their chemical composition; or of their geological age; or of their method of genesis. One or several of these principles enter into all schemes. On the basis of the first, rocks have been classified as *massive* and *stratified;* as *crystalline* and *fragmental* or *clastic,* each with subdivisions on one or more of the other principles. On the basis of minerals we have had those with only one mineral (simple rocks) and those with several (complex rocks). The chemical composition as shown by a total analysis without regard to special mineral components, is of almost universal application in advanced work. It is especially serviceable in the study of igneous rocks and of those highly calcareous or highly siliceous rocks that are deposited from solution. The principle of geological age was formerly much valued in connection with the igneous rocks, but it is almost completely abandoned. The principle of origin or genesis is the most philosophical of all as a fundamental basis, but while it may be readily applied to most rocks there are some puzzling members whose entire geological history is not well understood.

Very early in the development of the subject it was appreciated that there were two great, sharply contrasted groups, according as the rocks had consolidated and crystallized from a molten condition, or had been deposited in water either as mechanical fragments or as chemical precipitates. Two grand divisions have therefore been established, the igneous, on the one hand, and the aqueous on the other. Along with the aqueous rocks are included some deposited by air and by ice to form a group called sedimentary rocks. Even a limited field experience soon convinces the observer that there are many rocks which cannot be readily placed with either of the two great classes whose origin is comparatively simple.

Rocks for instance may have the minerals common to the igneous rocks but structures that resemble those of sediments in water. Great geological disturbances, especially if of the nature of a shearing stress, may so crush the minerals of any igneous rock and stretch them out in bands and layers as to closely imitate a recrystallized sediment.   The baking action of igneous intrusions on fine sediments, such as clays and muds, makes it difficult for an observer, without the aid of thin sections and a microscope, to say where the former sediment ends and the igneous rock begins. Sediments buried at great depths and subjected to heat and hot water become recrystallized with their chemical elements in new combinations.   These excessively altered rocks are grouped into a separate, so-called "metamorphic" division, which is a sort of "omnibus" of unsolved geological problems.

This metamorphic group is useful, but wherever possible it is well to appreciate the true affinities of its members, some of which though altered are still referable to their originals.   There is a rather strong trend among recent workers to describe and map as sedimentary rocks those metamorphic rocks, especially quartzites, whose origin is known.[6]   If a sediment is altered and its origin is not still clearly determinable, the problem of classification may be avoided by calling it "bedded" or "stratified."

In the following pages these three divisions will be adopted, but the metamorphic group will be reduced to a minimum by remarking in connection with descriptions of the unaltered rocks, the changes that igneous and sedimentary rocks undergo.

We take up, therefore, in this order:

A. The Igneous Rocks.
B. The Sedimentary Rocks.
C. The Metamorphic Rocks.

For laboratory practice, it is best to begin with rocks known to be igneous, and later to add material from the other classes. As the others are added it becomes necessary to have methods of distinction of these three classes.   For most rocks it is easy, on the basis of simple criteria, to determine this primary classification, but anyone of long experience has found many specimens the primary classification of which is very difficult, requiring all the skill of experts in microscopic and chemical tests.

[6] U. S. Geological Survey, Bulletins 814, 828, and 884; Folios 217, 223, and 225; Professional Papers 148, 160, 169, 171, and 176.

Some Criteria for Distinguishing Igneous, Sedimentary and Metamorphic Rocks

Igneous.

1. *Interlocking grains:* mostly hard rocks.
2. Characteristic mineral composition. Nepheline, olivine, chromite, leucite, perthite.
3. *Massive* (Figure 18); irregular shape, columnar joints (Figure 29); spheroidal weathering, only rarely banded.
4. Textures: glassy, porphyritic, amygdaloidal, cellular, orbicular, diabasic, graphic, miarolitic cavities, granitoid.
5. High in feldspar.
6. Enclosing rocks baked.
7. Gradation laterally into igneous rocks definitely identifiable.
8. Formation transgresses schistosity but seems influenced by it.
9. No fossils or strata.
10. Chilled borders.

Sedimentary.

1. *Stratification* (Fig. 53) and sorting; mostly soft rocks.
2. Textures: *Fragmental,* öolitic, pisolitic, porous, reniform, botryoidal, rounded and sorted grains.
3. Wide lateral extent.
4. The common rocks, clay, sandstone, limestone, and coal.
5. Intercalations with known sediments and gradations to them laterally.
6. Fossils.
7. Quartz chiefly, or calcite chiefly, or high in Al_2O_3 minerals, if soft.
8. Formation shows marked and regular differences in composition.
9. Formation persistently follows folds.
10. Minerals of chemical and organic precipitates. Salts, gypsum, glauconite, vein minerals, chert, and carbonates.
11. Textural changes in bands laterally and vertically.
12. Original textures such as cross-bedding, mud-cracks, ripple-marks foot-prints.
13. Not usually extremely basic.
14. Concretions, septaria, stalactites, crusts, etc.

Metamorphic.

1. *Parallelism* of mineral grains, *interlocking grains,* hard rocks.
2. Secondary *cleavage* independent of bedding.
3. *Banding* (Figs. 79, 80 and 84 to 87), foliation, *schistosity.*

4. Characteristic minerals, staurolite, andalusite, garnet, wollastonite, grossularite, tremolite, kyanite, sillimanite, cordierite, zoisite, talc, etc.

5. Distorted pebbles, fossils, crystals, etc.

6. Granulation, augen, mortar and flaser structures hornfels textures.

7. Presence of graphite in quantity (say 5 per cent).

8. Minerals as metacrysts (list, page 228).

9. Geographic and geologic position of outcrop: (*a*) in deeply eroded known pre-Cambrian regions, (*b*) next to rocks that may have affected it, (*c*) grading laterally into a recognizable metamorphic rock.

10. Rocks chiefly mica, chiefly chlorite, or hard rocks chiefly quartz or calcite.

CHAPTER II

GENERAL INTRODUCTION TO IGNEOUS ROCKS.
CLASSIFICATION

Igneous rocks are formed by the cooling or solidification of magma. Magma is a natural fluid in or on the earth, generally very hot, made up largely of a mutual solution of silicates, with some oxides and sulphides, and usually some water and other gases held in solution by pressure.

The igneous rocks are treated first because they have been the originals, according to our best light, from which the others have been directly or indirectly derived, either from the fragments, as afforded by their disintegration, or from the minerals and solutions, yielded by their alteration.

The igneous rocks occur in *dikes, sheets, laccoliths, bosses,* and vast irregular bodies for which we have no single term. Fragmental rocks form *surface beds* with little stratification. Dikes (spelled also dykes) have penetrated fissures in other rocks, and have solidified in them. They therefore constitute elongated and relatively narrow bodies, of all sizes, from a fraction of an inch in thickness and a few feet in length, to others a thousand or more feet across and miles in length. Sheets are bodies of relatively great lateral or horizontal extent, compared with their thickness. They are either surface flows which may be afterwards buried, or sills intruded between other strata. Intrusive sheets that are locally thickened to lenses are called laccoliths. The famous laccolithic sill of Shonkin Sag, Montana, is about 200 feet thick and a mile wide. Laccoliths of the type locality in southeastern Utah range from about one-seventh to one-tenth as thick as they are wide, and probably most show some complexity,—faulting or lack of symmetry. See Figures 3 and 4. Roughly cylindrical masses are called necks, if there is evidence of chilling in the conduit of a volcano, but such evidence is rarely conclusive. Irregular, projecting, rounded bodies are called bosses. The enormous masses of crystalline rocks like granite are called *batholiths*. They may be hundreds of square miles in area but are exposed in a variety of sizes. Those small masses 1 to 25 square miles in area, that re-

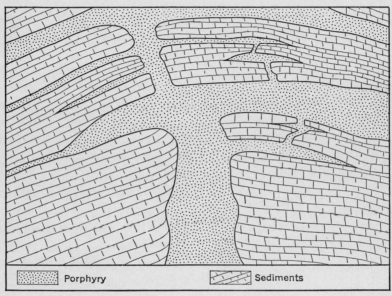

Porphyry   Sediments

Fig. 3.— Schematic section showing relations of intrusive forms, stock, sill and laccolith. La Plata Mountains, Colorado. (After E. B. Eckel.)

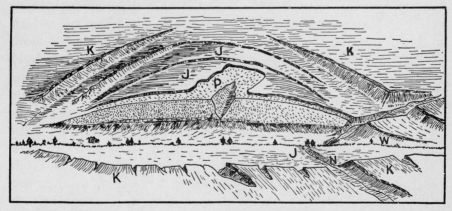

Fig. 4.— Stereographic sketch of Warm Springs laccolith (P), between sediments (J and K). The creek (W) cuts a section through the laccolith showing flat floor and domed roof. (After W. H. Weed.)

semble batholiths in material and origin are *stocks*.   Batholiths have in most if not all instances been uncovered only by long erosion, for the name means a rock belonging to the depths of the earth.   Intrusive masses of very irregular form are called *chonoliths*.   A large floored intrusive that is centrally sunken into the form of a basin is a *lopolith*.

Small dikes and *stringers* extending out from a large mass into its walls are *apophyses;* if they follow the foliation of a wall rock in thin *dikelets,* they form *lit-par-lit injection gneisses*.   It will be later brought out that the character of occurrence, whether as surface flow, dike, sheet, or batholith, has an important influence on texture.

Igneous rocks are commonly massive, as contrasted with the stratified structure of the sedimentary rocks, and the term massive has been employed as a synonym of igneous.   Other synonymous terms are *eruptive* and

Fig. 5. — A black dike in granite, Saganaga Lake, Minnesota.   Courtesy of the McGraw-Hill Book Company.

anogene, both meaning that the rocks have come up from below. Many years ago the distinction was made between those that have crystallized deep within the earth, the *plutonic,* and those that have been poured out on the surface, the *volcanic*.   The words intrusive and effusive or extrusive have been employed in much the same way.   Between surface flows and deep-seated masses (batholiths) every textural gradation is to be expected and is met, and some writers have even gone so far as to establish an intermediate group for rocks that have cooled as intruded

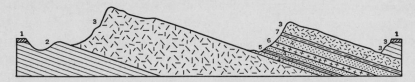

FIG. 6.— Two intruded sheets of andesite porphyry (3) near New Madrid, N. M.
Modified from D. W. Johnson.

sheets and dikes. The intrusive rocks at moderate depths are called *hypabyssal,* but no distinctive names are here based on occurrence. The textures are most satisfactory as a basis for classification, and the occurrence is only roughly indicated by the texture.

A small group of hypabyssal rocks with sugary texture or sugary groundmasses are distinguished in some schemes of classification, from the porphyries of more abundant dikes. Associated with certain stocks there are sugary dikes of two kinds, the more siliceous ones are *aplites,* and the more basic ones *lamprophyres.* If the two were mixed in the right proportions, they might yield a composition like that of the stock in which they are found,—they are "complementary" dikes. When this was first discovered some men jumped to the conclusion that the dikes had resulted from a splitting of the magma. The dikes were then classed as *diaschistic* (split in two) in contrast to the ordinary porphyry dikes which are *aschistic* (not split); but this is theoretical and not a good basis for terminology.

We are tending more and more to employ the word structure for the larger features of a rock, while the smaller features which may be seen even on a small fragment are described as textures. The structures of common igneous rocks (as distinct from stratified sediments) are massive; but there are some flow structures, and the almost universal joint systems. Columnar joints appear almost wholly in tabular igneous masses (Fig. 29). Many basic flows have ellipsoidal or pillow structures (Fig. 30). Mention should also be made of inclusions of several kinds (Fig. 17),

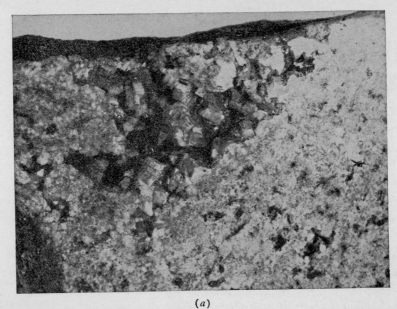

(a)

(b)

Fig. 7. — (a) Miarolitic cavity in granite, Minnesota. (b) Average granitoid
texture in granodiorite. Cottonwood County, Utah.

the *xenoliths* from outside, and cognate inclusions resulting from early solidification in the same magma chamber. Some inclusions and other irregularities in magmas may be drawn out into streaked structures of indefinite boundaries called *schlieren* (Fig. 17 (*c*)).

Textures cover the proportion of glass to crystals, the sizes of crystals, and the pattern of arrangement or fabric. *Glassy* texture, as the name implies, is that of glass or slag which has no definite minerals. It results when a molten magma is so quickly chilled that the minerals have no opportunity to form. *Porphyritic* implies large crystals, whether well formed or corroded and rounded, embedded in a more finely crystalline or even glassy groundmass. There may be several sizes and kinds of these crystals, and because of their prominence in the rock, they are called *phenocrysts,* i.e., apparent crystals. If a magma crystallizes as a mass of very fine or microscopic crystals without phenocrysts, its texture is described as *felsitic.* A *granitoid* texture has the coarse crystals all of about the same size, and very few grains possessing their own crystal boundaries. Strictly speaking, there is no groundmass in granitoid rocks. Some granitoid rocks, from a local abundance of mineralizers (as later explained) (pages 36–37), have small cavities into which the component minerals project with well-bounded crystals. Such are called *miarolitic* (Fig. 7 (*a*)). Those textures in which some part of the rock is too fine-grained or glassy to recognize minerals without a microscope are grouped together as *aphanites,* in contrast to *phanerites* which are granitoid. This serves to group all the textures into two groups and with any specific composition, the family name is indicated by combining the names of the aphanite (usually felsitic), and the name of a phanerite, as for example, the rhyolite-granite family.

A committee of British petrographers [1] delegated to study the matter have tentatively suggested that rocks with three sizes of grains be named as follows:

[1] A. K. Wells, Secretary: *Petrographic Nomenclature.* Geological Magazine, volume 73, pages 319–325, 1936.

MINIMUM DIMENSIONS OF

Plagioclase in Basalt-Gabbro Family		Quartz and Feldspar in Rhyolite-Granite Family	
> .5 mm.	Gabbro	> .5 mm.	Granite
.5 — .1 mm.	Dolerite	.5 — .05 mm.	Micro-granite (aplite)
< .1 mm.	Basalt	< .05 mm.	Rhyolite

This is still under consideration and will probably be applied chiefly in microscopic studies. The aplite and dolerite are here classed as fine granitoid.

Johannsen[2] divides the phanerites (granitoid rocks) into:

Very coarse .... above 3 cm.
Coarse .... 1–3 cm.
Medium .... 1–10 mm.
Fine .... below 1 mm.

The distinction of the several glasses, and the distinction of several porphyritic textures are perhaps more troublesome to the student than others. To gain familiarity with the glasses, it is probably necessary to work with labelled specimens. They show such a variety of appearances that no amount of text can serve as well as laboratory experience. One recognizes *perlite, pumice, scoria,* and others because he has seen them before.

The porphyries in classification (page 46) are aphanites, divided into those with less than half the rock in phenocrysts, and those with more than half. There are other porphyritic rocks besides these porphyries, however. If a granite—a phanerite, in which all grains are coarse—has large crystals, say one inch wide, in a matrix of grains about ⅛ to ¼ inch wide, the large grains are phenocrysts and the relatively fine grains form a groundmass, and the texture may be described as porphyritic with a granitoid groundmass. It is a porphyritic granite. This is a variety of phanerite, whereas the rhyolite porphyry and granite porphyry,

[2] A. Johannsen: *A Descriptive Petrology of the Igneous Rocks.* Volume 1, page 31, 1931.

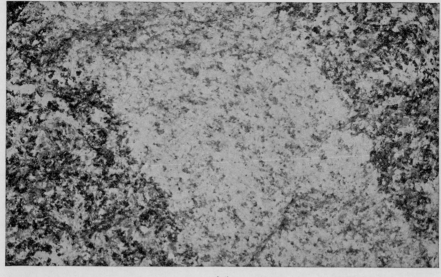

(a)

(b)

FIG. 8. — A wide range in granitoid textures. (a) Aplitic dike cutting St. Cloud, Minnesota, granodiorite of average granitoid texture. (b) Pegmatite of Vermilion batholith.

having groundmasses that are **actually** as well as relatively fine-grained, are aphanites.   See Figure 9 which shows *vitrophyre* and the three porphyritic rocks diagrammatically.   Porphyritic granite is a variety of granite, and only granite is named on page 46.

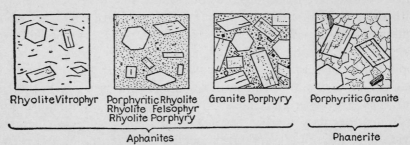

RhyoliteVitrophyr   PorphyriticRhyolite   Granite Porphyry   PorphyriticGranite
                     Rhyolite Felsophyr
                     Rhyolite Porphyry

Aphanites   Phanerite

FIG. 9.— Diagrams of the textural differences between the several porphyritic rocks of the rhyolite-granite clan.   Courtesy of ʹhe McGraw-Hill Book Company.   See also Figures 13, 20, 21, 23 and 32.

In spite of the fact that most igneous rocks are massive, there are some that have flow structures.   As a textural variety term to indicate flow structure in phanerites, it is proposed that *gneissoid* (like a gneiss) will serve to distinguish igneous structures (primary gneiss) from gneissic rocks, or gneisses, which are metamorphic.

The factors that largely determine whether lavas are erupted quietly or explosively, are the gas content and viscosity; and since most siliceous lavas are viscous, there are large volumes of siliceous fragmental rocks.   Most fragmental igneous rocks, however, have fragments of different sizes and compositions.   *Tuffs*[3] are the consolidated dusts and sandy fragments, and *breccias* are made of larger fragments (say over 1 cm. in diameter).   The explosive breccias are also commonly called *"agglomerates."*   Besides these there are some rare igneous breccias formed by forceful intrusion, breaking off and including fragments of wall rock; and some formed by the collapse of surface crusts on lavas, forming angular blocks in the liquid lava below.

Textures in igneous rocks are due to several factors that have influenced the consolidation of the magma.   The most important

[3] Formerly tuff was called "tufa" also, but that term is now usually reserved for precipitates from water.

are the rate of cooling, pressure, chemical composition, and the presence of dissolved vapors called mineralizers.

The fusibility varies with the chemical *composition*. The most silicic rocks prove to be most fusible (page 44). Anyone familiar with slags, however, will recall that ordinary slags, which are about equivalent to basalts, fuse to fluid slags, whereas the siliceous slags, though having a low melting temperature, are viscous and ropy. The importance of this as regards textures lies in the fact that the viscosity of siliceous melts interferes with crystallization and they are especially likely to yield glasses. The more fluid basic magmas flow farther from volcanic vents and are commonly crystalline, though a very quick cooling may form glass even of basaltic composition.

The *rate of cooling* has an important effect on size of grain. Cooling magmas tend to form crystals, and the rate of crystal formation largely determines the size of grain. There are several everyday examples. Granulated sugar is crystallized rather rapidly, but if larger crystals, "rock candy," are desired, a crystal is suspended in strong solution and allowed to stand at steady temperature for a long time. In the field it is very common to find that an intrusive rock of moderate size has a chilled margin of finer grain than the main central parts, with gradual transition from one texture to the other. In certain lavas it appears that crystals developed to notable size, it may be an inch or more in diameter, while the magma stood beneath the surface, in circumstances favorable to their formation. These are in suspension as the lava rises to the surface or near it where the final consolidation takes place and fixes them in the so-called groundmass. A quick chill makes a fine-grained groundmass when not a glassy one, and slow cooling yields one more coarsely crystalline, but in the final cooling or consolidation at or near the surface, crystals are seldom if ever developed of a size commensurable with those formed in the depths. By this process of partial crystallization below and final consolidation near the surface, the porphyritic texture is developed, but in strict accuracy it should be stated that rocks are known in which phenocrysts appear to have formed after the lavas came to rest. Magmas are solutions, and when they cool, they become saturated, first with one mineral and then another in sequence. If one constituent is abundant and its crystals grow large before the others in sequence begin to crystallize, it may form phenocrysts. There is also the complication that highly viscous magmas tend to become supersaturated, and in that state crystals grow only on the crystals already present—possibly "seed crystals" derived from adjoining rocks.

Many magmas flow to the surface with no phenocrysts (or "intratelluric" crystallizations) and then consolidate not as glass, but as finely crystalline aggregates. The resulting texture is called felsitic.

Pressure on magmas several miles below the surface may affect crystallization, but we are not certain just what the effects are. It is certain that pressure is necessary to hold gases in solution in magma, and the gases influence the texture.

Dissolved vapors in magmas include water, carbonic acid, hydrochloric acid, hydrofluoric acid, hydrogen sulphide, and many others. At first thought the student might suppose that red hot melted rock would not be able to dissolve such substances as water vapor. The solubility of gas, however, is a function of pressure and all are familiar with the use of pressure to hold gases in solution in liquids. The carbonated water at a soda fountain has carbonic acid held in solution by pressure. When the pressure is released by running the water into a glass, the carbonic acid gas separates from solution causing the effervescence. Basic magmas generally have a small per cent of dissolved gases, but acidic magmas seem to have more than basic, perhaps 5 to 10 per cent.[4] They affect the minerals that can be formed from a magma, for it must be evident that hydrous minerals like biotite could not form in a magma containing no water. They also affect the size of grains in the rocks, probably by reducing the viscosity of the melts; in the less viscous melt, diffusion permits the growth of large crystals, forming coarse rocks. It is doubtful if slow cooling can explain the growth of grains in a granite magma coarser than common granites. Even the largest batholiths, which needed thousands of years to crystallize, are mostly of normal granitoid tex-

[4] Gilluly, James: *The Water Content of Magmas.* American Journal of Science, volume 33, pages 430–441, 1937.

ture.   The coarser grain of pegmatite is then probably explained only by the concentration of vapors in a small part of the chamber. Because of these two effects, formation of new minerals and coarser minerals, the dissolved water and other gases are commonly called *mineralizers*.   They are the volatile or fugitive constituents.   Some may escape from the magma and "mineralize" the surrounding rocks.   The changes in the walls of a magma chamber, whether from mineralizers or simply from magmatic heat, are called contact metamorphism (pages 212–213).   When a lava with mineralizers reaches the surface, the release of pressure commonly results in a separation of steam bubbles, and a *cellular* lava; if the cavities are later filled with secondary minerals, it is *amygdaloidal* lava. In the siliceous lavas, the separation of gas may be so slow that not all escapes.   In an obsidian such as that at Obsidian Cliff, in Yellowstone Park, the mineralizers probably made it possible for certain parts of the mass to crystallize, forming stony layers and *stone bubbles*—lithophysae—in the glass.

For many years we have known that molten magmas behave essentially as solutions of some compounds in others and that solutions do not cease to be such even when the temperature is very high.   They tend to become uniform by diffusion, though their high viscosity makes this action much slower than in common water solutions.   They also cause the dissociation of some dissolved molecules.   At high temperatures rocks become mutual solutions rather than a solvent with other substances dissolved in it.   In spite of certain marked differences, therefore, the behavior of magmas may be inferred from the laws of solution and from the behavior of experimental melts in the laboratory.

Stages of magmatic action.—Many discussions of igneous action distinguish successive stages of magmatic action.   If the original magma is not as old as the earth, its first stage as magma is its formation and accumulation.   Early it may assimilate (dissolve) or "stope"[5] its walls, and be intruded.   If intruded near the surface, volatile constituents may "stream" to places of low pressure and may emanate to form pegmatites or react with the walls.

[5] Stoping is a term adapted by Professor Daly to igneous action, a technical mining term meaning to excavate to remove ore, commonly to excavate upwards.

Early cooling may cause the separation of partly miscible sulphides. The main cooling stage causes the normal crystallization of anhydrous silicates—the orthotectic stage; this may be accompanied by diffusion, convection, and crystal settling or floating. There is commonly a sequence of minerals formed, some early ones being zoned, some corroded. Stoping, emanation and assimilation may continue. The pegmatitic stage follows the orthotectic stage as mineralizers become concentrated and the magma reacts with early minerals to form others—the "deuteric" minerals as distinct from post-magmatic secondary minerals. Deformation at a late stage may squeeze out the last traces of liquid as from a filter press. Finally after all is solid, some solid solutions may break up on cooling. Where these magmatic changes in minerals and structures are conspicuous, some petrographers refer to them as *autometamorphism.*

In direct sequence after the truly magmatic and pegmatitic effects, there are commonly hydrothermal effects which are not truly magmatic, though the water may be of magmatic origin. These are indicated about the time chlorite forms from the mafic minerals.

Bowen[6] has given us the experimental basis for conclusions about the stages of crystallization of magma and calls his summary diagram "the reaction series."

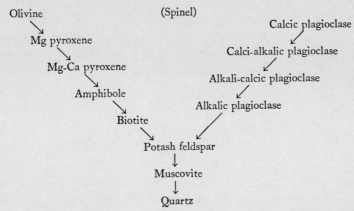

[6] N. L. Bowen: *The Reaction Principle in Petrogenesis.* Journal of Geology, volume 30, pages 177–198, 1922.

——: *The Behavior of Inclusions in Magmas.* Journal of Geology, volume 30, pages 513–570, 1922.

This arrangement gives us a logical basis for discussion of the sequence of growth of minerals in igneous rocks. It had been known for a long time that the granites seemed to have a *sequence* of minerals. By a study of the way one mineral included others and was molded around the corners of earlier crystals, Rosenbusch gave us the normal order, (1) ores, including apatite, magnetite, zircon, titanite, (2) ferromagnesian minerals, including olivine, augite, hornblende, biotite, (3) feldspars and feldspathoids, and (4) quartz. This is not opposed to the order seen in the lower part of Bowen's series. In granites it may be seen even in some hand specimens that hornblende is earlier than biotite, that albite is earlier than orthoclase, and that all these are earlier than quartz.

The Rosenbusch order is not so satisfactory, however, in basic rocks. Pyroxene and plagioclase may grow together, or either one before the other, the sequence depending on the compositions and abundance of the two minerals. This can be inferred from Bowen's series. Pyroxene and labradorite are at about the same level in the series, but the one in excess may start growing before the one in minor amounts. Vogt found[7] by measurements that, in gabbros over 55% plagioclase, the feldspars grew with lath-like crystal out-lines, making a texture called *diabasic,* whereas the similar rocks with less feldspar did not show laths, but irregular grains.

It is likely that the conditions in a large chamber of magma are more or less turbulent, because of injection and changes in temperature. It may and does often happen that crystals formed early in a magma are redissolved, or attacked, or that they react with the magma to form other minerals. It is because of these changes that Bowen's series (page 38) is called a reaction series. Near the upper part of the series, are the minerals that crystallize early, but as the magma changes by reason of their removal from solution, they may react with the late magma to form minerals lower in the series. Magnetite grows early in some basaltic glasses but, probably as a late reaction product, it may be one of the last minerals to crystallize in a diabase.

[7] J. H. L. Vogt: *The Physical Chemistry of the Crystallization and Magmatic Differentiation of Igneous Rocks.* Journal of Geology, volume 29, pages 439–443, 1921.

It may also happen that after one series of minerals, usually of large size and intratelluric origin, has formed, the series is repeated on a small scale as far back as the ferromagnesian silicates. Minerals of a so-called second generation thus result, but they are always much smaller than the phenocrysts and are characteristic of the groundmass.

Sharp division lines such as are drawn on page 46 are very artificial, and nature does not separate igneous rocks so sharply. At many places one kind of igneous rock grades into another by imperceptible steps. A large outcrop of coarse rock may be granite at one end and syenite or diorite a few rods away without any sharp contacts. It is possible that these grew from a magma that was much more nearly uniform when it was emplaced. It is not to be assumed that any magma is perfectly uniform [8] because such a liquid should be in vigorous reaction with its roof and walls. It seems clear, however, that some rock series result from a process of *differentiation*—a process by which a magma more or less uniform to start with separates to form two or more rocks of different compositions.

Two processes on a laboratory scale may serve to show that magmas may differentiate in more than one way. There are probably four or five ways in all. 1. If a mixture of alcohol and water in a barrel is frozen slowly, the outside freezes to ice with very little alcohol, and the center finally freezes with most of the alcohol. 2. If a saturated solution of salts in a beaker of water is frozen slowly, the salts crystallize early and being of higher specific gravity than the liquid, settle to the bottom forming a layer, before the mixture of salts and ice finally freezes above.

In a number of coarse igneous rocks, differentiation has resulted in the accumulation of a certain mineral or element in such concentrations as to prove valuable or interesting. These are then called magmatic segregations of the mineral or element. Most of them have bases concentrated and silica left in the magma and are therefore called "basic segregations." The criteria of segregated ores

[8] Sollas in 1894 wrote in the Transactions of Royal Irish Academy, volume 30, page 506, "An original homogeneous magma does not seem to be an existence discovered by observation; it is rather of the nature of a postulate . . . which to my mind is opposed to the general probabilities."

include not only the occurrence in large bodies of igneous rock, but a restricted group of ore minerals, a granitoid texture, and the occurrence of euhedral rock silicates in a matrix of ore minerals (Fig. 35).

Since about 1900 the theory of differentiation has been very popular as an explanation of the differences in different parts of igneous masses. It has perhaps been applied too many times when other explanations would serve as well. Igneous rocks may differ as a result of assimilation, of partial or complete fusion, of mixing of different magmas and of gradation by *lit-par-lit* injection into schists (page 233).

A word should be added about the chemical compositions of rocks and the interpretation of analyses. Even as in mineralogy the student learns the compositions of minerals, commonly without any skill at mineral analysis, so the student of rocks should have some general ideas of rock composition even if he has not the skill to make a rock analysis—the course in rock analysis is about a term's work. No one attempts to memorize the chemical analyses of a long list of rock varieties, but after some experience one may have a fair idea of the mineral composition of common rocks. Since the minerals are more definite in composition and the common ones are not too numerous, one may easily calculate an approximate chemical analysis for any common rock. Such a process is outlined in Chapter XIII.

Chemical analyses are commonly reported in percentages of oxides, for the most part, and these are arranged in the following series: SiO_2, Al_2O_3, Fe_2O_3, FeO, MgO, CaO, Na_2O, K_2O, $H_2O +$, $H_2O —$, CO_2, TiO_2, ZrO_2, P_2O_5, S, MnO, BaO, and others more rarely. If H_2O and CO_2 are abundant in igneous rocks they indicate decay and throw uncertainty over the relations of the rest. When an analysis is available, it may be used as a basis for calculation of minerals,—either theoretical or observed minerals. A well-known scheme of calculation proposed in 1903 by four eminent petrographers led to a mineral analysis in terms of possible minerals, a "norm." See Chapter XIII, Problem 6, page 259. It might happen that none of "normative" minerals was actually in the rock analyzed, and the scheme has not been as widely used as its authors hoped. The actual mineral composition, in contrast, is called the "mode."[9] It can be calculated from the analyses of some rocks if the particular minerals present are known and not too complex. In Chapter XIII this subject is further treated with an illustrative example.

Using the data of chemical analyses, with more or less calculation, some diagrams have been devised. On page 43 a variety of rocks are shown in diagrams of a kind credited to Michel-Levy, but modified successively by Broegger, Hobbs, and Spurr. With a little study these could easily be interpreted into the minerals that would result. Only those with a long silica line yield quartz. Potash is needed for orthoclase, and soda for albite and nepheline, —nepheline when the silica line is short. MgO in large amounts yields olivine, or with abundant silica the orthorhombic pyroxene. See also the diagrams on pages 116–119.

The specific gravity or density of an igneous rock is an important feature in its practical bearings. While it may in ice be less than 1, and in glasses reach 2.25, yet in the common rocks it is seldom below 2.50, and ranges from this to over 3.00. Determinations are important in those rocks used for building purposes, and are expressed in pounds per cubic foot. For data on the several igneous rocks, see page 111.

The temperatures of magmas are variously estimated as from 500° to 1300° C. and by some petrologists much higher. There is little evidence that underground magma is hotter than 1100° C. and the higher temperatures are observed only at lava lakes where burning gases cause a local heating. No mineral remains solid above its own melting temperature at the prevailing pressure, but magmas do not commonly require such high temperatures as are needed to melt minerals. Mixtures of minerals melt at lower temperatures than pure compounds, and the mineralizers are especially effective in reducing the temperature needed to keep a magma fluid. Pegmatite magmas probably remain fluid to 500° C. Some minerals break up into other compounds as they begin to melt, and

---

[9] In the norm system, hypothetical minerals are grouped as *salic* and *femic,* terms which should not be used for actual minerals. The corresponding terms for the minerals of the mode are *felsic* and *mafic* (page 21).

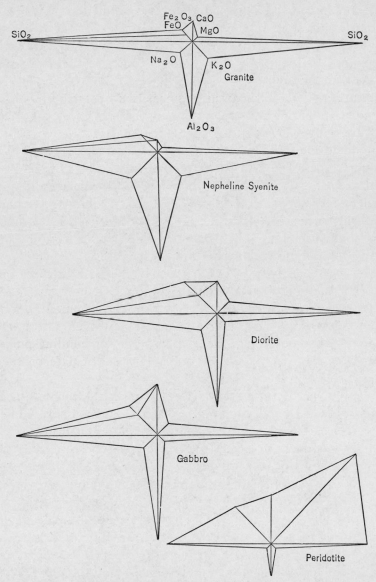

Fig. 10. — Diagrams of the chemical composition of typical rocks in several clans. The method is credited to W. C. Broegger. As here drawn, the lengths of the lines radiating from the centers are proportional to the percentages of the constituents reported in analyses. The directions for each constituent are constant for the whole series. From a study of the diagrams, the probable mineral compositions can be predicted.

are said to melt "incongruently." The accompanying table is of interest in this connection.

MELTING TEMPERATURES OF SOME ROCK-FORMING MINERALS

Degrees Centrigrade

Orthoclase (incongruent) .... 1170–1530 ± 5
Plagioclase
    Albite .... 1100 ± 10
    Anorthite .... 1550 ± 2
Olivine
    Forsterite, Mg_2SiO_4 1890
    Fayalite, Fe_2SiO_4 (incongruent) .... 1205 ± 2
Enstatite (incongruent) 1557–1577
Diopside .... 1391 ± 2
Leucite .... 1755 +
Silica (cristobalite) .... 1710 ± 10
Spinel, $MgAl_2O_4$ .... 2135 ± 20
Corundum .... 2050 ± 4
Magnetite .... 1591 ± 5
Pyrrhotite .... about 1185

The more complex micas, amphiboles, and pyroxenes have less definite temperature ranges of melting.

Igneous rocks commonly melt in a range of temperatures around 900° to 1100° C. The melting process is complex and progressive, the first liquid being formed by reaction between minerals in contact. Very little careful work has been done on rocks themselves, as compared to work on minerals, but Goranson has furnished data for Stone Mountain granite.[10] At 700 ± 50° C. and under a water vapor pressure of 980 bars, the granite became almost completely liquid, and had 6.5% water in solution. A typical granite, powdered, heated for a week at 800° C. without water became about half liquid. It required a temperature about 300° C. higher to develop a corresponding degree of melting in basalt.[11]

Distribution of Igneous Rocks as a Whole. — Igneous rocks crop out at the surface of the earth chiefly in mountainous regions, or in the older "Shield" areas that were once mountainous. This

[10] R. W. Goranson: *Some Notes on the Melting of Granite.* American Journal of Science, volume 23, page 236, 1932.

[11] Greig, Merwin, and Shepherd: In Carnegie Institution of Washington, Year Book 30, pages 77–78, 1931.

means that in North America, for example, there are many exposures of igneous rock in the Appalachian Mountains, in the Cordillera, and in the Canadian Shield. Smaller areas are in the Black Hills and Ozark Mountains. Relatively few igneous rocks are known in the great plains and Mississippi Valley.

The Naming of Rocks. — Some very ancient names for rocks are retained without any attempt to give them systematic form. Most rock names end in *-ite,* as do mineral names. J. D. Dana once suggested the use of *-yte* for rock names, so that there would not be any confusion with mineral terms in the printed name. The suggestion was not widely adopted and appears now only where the root-word ends in the letter *y,* as in trachyte and tachylyte.

The Classification. — In the matter of the study and determination of a rock species, especially of an igneous rock, it is desirable to procure materials as fresh and unaltered as possible. If feldspars have all changed to clay, if ferromagnesian silicates are merely chlorite or serpentine, and if secondary quartz, calcite and the like have formed, it is very difficult if not impossible to draw correct or even well-grounded inferences. Many rocks near ore bodies are of this character.

Bearing in mind the differences of texture and the causes of them, we can group igneous rocks in such arrangement that they can be intelligently studied, and identified with a reasonable close approximation to the truth. It should be appreciated, however, that with finely crystalline rocks, whose components are too small for the unassisted eye, the microscope is the only resource, and with this as an aid much greater subdivision can be attained. The object here in view is to limit the discussion purely to the study without the microscope.

The scheme of classification of the igneous rocks has two principles underlying it, namely: (1) texture, related to occurrence and (2) mineralogic composition, related to chemical composition. The textures are five: granitoid, porphyritic, felsitic, glassy, and fragmental, and the table is arranged from top to bottom so that they come in this order. The arrangement is adopted because it brings at the outset the rocks in which minerals and textures can be clearly seen. The word porphyry as a suffix has been adopted

ACIDIC ⟸⟸⟸ Excess of light-colored minerals   **Table II for the megascopic classification of**   ⟹⟹⟹ BASIC   Excess of dark-colored minerals

IGNEOUS ROCKS

Usual Occurrence	Texture	Chief Feldspar Orthoclase — ± Biotite ± Hornblende ± Augite			Chief Feldspar Plagioclase — Biotite (or) (and) Hornblende		Pyroxene (usually Augite)		Nepheline or other Feldspathoid	No Feldspar or Feldspathoid — Augite (or) (and) Hornblende ± Biotite		Ultra-basic Rocks
		+ Quartz	− Quartz − Nepheline	+ Nepheline	+ Quartz	− Quartz	− Olivine	+ Olivine		− Olivine	+ Olivine	
Batholiths, Laccoliths	Granitoid	Granite	Syenite	(Rare) Nepheline-Syenite	Quartz-Diorite	Diorite	**G A B B R O** Gabbro	Olivine-Gabbro	A series of dark rocks not readily distinguished	**G R O U P** Pyroxenite (Hornblendite)	Peridotite	Basic Segregations in normal magmas
Intrusive Sheets Dikes, Laccoliths	Porphyritic, Phenocrysts Predominant	Granite-porphyry	Syenite-porphyry	(Rare) Nepheline-Syenite-porphyry	Quartz-Diorite-porphyry	Diorite-porphyry	Gabbro-porphyry	Olivine-Gabbro-porphyry		(Rare) Pyroxenite-porphyry	Peridotite-porphyry	
Dikes, Laccoliths	Porphyritic, Phenocrysts Prominent	Rhyolite-porphyry	Trachyte-porphyry	(Rare) Phonolite-porphyry	Dacite-porphyry	Andesite-porphyry	Basalt-porphyry	Olivine-Basalt-porphyry	(Rare in America)	(Rare) Augitite-porphyry	Limburgite-porphyry	
Surface Flows	Felsitic, Glassy, Cellular, Phenocrysts Few	Rhyolite **FELSITE**	Trachyte	Phonolite **GROUP**	Dacite	Andesite	Basalt **BASALT**	Olivine-Basalt		(Rare) Augitite **GROUP**	Limburgite	Meteorites
Crusts, Surface Flows	Glassy	Dense: Obsidian; Very vesicular: Pumice; Special features: Perlite, Pitchstone; With phenocrysts: Vitrophyres				Andesite-obsidian	Basalt-obsidian = Tachylyte Scoria					
Beds Strata	Fragmental	Fine-grained,—Ash, if in loose grains; Tuff, if well cemented. Coarse-grained,—Breccia and Agglomerate. Note: Most of these rocks contain fragments of several different compositions. If one kind dominates, prefix to the term Breccia or Tuff, the name of the felsite or basalt of that composition.										Ice

for the intermediate members, which roughly correspond with the intrusive rocks.   Older classifications, after which this is modelled, used the occurrence as a basis for names, but occurrence is not so readily determined in hand specimens as the texture, here used. It must be appreciated that the methods of field occurrence follow these textural differences only in a general way.   Thus thick surface flows will have porphyritic textures at their centers, and dikes are known with glassy borders.   Thick intrusive sheets and laccoliths are practically granitoid, like the batholiths, and the batholiths themselves locally become roughly porphyritic from the exceptional development of the feldspars.   Nevertheless an important general rule is emphasized by the arrangement, and the truth that texture is largely a function of depth and pressure, is brought out.   Not all the rocks described in the text appear in the table, since some are of rare occurrence and would prevent a due sense of proportion. All these together with synonyms and relatives will be subsequently emphasized, so far as is appropriate for an elementary book.

The rocks are arranged from left to right on a mineralogical principle, and chiefly on the basis of the predominant feldspar, as is the usual custom.   This also makes possible a general succession from those most acidic on the left to those most basic on the right, but while this is true for the extremes, it is not strictly so for intermediate points because dacites and quartz-diorites are far higher in silica than are phonolites and nepheline-syenites, and even than trachytes and syenites.   The importance of the bases is not to be overlooked and tables of average analyses are given on page 107. For brevity the mineral headings in the table are much shortened.   The student should understand, for example, that "— Quartz" means "without essential amounts of quartz," perhaps less than 5 per cent.

The subdivisions of plagioclase rocks are here based on the nature of the ferromagnesian minerals.   In more advanced microscopic work, it may be better to use the kinds of plagioclase, but these are clearly impossible of distinction in the hand specimens.   In the naming of most rocks, it makes no difference whether plagioclase or the dark minerals are used.   See page 38 giving Bowen's reaction series.   At the level of augite, the plagioclase is labradorite, and at the level of hornblende and biotite the plagioclase is andesine or oligoclase. This association is found in probably 90 per cent of the plagioclase rocks. In a few rare rocks labradorite may be intergrown with hornblende, or augite with andesine. These exceptional rocks might be differently named by the field worker and the petrographer with a microscope.

Several men in recent years have emphasized the importance of the volume percentage of dark (or better mafic) minerals as a basis for classification of rocks. This appears on page 46 only in the distinction of

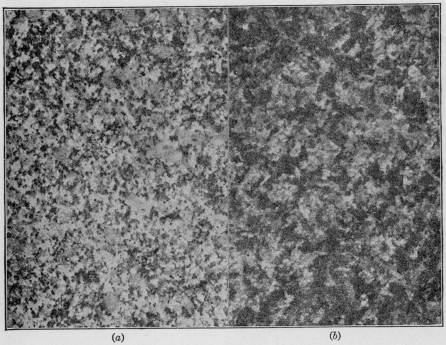

(a)   (b)

FIG. 11. — Granitoid rocks of different color tones (a) Granite, a leucocratic rock, Giants Range, Minnesota. (b) Gabbro, a melanocratic rock, Salem neck, Massachusetts. About natural size. Courtesy of the McGraw-Hill Book Company.

rocks with "no feldspar." In other families, detailed variety names may be based on percentages, as for example, anorthosite (page 84) as a variety of *gabbro*. Exceptionally light rocks in any clan may be indicated, if desired, by a prefix, leuco-, and dark rocks by the prefix, mela- (Fig. 11), but the average granite is very light and average gabbro is about half mafic.

There are also, especially among microscopic petrographers, those who favor more use of alkalies in classification, distinguishing alkalic from less alkalic groups. Alkalic rocks have (1) more than average alkali for that clan in which they occur, or (2) minerals in which the molecular ratio of alkali to silica is greater than 1 to 6, including feldspathoids and some sodic amphiboles and pyroxenes. These are not very easily distinguished in the field.

The Determination of Igneous Rocks. — In determining an igneous rock, the texture should be noted first, the feldspars next. If orthoclase prevails, the presence or absence of quartz establishes the rock. If plagioclase prevails, we look for biotite, hornblende, pyroxene, quartz and olivine. If no feldspar is present, we look for the presence or absence of olivine. We then refer to the table on page 46. While books are of great assistance, the only way to become really familiar with rocks is to use the books in connection with correctly labeled and sufficiently complete study collections. The fine-grained rocks and tuffs elude the power of the unassisted eye. If light colored they are referred to the felsites. A few felsites may be medium dark colored (as obsidian is) from magnetite in very fine particles, but the more common colors are white, pink, red, purple, light gray, yellow, or brown. Basalts are much darker, black, dark gray, or dark green. Weathering turns some basaltic rocks lighter gray, or red from hematite, but the red is commonly different from the redness of pink feldspar and of felsites.

Care should be used not to confuse phenocrysts and *amygdules*.

Phenocrysts	*Amygdules*
Crystal forms common, plane faces, sharp corners, parallel sides, regular arrangement.	Spherical, almond-shaped (Figure 12), or pipe-like.
Usually single crystals.	Commonly aggregates, radial or concentric.
Common in many felsitic rocks.	Common in dark felsitic rocks.
Quartz, feldspars, hornblende, augite, and olivine.	Quartz, calcite, zeolites, chlorite, epidote.

Porphyries are commonly classified from the minerals which are visible as phenocrysts, with little regard for the groundmass even if it is much over half the rock. This may lead to error, but no alternative is available until the microscope or chemical work reveals the nature of the groundmass.

The student should be reminded of the methods of distinction of feldspars (page 13). If crystals of feldspar are too small to recognize by their inherent characters, but the light color indicates their presence, their nature should be estimated by association. In a light-colored porphyry with only quartz phenocrysts the feldspar should be considered orthoclase. In a gray porphyry with only olivine, or only augite phenocrysts, the feldspar should be considered plagioclase. If the same minerals appear in a black groundmass, there is a possibility that no feldspar is present; but such rocks with no feldspar are so rare that none should be assumed to occur without strong reasons. In a gray porphyry with only hornblende or only biotite phenocrysts, orthoclase may be assumed, but is not at all certain.

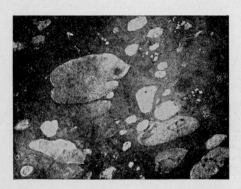

Fig. 12. — The forms of amygdules, almond-shaped to ellipsoidal. Natural size.

A similar situation arises in the distinction of hornblende and augite when crystals are too small to recognize by their inherent characters. If a granitoid rock with nearly 100% plagioclase is to be classified on page 46, the dark mineral is assumed from its association to be augite (page 16) and the rock is a gabbro. Similarly a rock with only plagioclase phenocrysts in a black groundmass, is assumed to have augite in the groundmass, and is therefore a basalt-porphyry. No other minerals are assumed to be present unless they can be seen.

These estimates are not pure guesses but are made according to rule and custom, and the names so given are used and agreed to by other students so that there is uniformity in the naming, unless microscopic work shows that some feature was missed.

The commonest errors in field identification result from the difficulty in distinguishing orthoclase and plagioclase so that some quartz diorites may be called granites; some *syenite* may be called diorite, and *vice versa*. It is a common practice in field work in the pre-Cambrian Shield areas to call many rocks "feldspar-porphyry," not distinguishing whether the feldspar is orthoclase or plagioclase. Almost as difficult is the distinction of hornblende from augite, in consequence of which some gabbro may be supposed to be diorite, and *vice versa*. These errors must be expected by field workers at places, and the corrections made by laboratory study afterward are no reflection on the character of the field work. With increased equipment more accurate work is expected, but the work on hand specimens should be carried as far as convenient.

CHAPTER III

THE IGNEOUS ROCKS, Continued

The Rhyolite-Granite Clan. The Trachyte-Syenite Clan. The Phonolite-Nepheline-Syenite Clan

PHANERITES OF THE RHYOLITE-GRANITE CLAN

General Description. — The rocks of this clan are a large and diversified group. All its members have the light-colored minerals, quartz, orthoclase and plagioclase in great excess. The dark-colored minerals, biotite, hornblende, and augite, of which biotite is the commonest, are greatly in the minority. The accessory minerals, magnetite, hematite, pyrite, etc., are few and inconspicuous. The prevailing colors are light grays, yellows, and pale reds, but darker shades especially of red are not uncommon.

Mineralogic Composition and Varieties of Granite. — Granites are granitoid rocks consisting of orthoclase or microcline, silicic plagioclase, quartz, and a small amount of mica or some other ferromagnesian mineral. The dark minerals range from 1 to 25% of the rock, but rarely more. Biotite is much the commonest mica, and when it is present alone the rock may be called *biotite granite* or *normal granite.* Fine-grained light-colored granite in dikes is called *aplite* and commonly has more muscovite than average. The grain sizes are such as characterize *microgranite* (page 32). The same texture may appear in syenite aplite, quartz-diorite aplite and others, but the term aplite without qualification indicates a rock of the granite clan. Hornblende is common, either with biotite or by itself, giving then *hornblende granite.*[1] *Augite granite* is much less common. Where quartz and feldspar are the only two minerals, we have the so-called *binary granite,* though that term has been applied also to granites with two micas. Granites with almost

---

[1] In former years this aggregate was called syenite, but the modern usage is different.

half the feldspar plagioclase (especially if andesine) are called *quartz monzonites*. Granites with exceptionally coarse feldspars scattered in a normal granitoid groundmass are *porphyritic granites* (Fig. 13).

Near the borders of large intrusives and more rarely near the centers, there are very coarse crystalline aggregates of the same

FIG. 13.— Porphyritic granite, Goudreau, Ontario. Groundmass has grains about one-eighth inch in diameter. About one-half natural size.

minerals as granite, called *pegmatites* (Fig. 8 (*b*)). If the same coarse textures appear in rocks of other clans, they may be called syenite pegmatite, diorite pegmatite, etc., but the term pegmatite without qualification indicates a rock of the granite clan. In the pegmatites is the home of the *graphic granite* (Fig. 14), the curious intergrowth of quartz and feldspar such that on certain feldspar cleavage faces the quartz makes a pattern suggesting cuneiform or runic characters.   Here also is the home of the soda-potash feld-spars that have "unmixed" on cooling to form perthite,—a potash feldspar with streaks of intergrown albite.   Only about one per cent of a large intrusive is pegmatite, and most of that is near the border or in the schists around the intrusive, in veins or dikes—it is an open question which is the more correct term.   Pegmatites may be associated in the same dike with aplites and both may grade imperceptibly into the main intrusive and into quartz veins (*silexite*

FIG. 14. — Graphic granite, about natural size.

if formed from magma with little feldspar), though the aplites commonly have sharper walls than pegmatites. At a few places pegmatites contain remarkable concentrations of rare elements and of mineral-izers. They have received a great deal of attention because they supply some commercial ores, such as those of lithium, tin, and radium. Pegmatites are direct sources of feldspars, muscovite, and a variety of gem minerals. We conclude from laboratory studies of melts containing volatile constituents that the early crystallization of non-volatile constituents in a magma left the late residue so rich in volatile matter that the vapor pressure be-came enormous and the residual magma with its mineralizers had a violent tendency to break out through the outer and already solidified parts of the rock. The granites crystallize at about 700° C., but the optical study of quartz in pegmatites indicates that mineralizers keep the residual pegmatite magma liquid down to temperatures below 575° C. At such temperatures the magma may be highly aqueous and perhaps even above its critical tem-perature, so that it is very fluid. It can circulate through early rocks, formed at the borders of the chamber, and replace them largely with rare minerals. Thus may be formed the great "logs" of spodumene, 42 feet long, beryl crystals weighing tons, as well as other large crystals.[2]

At still lower temperatures, the outer portions of granite masses may be attacked in a different way by escaping mineralizers,—hot water and boric and hydrofluoric acid. These develop tourmaline in quantity and in rare instances fluorite and cassiterite. At the extreme of such an alteration is a quartz-tourmaline aggregate without feldspar—a *tourmalite*. The vapor may change the borders of granites to a mass of quartz and white mica, affording the rock that is called *greisen* and that is a familiar gangue for tin ores. The changes are so great that the rocks are no longer granites as classified on page 46, but the changes come so soon after crystallization that they are not commonly described as metamorphic. They may be called autometamorphic.

FIG. 15.— Orbicular granite, Idaho. About one-half natural size.

Granites are commonly gray, white, reddish or bluish in color. The feldspar is mainly responsible for this, as quartz is colorless and transparent and biotite and hornblende are not specially abundant; but unusual richness in the last named silicates tends to darken the rock. Irregular dark streaks are called schlieren, and where the dark minerals assume concentric layered structures, the granite is called *orbicular*. Such rocks are commonly local facies of large masses.

Wall rock fragments of all sizes may become dislodged and form dark inclusions in magmas, and the minerals of the inclusions commonly react with the magma to form those minerals that are crystallizing from the magma.[3] Shales and slate are especially

[2] J. F. Kemp: *The Pegmatites.* Economic Geology, volume 19, page 697, 1924.

[3] N. L. Bowen: *The Behavior of Inclusions in Igneous Magmas.* Journal of Geology, volume 30, pages 513–570, 1932. Some dark spots have been considered segregations, but such segregation has not been demonstrated.

J. F. Kemp noted that some masses called "segregations" were no doubt partly digested inclusions. Economic Geology, volume 19, page 713, footnote.

subject to recrystallization and become deceptively like igneous rocks in minerals and textures, commonly with a texture that resembles a porphyry. Some large intrusions, however, have dark border facies that solidify early and furnish some "cognate" fragments to the later main facies as inclusions. Thus the origin of the dark inclusions is not easily determined in most granites. Those from outside the magma chamber are called xenoliths.

Fig. 16.— Granodiorite, Alta stock, Utah. About one-half natural size. The length of the dark inclusion is parallel to the needles of hornblende, and both are normal to the aplite dikes.

Many granites, which on casual inspection seem to be massive or lacking in oriented grains, have in recent years been found to show some structure (see page 5). If there is no clear evidence of metamorphism, and especially if the related aplites and pegmatites show no internal structure, the rocks are igneous and properly still called granites. Rocks of much the same character may result from metamorphism and are called granite gneisses. To distinguish the granites with flow structures from metamorphosed granites, they may be called *gneissoid granites*,—the suffix *oid* meaning like. Many students have referred to them as "primary gneisses" (Fig. 17 (*b*)).

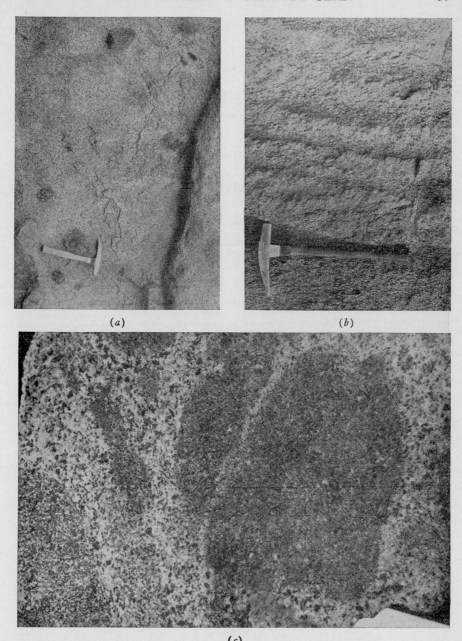

(a)

(b)

(c)

FIG. 17. — Dark inclusions and schlieren, Boulder batholith, Montana. (a) Small scattered inclusions. (b) Ill-defined layers with slight concentration of dark minerals. (c) Inclusions; some are distinctly outlined and others grade into schlieren.

The average granite contains nearly 50 per cent potash feldspar, 20 per cent plagioclase, over 20 per cent quartz, and 3 to 15 per cent biotite. These values range widely without transgressing the boundaries set by the table, page 46. It must be admitted, however, that the term granite has been used for many quartz rocks in the field (a) without careful examination of the feldspar. The so-called granites may be over half plagioclase. It may be added also that commercial dealers in building and ornamental stone use the term for granitoid rocks of all sorts, including even gabbros under the name "black granite."

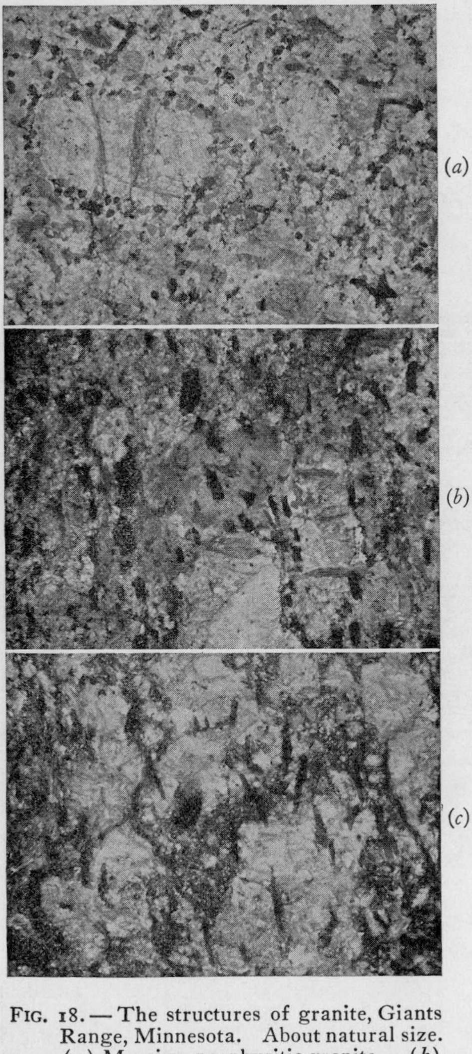

The student should attempt to fix in mind rather accurately these mineral percentages. If they can be remembered along with the chemical nature of minerals given on pages 11 to 21, the chemical nature of the granite clan can be estimated very (c) closely. Chapter XIII gives illustrative estimates.

Relationships. — The gradation of granites, through granite-porphyries and microgranites, into rhyolite-porphyries and felsites, has been remarked. Along the borders of some intrusions, this can be traced inch by inch to a

Fig. 18. — The structures of granite, Giants Range, Minnesota. About natural size. (a) Massive, porphyritic granite. (b) Gneissoid porphyritic granite. (c) Porphyritic granite gneiss. (a) and (b) are igneous structures, but (c) may be metamorphic.

place where the porphyritic texture is due to a quick chill. Mt. Willard, in the Crawford Notch of the White Mountains, is a classic locality for this transition. It was described in 1881 by Geo. W. Hawes, and will be referred to again under the products of contact metamorphism. The close relationship of the granite porphyries with granite hardly needs to be mentioned. As quartz decreases, they grade to syenites by insensible steps, and as horn-blende or biotite and plagioclase increase, they grade to diorites. Intermediate varieties, which are very common, are quartz-mon-zonites. Transitional passages to gabbro, from increase of augite and plagioclase, are also well recognized.

Uses. — Granites are much more extensively employed for structural purposes than any other igneous rock, and indeed in the trade almost any crystalline rock consisting of silicates is called granite. They are in general the strongest of the common build-ing stones. Crushing resistances range from 10,000 to 40,000 pounds per square inch in a 2-inch cube. The important points are homogeneity of texture, good, rectangular jointing in the quarry, adaptability to tool treatment, durability, and pleasing color.

Alteration, Metamorphism. — In ordinary weathering granites suffer first by the oxidation of the protoxide of iron in the ferro-magnesian silicates (biotite, hornblende), and the formation of other secondary minerals. The feldspars are soon kaolinized, and the rock thus becomes hydrated. Pyrite, if present, is an active agent in decay. Recent studies show the progressive changes dur-ing prolonged weathering (page 130). Similar sets of analyses have been made at a number of places with analogous results. The rocks are mechanically broken up at the same time leaving soils, in which spires and boulders indicate the nature of the original rock (page 125).

Hot water or hydrothermal attack results in sericite most com-monly, turning the rock soft, dull, and light-colored; it is then very easily deformed by stresses to sericite schist.[4] Some impor-

[4] G. M. Schwartz: *Alteration of a Colorado Granite to Sericite Schist.* Journal of Geology, volume 41, pages, 537–45, 1933.

tant china clay deposits are believed to result from hot water attack on pegmatites, a deep-seated kaolinization.   At places, hot waters also cause silicification and various other mineralogical changes. The formation of tourmalite and greisen was noted on page 55.

Under dynamic stress granites are more or less crushed and have their minerals drawn out into laminations so that they become gneissic.   Beyond question many gneisses have resulted in this way, as for example in the Archean of the Canadian Shield and in the Front Range of Colorado.   The structures were doubtless induced while the granite was deeply buried and subjected to pressure while closely confined, so that the yielding came in a gradual flow.   Some coarse orthoclase of the pegmatites or porphyritic granites may be left as "eyes," or to adopt the German term *"augen,"* affording augen gneisses of granitic composition.

Other gneisses, however, result from the injection of true granite or pegmatite in relatively narrow but numerous dikes into laminated rocks.   These mixed rocks are partly igneous and partly metamorphic, but are commonly listed as metamorphic because of their pronounced structure (Fig. 86).   Sederholm proposed for the mixed rocks the term, *migmatites*.   Where the magma followed thin layers of schist, the gneiss is said to result from *lit-par-lit* injection (page 28 and Figs. 85–6).

Distribution. — Granites are abundant along the Atlantic coast, and are near tidewater from Canada to Virginia.   Farther south they lie back of the Coastal Plain.   They are extensively quarried. A famous hornblende granite is obtained at Quincy, Massachusetts. In the old crystalline areas of Michigan, Wisconsin, and Minnesota, and north throughout the Canadian Shield granites are common. Missouri has many in the region of the porphyries, cited below, and Texas has a building stone quarry in fine granite.   In the West, the Black Hills, the Rocky Mountains, the Wasatch, and the Sierras are abundantly supplied.   They are equally common in Europe and elsewhere the world over.   The famous hornblende biotite granite of Syene was quarried in early Egyptian times for pyramids and oblelisks, and in recent years for the Nile dam.

Silexite, the quartz-rich dikes, crop out in the Adirondacks and many batholithic areas.   Interesting complex pegmatites are known

in New England, in the Black Hills and near San Diego, California.
Famous aplites occur in the quartz monzonite at Butte, Montana.
All of these rocks, however, are well known in hundreds of places.

Aphanites of the Rhyolite-Granite Clan

General Description. — The rhyolites are high in silica and
their melts are therefore usually viscous and thick, and their movements are not marked by the fluidity shown by the more basic

Fig. 19.— Platy parting, flow lines and inclusion in rhyolite.
Black Hills, South Dakota.

rocks.   When solidified many show flow layers which originally
suggested their name from the Greek verb meaning to flow.   Technically the structure is called *eutaxitic,* and it commonly results in
a platy parting in the .rhyolites of the American Cordillera, and
to some extent in those of the older Shield areas (Fig. 19).

The textures of the aphanites in this clan range widely and
upon them are based the principal variety names.   The *Rhyolites
proper,* are felsitic to slightly porphyritic rocks.   A few of them

are somewhat cellular because of their occurrence as surface flows, whose dissolved vapors have separated from solution at atmospheric pressure and formed the cells. Such cells are less common in this clan than in basic flows, but are fairly well distributed. When the texture is felsitic, it is impossible to tell rhyolites from trachytes and dacites without tests with the microscope or analysis, and the non-committal term *felsite* is convenient. With the development of a few phenocrysts, the determination of the rock is more certain. Glassy varieties are noted on pages 100–102.

It is not very certain that the nature of the groundmass is determined by the minerals of the phenocrysts, but quartz and orthoclase phenocrysts are good signs of rhyolitic composition. The dark silicates are scarcely apparent and since quartz and orthoclase have clearly crystallized early (before the groundmass) this might seem to be an exception to the normal order of crystallization. The fact is that some ferromagnesian mineral was probably formed still earlier, but is in small grains and in such small amounts as to be inconspicuous. The groundmass is usually felsitic, but it may be glassy, and in old rocks, felsites may show spherulites (Fig. 34), perlitic cracks and stone bubbles, indicating their *devitrification* from a former glassy state. Re-crystallized and usually more or less silicified rhyolites which have suffered metamorphism in the long course of geologic time are called *aporhyolites*.

The *Rhyolite-porphyries* have abundant phenocrysts, say 1/10 to 1/2 the rock, in a groundmass that is commonly dense but not cellular. These rocks are characteristic of the central portions of thick flows, of dikes, of intruded sheets, and of the outer parts of laccoliths.

The quartz phenocrysts are double six-sided pyramids, almost never with a visible prism, and as a consequence they are nearly equi-dimensional. With a little corrosion by the magma they commonly become rounded and may be mistaken for sand grains rounded by transportation. They are distinguished by their association with crystals of orthoclase and biotite, and by the contrast in size of grains in the phenocrysts and groundmass—such contrasts are rare in sediments.

Where the phenocrysts are in marked excess over the ground-mass, the rocks are *Granite-porphyries*. Where the phenocrysts are numerous, they are generally larger, and the groundmass be-tween them is slightly coarser than in the rhyolite-porphyries. These rocks are met in the deep-seated dikes, in thick sheets, and in the central parts of laccoliths. They mark a textural transition to the granites.

Rhyolite Tuffs are the fragmental ejectamenta from explosive eruptions that may form many extensive strata of rock. Although

FIG. 20.— Granite porphyry, Saganaga Lake, Ontario. Phenocrysts predominate, but the groundmass is fine-grained. Natural size.

loose at the time of falling, they may become consolidated in the course of time or, before this occurs, they may be sorted and rede-posited in water so as to share the nature of a true sediment. They are made up of small fragments of volcanic glass and of all the component minerals of rhyolite and even some other rocks. Larger fragments of rock and volcanic bombs make *rhyolite breccias*. Tuffs of ancient geological date become metamorphosed and re-crystallized, so as to afford products not to be easily distinguished from compact felsites.

Synonyms and Relatives. — The name rhyolite was first given by von Richthofen in 1860 to the rocks which had previously been

called quartz-trachytes.   About a year afterward Justus Roth suggested *liparite* for the same group, a name derived from the
Lipari Islands between Naples and Sicily, where these rocks are
characteristically developed, and liparite in consequence is much
used by European geologists.

> When both these names were applied and first used, they were in-
> tended for Tertiary and later eruptives alone.   The pre-Tertiary repre-
> sentatives were called *quartz-porphyries*.   With the disappearance of this
> time-distinction the term "quartz-porphyry" became restricted to the in-
> trusive dikes and sheets with their dense textures as contrasted with the
> rhyolites proper or surface flows.   It is now practically a synonym of rhyo-
> lite-porphyry, and wherever possible the dacite porphyries, also carrying
> quartz, should be distinguished.   The term rhyolite-porphyry is preferred
> to quartz porphyry because it permits the use of analogous and uniform
> names all though the clans of igneous rocks.

Rhyolites pass by insensible gradations into glasses on one side,
trachytes on another, granites on a third, and dacites on a fourth.
Without the microscope rhyolites can be identified with certainty
only by recognizing the quartz, and may then be confused with
dacites.   The striated feldspar of the latter is our chief means of
distinction between the two.   Where both orthoclase and plagioclase occur with quartz in phenocrysts, the rocks are *quartz latite-
porphyries,* or with excess of phenocrysts *quartz monzonite-por-
phyries.*

Alteration. — Ordinary weathering leads to the formation of
clays and kaolin.   In metamorphic alterations the rhyolites pass
into very finely crystalline aggregates of quartz and feldspar, and
then it is difficult to decide what minerals are original and what
secondary, and whether the original rock was a massive one or a
tuff.   Shearing stresses develop schistose structures, and when hydrothermal attack accompanies them, may result in sericite schists,
which are extremely difficult geological problems.

Distribution. — Rhyolites are common in the Western States,
and are well known in the Black Hills, in Yellowstone Park, in
Colorado, in Nevada, both near Eureka and near the Comstock
lode, and in California.   The rhyolite-porphyries have been met

in many Western districts, but are of especial importance at Leadville, where they are intimately associated with the ores. Rhyolite-porphyries have also an important development on Lake Superior, in both the Archean and Keweenawan series. The greater part of the boulders in the Calumet copper-bearing conglomerate consists of them, and Lighthouse Point, near Marquette, furnishes an outcrop. Along the Atlantic Coast the pre-Cambrian rhyolites (felsites) are known from New Brunswick to Pennsylvania. Recent rhyolites are in vast quantity in Iceland. Many are known in Europe, but the enormous development in Hungary is especially worthy of note. The sheets of rhyolite on the Lipari Islands suggested the name liparite. In the Tyrolese Alps rhyolite-porphyries are of great extent, and in Scandinavia and in Cornwall, they form important dikes.

Rhyolite tuffs are abundant along the eastern foothills of the Front Range of Colorado, and are extensively quarried for a rather soft building stone. Beds of loosely coherent volcanic ash are widespread in the states east of the Rocky Mountains. Their grains are sharp broken bits of glass, equivalent to powdered pumice, and the rock is a useful abrasive.

PHANERITES OF THE TRACHYTE-SYENITE CLAN

Mineralogic Composition, Varieties. — The syenites embrace a group of rocks of considerable diversity. The name syenite was suggested by Syene, now Assuan, an Egyptian locality, where a hornblende granite was formerly obtained for obelisks, and if its local significance were perpetuated, the name should be applied to this rock. But Werner used it in the last century for the well-known rock from the Plauenschen Grund, near Dresden, that contains only a little quartz, and of recent years correct usage implies little or no quartz. Typical syenites have orthoclase and hornblende; those with biotite are called *biotite-syenites.* Some plagioclase, magnetite, and in microscopic grains apatite, and zircon, are invariable.

When plagioclase becomes conspicuous, or nearly equal in amount to orthoclase, the rocks are called *monzonites,* and they mark a transition to the diorites. Ordinarily the orthoclase is redder than the plagioclase, and wherever feldspars of two colors are seen side by side, one is likely to be plagioclase. The feldspars of syenites tend to be slightly more sodic than those of granites and perhaps for that reason more lath-like in form. Many syenites have oriented feldspar laths, forming *gneissoid syenites*. Several syenites have exceptional coarse feldspars scattered in a normal granitoid matrix, forming *porphyritic syenites*. Syenites are known in which all the grains are coarse, forming *syenite pegmatites,* but they are much less common than granite pegmatites. Dark biotite syenites in dikes, especially if of sugary texture, or with phenocrysts of biotite in a sugary groundmass, have been called *minettes*. The corresponding dark dikes with hornblende and such textures are called *vogesites*. Both these dike rocks weather easily and belong with lamprophyres (page 96). Where the dark mineral is augite, we have *augite-syenite,* and rarely some other dark minerals form other varieties. A very basic augite syenite over 50 per cent dark minerals occurs at Shonkin Sag in the Highwood Mountains, Montana. It shows that orthoclase is not strictly limited to acidic, light-colored rocks. Still the table on page 46 expresses the general truth, the exceptions being very rare rocks. With high soda, the mineral sodalite may develop and yields *sodalite syenites* which are passage forms to nepheline syenites.

The average syenite has about 80 per cent feldspar, perhaps 50 to 70 per cent of which is orthoclase; leaving about 20 per cent for dark minerals, hornblende, biotite, pyroxene, or a mixture. Magnetite and quartz are in very small amounts.

Relationships. — Syenites are closely allied to granites on one side and nepheline-syenites on the other. They also grade through monzonites to diorites, and the augite syenites may grade to gabbros.

Geologic Occurrence. — Syenites are abundant as border facies of granites, and as satellitic stocks related to larger granite batholiths. Some, however, form independent dikes and masses of irregular shape, as do the granites.

Alteration. — There is little to be said that was not covered under granite. The rarity of syenite makes comment unnecessary.

In metamorphism and by *lit-par-lit* injection, syenites pass into gneisses.

Distribution. — Syenites occur in large volumes in the Canadian Shield and the Cordillera. In the Haliburton-Bancroft area of Ontario, syenite is transitional between granite and nephelite-syenite. A well-known syenite is associated with the anorthosite of the Adirondack Mountains, and probably that association is characteristic of anorthosites in many places. Minettes are prominent in the group of radial dikes at Spanish Peaks, Colorado, and one is known on Conanicut Island, Rhode Island. Syenites occur in the great igneous complex of the White Mountains. They form large knobs and dikes near Little Rock, Ark., and a dike is known in Custer County, Colorado. Some stocks and laccoliths of syenite in Montana are well studied. Monzonites are not restricted to Monzoni in Tyrol, but are widely exposed in the Rocky Mountains. The syenite quarries in Laurvik, Norway, supply a dark ornamental stone with a blue chatoyancy.

Aphanites of the Trachyte-Syenite Clan

General Description. — The Trachytes have the light-colored minerals in excess. The feldspars are much the most prominent components and give character to the rock. Quartz practically fails although an occasional crystal may be seen. Biotite is perhaps the most common of the dark silicates, but both hornblende and augite are well known. As with the rhyolites the prevailing colors are light grays, yellows, and pale reds, with occasional darker shades. The trachytes afford glasses much less often and less readily than the rhyolites, and show a greater tendency to appear as thoroughly crystalline rocks.

The textures of the trachytes range from felsitic to coarsely porphyritic. The *Trachytes proper* are felsitic or slightly porphyritic rocks, some of them cellular from their crystallization as surface flows. When finely felsitic they cannot readily be distinguished from rhyolites, dacites, and andesites without microscopic examination, and then *felsite* is the only name which can safely be applied to them. Many trachytes have a flow structure, in which

elongated feldspars point in the direction of flow, but it is rarely
seen except under the microscope.   It is so common that all such
structures in felsitic rocks may be called trachytic.

With the development of phenocrysts, the exact determination
of the trachytes becomes less difficult.   Quartz fails and feldspars
constitute the prominent porphyritic crystals (Fig. 21).   The
greater number of the feldspars should show no striations when
the cleavage faces are examined with a lens.   The clear vitreous
variety of orthoclase which commonly appears in the later volcanic
rocks and especially in the trachytes is called sanidine.   The dark
silicates, though visible, constitute but a subordinate part of the
rock.

FIG. 21. — Trachyte porphyry, Good Springs, Nevada, with exceptionally large phenocrysts of orthoclase.   Weathering has loosened some phenocrysts, shown beside
the rock.   Natural size.   Courtesy of the McGraw-Hill Book Company.

Where the phenocrysts are abundant these rocks are *Trachyte-
porphyries*.   The cellular structure is not common, but the groundmass is dense and felsitic.   The interiors of thick flows, the dikes,
the intrusive sheets, and the outer parts of laccoliths are their
special homes.

Where phenocrysts are in marked excess over the groundmass,
the rocks are *Syenite-porphyries*.   Where the phenocrysts are nu-

merous, they are generally larger and the groundmass between them is slightly coarser than in trachyte-porphyries. These rocks are met in deep-seated dikes, in thick sheets, and in the central parts of laccoliths. They mark a textural transition to syenites.

Synonyms and Relatives. — The name trachyte is an old one, having been first given in 1822 by the Abbé Hauy to volcanic rocks from the Auvergne in France, whose rough and rasping surfaces suggested its creation from the Greek adjective meaning rough. For thirty years or more, it was used for the light-colored volcanic rocks which now include all the felsites,—rhyolites, trachytes, dacites, and andesites; and in earlier writings the word must often be interpreted in this general sense. For many years subsequent to 1860 and after its mineralogy became defined as now, it was restricted to the lavas of Tertiary and later age, while "porphyry" was employed for the corresponding rocks of earlier geologic time. Porphyry, where accurately used, is now a strictly textural term but in common speech it is applied loosely to almost any eruptive which happens to be associated with an ore-body in the Cordilleran region.

When soda is especially pronounced in the composition of a member of the trachyte series, it leads to several mineralogical variations from the type. The principal feldspar may be anortho-clase, without change in appearance, but if phenocrysts are partly orthoclase and partly plagioclase, the rocks are called *latite-porphyry,* or with predominant phenocrysts *monzonite-porphyry.* These are transitional to andesite-porphyry and diorite-porphyry. In any rock where two abundant feldspars have different colors, it is to be suspected that one is orthoclase and the other plagioclase. Further increase in soda gives rocks transitional to phonolites.

Alteration. — The alteration is practically the same as that described under rhyolites.

Distribution. — True volcanic trachytes are rare in this country, for many of the cited localities, as, for instance, some of those in the reports of the Fortieth Parallel Survey, have been shown to be andesites. Beautiful examples do, however, occur in the Black Hills, with superbly developed orthoclases. Others are known in Custer County, Colorado, and in Montana. The trachyte-porphyries occur in many dikes in the West. Exceptionally fine examples are collected at Goodsprings, Nevada. In southeast Missouri, at Iron Mountain and Pilot Knob, they are very abundant. Many interesting dikes of them occur around Lake Champlain, and among the pre-Cambrian volcanics of the Atlantic Coast they are not lacking. Abroad trachytes are common, notably along the Rhine, in Sardinian lava flows, in Italy, in the Auvergne, and in the Azores.

Trachyte Tuffs are not common in America and are not very different from the rhyolite tuffs, except that they lack quartz, and this may be too fine to detect by the eye.

Phanerites of the Phonolite-Nepheline-Syenite Clan

Mineralogic Composition, Varieties. — The nepheline rocks are rare and seldom recognized by geologists in the field. Daly estimates that all nepheline rocks together make less than .1 per cent of the igneous rocks. The minerals of nepheline-syenite are in general the same as those of syenite proper, with the addition of nepheline and several minerals in which the rare earths enter as bases. Zircon is widespread and at a few places affords megascopic

FIG. 22. — Nepheline syenite, Bushveld complex. Nepheline in blocky hexagonal grains weathers to differ from feldspars. About natural size. Courtesy of the McGraw-Hill Book Company.

crystals, so that the rocks were named *zircon-syenite* before the nepheline was recognized.

The texture of nepheline-syenites ranges widely. At places it is very coarsely granitoid or pegmatitic, and elsewhere it is gneissoid with rods of feldspar, more or less in flow lines. *Porphyritic nepheline-syenites* are known (Fig. 22).

A great many names have been proposed for different nepheline rocks, but they are based on slight mineralogic differences, and are not to be recommended. The best names use, as a prefix, the name of the dark silicate, thus: *biotite nepheline-syenite,* and *acmite nepheline-syenite*. Acmite, the sodic pyroxene, is logically to be expected in rocks so rich in soda as to form nepheline. It is more needle-like than most pyroxene and may be mistaken for hornblende in hand specimen study.[5]

With the nepheline are commonly other feldspathoids such as leucite, and the names of these minerals also may be used as qualifying prefixes to the nepheline-syenites. These may occur without nepheline, but such rocks are so rare that their classification is not much of a problem. They are *leucite-syenites,* etc., but related to this clan.

The nepheline-syenite clan, however, is a difficult clan for the student. Nepheline is hard to identify with certainty so that whenever it is suspected for any reason there are a number of points to observe or tests to make.

(1) The rocks commonly have a greasy luster from the nepheline. (2) Nepheline in phenocrysts forms stout hexagonal prisms with basal pinacoids. (3) Nepheline weathers more rapidly than the feldspar, and the simple fact that something in the rock weathers differently may lead to the suspicion of nepheline. Large grains result in pits on the surface of the rock dusted with white or bluish gray. (4) The presence of quartz at once throws out all suspicion that nepheline is present. (5) After all these points are given due consideration, most students still feel a good deal of doubt in the determination and make a test for silica jelly. A small sample of the rock in question is powdered and gently warmed

[5] It was formerly the custom to refer to pre-Tertiary nepheline as *eleolite* (or *elaeolite*), but this is gradually falling into disuse.

in dilute (1:4) nitric or hydrochloric acid. The nepheline passes readily into solution and when the liquid is decanted from the undissolved grains and is boiled down well toward dryness, gelatinous silica results. No other common, rock-making and gelatinizing mineral is so easily soluble as nepheline, and olivine alone approaches it.

The average nepheline-syenite has about 80 per cent light minerals and 20 per cent dark, the latter very commonly a sodic pyroxene. The light minerals range widely but average over 15 per cent nepheline, with much potash feldspar, some plagioclase, and traces of other feldspathoids.

Relationships. — The nepheline-syenites are closely related to the true syenites, and to the phonolites; also to some rare rocks containing nepheline and plagioclase.

Geologic Occurrence. — The nepheline-syenites are especially prone to appear as irregular intrusives, and at places along the borders of batholiths of granite where in contact with limestones or other basic rocks. From their common irregularity in texture and composition, and from their small total volume and relations to granites and other rocks, has come the suggestion that special conditions are needed for their formation, such as a high concentration of mineralizers in the late residual magma, or the contamination of magma by basic inclusions and walls. Some nepheline-syenites may have been formed by the action of magmatic emanations on their wall-rocks rather than by direct cooling of magma. This is confirmed by the common presence of some CO_2 and other "mineralizer" minerals. Probably some have formed in different ways from others, for the phonolite flows show that a magma with the composition of this clan can exist underground and be intruded and extruded.

Alteration. — In addition to the alteration products of granite and syenite, there may be formed from nepheline some zeolites, muscovite (liebenerite), kaolinite (gieseckite), and cancrinite. Descriptions of metamorphic rocks rarely refer to this clan partly because nepheline rocks are rare to begin with and partly because the nepheline may be lost in metamorphism.

Distribution. — In spite of their small volume, the nepheline-syenites have been noted in a number of American districts; in the Monteregian Hills of Quebec; in the Haliburton-Bancroft area, Ontario; Litchfield, Me.; Red Hill, N. H.; Salem, Mass.; Beemerville, N. J.; near Magnet Cove, Ark.; in central Wisconsin; in the San Carlos Mountains, Tamaulipas, Mexico; in the Ice River district, British Columbia; and at several less well known localities. Abroad, a section in the Monchique Mountains of Portugal, the example at Ditro, Hungary, and the wonderful dikes near Christiania, in Norway, so prolific in rare minerals, are of especial interest. The largest areas are in the Kola peninsula of Russia, in Pilansberg, South Africa and in Julianehaab, Greenland.

The Aphanites of the Phonolite-Nepheline-Syenite Clan

General Description. — Most phonolites are gray or green and rarely distinguishable in hand specimens from trachytes and andesites. They should be called felsites. In the aphanites nepheline is rarely coarse enough to be recognized without the microscope, and the tests and observations described for nepheline in the phanerites are even more important when its presence is suspected for any reason.

The *Phonolites proper* are felsites, characteristically dense and commonly with a slabby parting. They form surface flows and dikes.

The *Phonolite-porphyries* result when the phenocrysts become notably abundant. The phenocrysts are then chiefly orthoclase, acmite, and perhaps an occasional sphene. Nepheline in phenocrysts is known from only a few localities. The phonolite-porphyries occur in dikes and intruded sheets. *Nepheline-Syenite-porphyry* is known but is a rare rock.

Synonyms and Relatives. — The name phonolite is an old one. It was given by Klaproth in 1801 to the rocks which had long been called clinkstone and was merely the Greek equivalent of this colloquial term. The phonolites have more soda and alumina than the trachytes and at the same time not enough silica to form albite (see page 19). Where leucite occurs without nepheline, the rock is a *leucite-trachyte,* but is more closely related to the phonolites than to the other trachytes because it is undersaturated with silica. With increase of plagioclase and the dark silicates, phonolites grade into basaltic rocks with nepheline.

Alterations. — Nepheline changes readily to zeolites and feldspar, while leucite yields analcime. Metamorphic processes are yet to be studied.

Distribution. — The true volcanic phonolites are known in only a few localities in this country, such as the Black Hills of South Dakota and Wyoming, and the Cripple Creek mining district of Colorado, where the dikes are associated with gold ores. A basic phonolite is exposed in the Uvalde district, Texas. Porphyries with nepheline or leucite occur near Magnet Cove, Ark., and Beemerville, N. J. A leucite rock gives the name to the Leucite Hills, Wyoming, and such rocks are known in the Highwood Mountains, Montana, and near Rio de Janeiro, Brazil. Phonolites are well known in many parts of Germany. The varieties with leucite are especially familiar from the vicinity of Rieden, in the extinct volcanic district of the Eifel. Several prominent phonolites have been discovered in South Africa and in the Great Rift Valley of eastern Africa.

CHAPTER IV

THE IGNEOUS ROCKS, Continued

The Dacite-Quartz-Diorite Clan. The Andesite-Diorite Clan

Phanerites of the Dacite-Quartz-Diorite Clan

Mineralogic Composition, Varieties.—The quartz-diorites are granitoid rocks which contain plagioclase as the chief feldspar and quartz as an essential component. From all other granitoid rocks except granites, the quartz-diorites are distinguished by their quartz. From granites the prevalence of striated feldspar is the chief distinction. Where a little orthoclase appears the rock is *granodiorite,* and where two feldspars are nearly equal, *quartz monzonite.* The dark silicates are biotite or hornblende or both, and these mineral names are prefixed to indicate mineralogic varieties, as *biotite quartz-diorite,* and *hornblende quartz-diorite.*

The textures of most quartz-diorites are medium granitoid, but some fine granitoid dikes are *quartz-diorite aplites.* Where a quartz-diorite of medium grain has notable phenocrysts an inch or more long, it is a *porphyritic quartz-diorite,* and at a few places a rock with all the grains coarse, is a *quartz-diorite pegmatite,* corresponding to granite pegmatites and probably formed in much the same way. The common plagioclase, hornblende and biotite of this clan, are characteristically lath-like or platy, and many of the intrusives of this composition show flow structures—they are *gneissoid quartz-diorites* or *gneissoid granodiorites.*

The average quartz-diorite contains about 20% quartz, nearly 60% feldspar, and 20% of dark minerals, usually biotite or hornblende. There is a little magnetite. The potash feldspars are negligible except in the fairly abundant granodiorites which average about 15% potash feldspar and 45% plagioclase.

Relationships.—The quartz-diorites are close relatives of the granites on one hand and the diorites on the other. To the granites there is an easy transition through grano-diorites and quartz-monzonites.

Geological Occurrence. — The quartz-diorites form batholiths and dikes.

Alteration. — The alteration is in all essentials similar to that of granite.

Distribution. — Quartz-diorites appear in a few areas in the crystalline rocks of the eastern United States, notably near Peekskill, New York. Others are known in Yellowstone Park, at Marysville, Montana, and in the Sierras. Granodiorites are abundant in southwestern states and widely scattered in the Canadian Shield. The Boulder batholith at Butte, Montana, is a famous mass, partly granodiorite and partly quartz-monzonite.

APHANITES OF THE DACITE-QUARTZ-DIORITE CLAN

General Description. — The Dacites are a group of rocks which so strongly resemble the rhyolites that it is difficult for the student to distinguish them without microscopic or chemical work. The light-colored minerals, quartz and feldspar, give character to both, but in the dacites the predominant feldspar is a plagioclase of acidic or medium composition. Biotite is perhaps the most common of the dark silicates, but hornblende is next and augite appears in some. Other minerals are rarely visible to the eye. The prevailing colors are light grays, yellows, and pale reds. Glasses and cellular lavas are not uncommon.

The *Dacites proper* are *felsites* and not distinguished from other felsites in hand specimens. They range from dense to cellular, and where a few small phenocrysts appear, they grade to dacite-porphyries in which the cleavage faces of feldspars need study with a lens.

Where phenocrysts are abundant these rocks are *Dacite-porphyries* (Fig. p. 23). The cellular structure is not common, but the groundmass is dense and felsitic. Quartz and striated plagioclases form recognizable phenocrysts. The interiors of thick surface flows, the dikes, the intrusive sheets, and the outer parts of laccoliths are their special homes.

Where phenocrysts are in marked excess over the groundmass, the rocks are *Quartz-diorite-porphyries.* Where the phenocrysts are numerous they are generally larger, and the groundmass between them slightly coarser than in dacite-porphyry. These rocks are met in deep-seated dikes, in thick sheets, and in the central parts of laccoliths. They mark a textural transition to quartz-diorites.

Fig. 23.— Dacite porphyry, Mt. Shasta, California. About two-thirds natural size. Courtesy of the McGraw-Hill Book Company.

Synonyms and Relatives.— The name dacite was created in 1863 by an Austrian geologist, G. Stache, who had been working upon the eruptives of the province of Dacia, now in Romania known as the Siebenburgen. Under it was embraced a series of rocks somewhat indefinitely called by earlier lithologists andesitic quartz-trachytes, and other undesirable names. The name dacite has proved to be a useful one and is universally employed today. Varieties are made on the basis of the dark silicate present such as *mica dacite,* or *hornblende dacite.* The dacites are close relatives of the andesites into which they grade with increasing basicity, and with the disappearance of quartz. They are also very closely akin to the rhyolites and to intermediate rocks between rhyolites and dacites, called *quartz latites,* recognized only if there are phenocrysts of quartz and two feldspars. *Quartz porphyrite* is an old synonym of dacite-porphyry.

Alteration, Metamorphism. — The alteration of the dacites is practically like that of the rhyolites, but the greater abundance of soda-lime feldspar may yield more calcite. The light-colored silicates change to kaolinite. In metamorphism the dacites yield siliceous schists especially when greatly mashed or sheared.

Tuffs. — The tuffs and breccias are essentially like those of the rhyolites. They cannot readily be distinguished without the microscope.

Distribution. — Dacites usually appear as subordinate members in eruptive regions where the andesites are the chief rocks. They are therefore widespread in the volcanic districts of the Cordilleran regions of North, Central, and South America. Quartz-latites have been noted in the mining districts of Globe, Arizona, and Tonopah, Nevada, and others. The lavas of Santorin are dacites and quartz latites.

Phanerites of the Andesite-Diorite Clan

Mineralogic Composition. — The diorites are granitoid igneous rocks, whose chief feldspar is plagioclase and whose chief dark silicate is either hornblende or biotite. Some augite may be present, marking a passage to the gabbros. It is however a matter of much difficulty to distinguish hornblende from augite with the eye alone, and unless the observer can make certain of the cleavages— approximately 120° for hornblende, and 90° for augite—doubt may arise. In the typical diorites the feldspars are in marked excess over the dark silicates, and contrasts are thus afforded with average gabbros, but the name diorite in ordinary use is often applied to rocks with a decided excess of hornblende. Additional difficulty in the sharp application of the word arises because under the influence of metamorphism original augite changes readily in whole or in part to hornblende, and a mineralogical aggregate thus results which corresponds to diorite, yet which did not crystallize directly in this form.

There is a decided disposition among students of rocks, especially when working with the microscope, to apply the name diorite to those varieties of the plagioclase rocks whose feldspar is more acidic than labradorite; that is when the plagioclase comes within the oligoclase-andesine ranges. The dark silicate may then be hornblende, biotite, or pyroxene. The rocks with the more basic plagioclases are classed with the gabbros. Without the microscope, however, these distinctions among the plagioclases are impracticable. See pages 47–48 for a discussion of this problem.

The name diorite was first applied in 1822 by the Abbé Hauy. It is derived from the Greek verb, to distinguish, and was suggested by the fact that, in the rocks first named, the white feldspar could be easily distinguished from the black hornblende. In the course of time it became a very widely used field name among geologists and miners.

Varieties. — The varieties *biotite diorite* and *hornblende diorite* are abundant, and the possible *augite diorites* have already been noted. If potash feldspar is nearly as abundant as plagioclase, the rocks are *monzonites.* Dike rocks with sugary groundmass and the composition of a biotite diorite are called *kersantite.* Similar dikes with large hornblende phenocrysts are *camptonite.* These are members of a group of dike rocks called *lamprophyres* (page 96), in which distinctions are difficult without the microscope. Contrasting with the dike rocks that are so fine as to be almost felsitic, there are coarse diorites that may be called *diorite pegmatites,* but these are much less common than the quartzose pegmatites. The diorites with phenocrysts are best called *porphyritic diorites,* and those with flow structures are *gneissoid diorites. Orbicular diorites* are known from several districts. A considerable number of diorites with grain about 1 mm., occur in sills of moderate size, and are very difficult to identify and distinguish from gabbro, because the feldspar is gray and because hornblende in such small grains is not easily distinguished from feldspar and augite. It is common to use the term *dolerite* (meaning deceptive) to indicate that the rock may be a diorite or gabbro, but that, because of the fine grain, there is uncertainty between them.[1]

---

[1] The English petrographers use the term dolerite for rock with plagioclase needles earlier than coarse augite,—a diabase (see page 98), and many dolerites as here defined are diabases.

The average diorite contains about 65% plagioclase and 35% ferromagnesian minerals—biotite or hornblende or both, with minor amounts of pyroxene. Magnetite, quartz, and potash feldspars are rarely more than one per cent. With increasing potash feldspar they grade through monzonites to syenites, and with increasing pyroxene they grade to gabbro.

Alteration, Metamorphism. — In ordinary alteration the feldspar of diorites kaolinizes and the hornblende changes to chlorite, affording one of the varieties of the so-called greenstones. Under shearing stresses in metamorphism the diorites pass into gneisses, and into hornblende schists or amphibolites. In many mining regions even decidedly schistose varieties are still called diorite. A final stage is chlorite-schist, wherein the hornblende has altered to chlorite.

Distribution. — Diorites form fairly large parts of some of the batholiths of the Cordillera and the Canadian shield areas. Mt. Davidson, above the Comstock Lode, is either a true diorite or a granitoid facies of the andesite, but authorities differ as to its interpretation. Diorites are well known abroad, and have been described from various places.

APHANITES OF THE ANDESITE-DIORITE CLAN

General Description. — The Andesites embrace a large and wide-spread group of rocks, which marks an important step from the more acidic to the more basic limits of the igneous clans. Its members are emphatically rocks of medium acidity, with the light-colored minerals still in excess over the dark-colored ones. The feldspars are therefore the most prominent components but there is commonly much more ferromagnesian silicate than in the dacites. Quartz fails except as a rare and sporadic component. Hornblende and augite begin to take precedence over biotite, but all three are common. The prevailing colors are grays or greens, mottled by the light and dark phenocrysts. They rarely afford large amounts of glass.

Andesites proper are felsitic in texture, and the flows that contained mineralizers are commonly cellular or amygdaloidal.

Where wholly fine-grained they cannot be distinguished by the eye from other felsitic rocks acidic or basic. In the average, andesites are darker than other felsites and lighter colored than basalts, but there are many exceptions. If a few small phenocrysts are visible the identification of andesites is more definite, and the rocks grade into andesite-porphyries.

Andesite-porphyries have abundant phenocrysts in a groundmass that is felsitic and dense, without cellular openings. The interiors of thick flows, the dikes and the intrusive sheets are their homes. The mineral phenocrysts should be studied with a lens to find the striation on most of the feldspars, and the elongate forms of both feldspar and hornblende; minute biotite grains if visible can be tested for hardness with a pin-point. A noteworthy modification of texture results from clustering of phenocrysts into small groups or rosettes, forming rocks called *glomeroporphyries* (Fig. 24). Another textural variety is the *diabase,* more common in the basalt-gabbro clan (page 98).

FIG. 24. — Pebble of glomeroporphyry. About natural size.

Where the phenocrysts are in marked excess over the groundmass, the rocks are *Diorite-porphyries.* Where the phenocrysts are numerous they are generally larger and the groundmass between them is slightly coarser than in andesite-porphyry. These rocks are met in deep-seated dikes, in thick intrusive sheets, and in the central parts of laccoliths. They mark a textural transition to the diorites.

Synonyms and Relatives. — The name andesite was first proposed by L. von Buch in 1835 for certain lavas from the Andes Mountains which consisted of albite and hornblende. The name did not come into general use until 1858 since which time it has been universally employed for the porphyritic and felsitic plagioclase-bearing eruptives of medium acidity. Andesites whose chief dark silicate is biotite are called *biotite andesites;* those with horn-blende, *hornblende andesites,* or *amphibole andesites.* Aphanites with plagioclase and pyroxenes are classed as basalt on page 46, but show close relations to the hornblende andesites (pages 47–8 and 94). Commonly the rocks with biotite and hornblende are lighter colored than those with augite.

While the time-distinction was still preserved in the classification of igneous rocks, the term andesite was restricted to Tertiary and later rocks, and the pre-Tertiary andesites were called *porphyrite,* to which name the several prefixes, mica, hornblende, and augite were attached. Later porphyrite was employed for the deep-seated or intrusive andesites, which are here called andesite-porphyry and diorite-porphyry, but even this use is practically obsolete as it is certainly unnecessary.

Andesites with almost as much orthoclase as plagioclase are latites, but are recognized only if the feldspars appear as pheno-crysts. With the increase of the dark silicates, especially augite, and corresponding decrease of feldspar, andesites grade into the basalts. The appearance of quartz in notable amounts marks a transition to the dacites. Practically unbroken series can easily be selected to all these related groups. *Propylite* is a useful term for any of the aphanites in this and related clans which have suffered some alteration by hot waters so that they are green, from chlorite, epidote, or serpentine. The term propylite means "before the gates," signifying that they came before the true volcanics, but the term no longer indicates age. Having been used at the Com-stock Lode, Nevada, it is well known in western states.

Alteration, Metamorphism. — The andesites weather to kao-linized material and mixtures of this with chloritic products that are very difficult to identify. Thus the andesitic breccia at Cripple Creek, Colo., can rarely be shown to the eye to be other than a white, kaolinized mass, and decomposed outcrops of massive flows are no less unsatisfactory. Where metamorphic processes affect older andesite flows, fine sericitic to green chloritic schists are formed. The tracing of the history of the rock is then a matter for the microscope and chemical analysis if indeed it can be done. The propylites have already been noted.

Tuffs and Breccias. — Andesitic tuffs and breccias are rather common in the western volcanic districts. With ordinary observation they can be identified only by finding fragments large and fresh enough to indicate the original. Such have proved of great economic importance at Cripple Creek, Colorado.

Distribution. — Andesites are very wide-spread in the West. The vast laccoliths that form many of the peaks in Colorado are andesite-porphyries of a rather acidic type, commonly with some orthoclase. In the Yellowstone Park they are important. In Nevada, as at Eureka and the Comstock lode, they have proved of great geological interest, and especially in and near the latter, with its many miles of drifts, shafts, and tunnels, very important data for the study of the hydrothermal alteration of rock masses have been afforded. The old cones along the Pacific, Mt. Hood, Mt. Shasta, Mt. Rainier, and others are chiefly andesite. The products of Mexican and South American volcanoes are also of this type, and indeed along the whole Pacific border the recent lavas have many features in common. In great volcanic districts abroad andesites are seldom lacking.

CHAPTER V

THE IGNEOUS ROCKS, Continued

The Basalt-Gabbro Clan. The Feldspar-free Basalts. The Pyroxenites and Peridotites. The Glasses. The Ultra-Basic Rocks

PHANERITES OF THE BASALT-GABBRO CLAN

Mineralogic Composition, Varieties. — The name gabbro is of Italian origin, and has been applied in recent years, and with growing favor to the great group of granitoid rocks which consist, in the typical cases, of plagioclase and pyroxene. The group is a very large and characteristically variable one. Originally the name gabbro was applied only to a mixture of plagioclase and the variety of monoclinic pyroxene called diallage, which has pinacoidal parting as well as prismatic cleavages, but of late years all granitoid, plutonic, pyroxene-plagioclase rocks are collectively spoken of as the gabbro group. In the typical gabbros the dark silicates are about as abundant as the light-colored ones, but there are a number of gabbros with very different mineral ratios. At the feldspathic extreme we have enormous masses of rock that are practically pure, coarsely crystalline labradorite. Pyroxene is the dark silicate but in many rocks it is insignificant. These pure feldspar rocks are best called *anorthosites,* from the French word for triclinic feldspar, but the word is not to be confused with anorthite, the lime feldspar, with which it has no special connection. Most anorthosites are very coarsely granitoid, and seem to have formed as differentiates of large bodies of gabbro. It is not certain that any large mass of magma had that composition when liquid.

Many gabbros have nearly equal amounts of plagioclase and augite, and some have small amounts of hornblende or biotite. If the pyroxene is orthorhombic, the rock is called *norite,* but this is rarely distinguished except under the microscope. If it happens that the orthorhombic pyroxene is bronzite with its characteristic brown color, it can be recognized in hand specimens, but such rocks are not common. The interest in distinguishing norites arises from their association with nickel ores at Sudbury, Ontario, with chromite ores in Africa, and with similar ores elsewhere.

Gabbros with olivine are abundant, giving *olivine gabbro* (and *olivine norite*). Most of the olivine is in small yellowish green grains with glassy luster, and so transparent that the student must have good light and commonly use a lens to detect it. On weathered surfaces most ferruginous olivine turns brown, resembling limonite spots, long before the black augite and magnetite are affected. A few gabbros may have olivine without visible augite, though traces may be assumed to be present even when not visible. Such are called *troctolites*. In the absence of olivine, it is possible to have *quartz-gabbros,* but these are rare and suggest contamination. *Grano-gabbro,* with both quartz and orthoclase, is still more rare.

At the dark extreme the gabbros grade into *pyroxenites, peridotites,* and *ores.*

Texturally a number of gabbros are *gneissoid,* that is, they show flow structures by the parallel orientation of plates of plagioclase (Fig. 25). There are also in many gneissoid gabbros "flow layers," or bands, or beds, in which the proportions of light and dark minerals differ in layers with rather irregular alternations. The layers may be from a fraction of an inch to many feet thick, may divide or pinch out, and may be as irregular as sedimentary beds. These layers have the same strike and dip as oriented plagioclase plates if any occur. Very coarse facies are *gabbro pegmatites* and these occur locally in segregated spots or dikes near the borders of gabbro masses, but are less abundant than granite pegmatites, into which they commonly grade by imperceptible stages. Anorthosite also may be very coarse-grained, but this is attributed to its monomineral character and not to a concentration of mineralizers as in pegmatites. Very fine granitoid gabbros are called *dolerites* (see pages 32 and 79). There are several well-known *orbicular gabbros.*

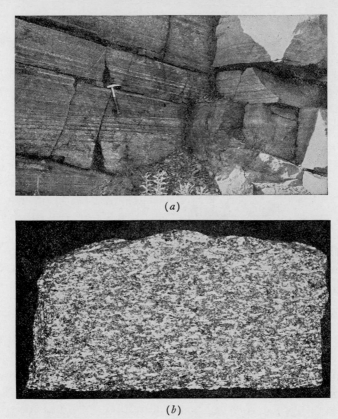

(a)

(b)

Fig. 25. — Flow structure in gabbro, Duluth, Minnesota. (a) Regular layers with different proportions of plagioclase. (b) Hand specimen showing oriented plates of plagioclase. About one-half natural size.

The average rock of the gabbro clan probably contains a little over 50% plagioclase, 30% augite, and 10% olivine, with smaller amounts of magnetite, and locally some hornblende and biotite. These proportions, however, are far from constant, since as noted above, gabbros range from rocks that are almost pure feldspar to rocks with only about 10% feldspar.

Alteration. — The gabbros alter chiefly by the formation of serpentine from olivine. Later the other dark silicates alter to hornblende and chlorite, and all the minerals may be changed. Dynamic stresses may change gabbro and anorthosite to gneisses with hornblende and garnet. The larger feldspars of anorthosites are commonly left in the gneisses as "eyes," or lenses, which are called "augen" from the German word for eyes. Augen gneisses result.

Distribution. — Gabbros occur in vast quantity in the Adirondacks and are well known in the White Mountains, in the famous Cortlandt series, near Peekskill, on the Hudson, and in the vicinity of Baltimore. Around Lake Superior gabbros are of great importance. The Keweenawan rocks and other older intrusions are largely formed of them. Fine specimens can be had at Duluth. The Stillwater complex in Montana has a similar rock series. The anorthosites occur in several Canadian areas, as at the headwaters of the Saguenay River, and again north of Montreal; in the higher peaks of the Adirondacks; and to the northeast of Laramie, Wyoming, in the Laramie range.

Abroad, gabbros and anorthosites are abundant in the Scandinavian peninsula, whose geology is in many respects like that of Canada and the Adirondacks. In the north of Scotland gabbros are of especial interest because they have been shown by Judd to be the deep-seated representatives of the surface basalts. On the continent they are important rocks at many localities. They are scattered in Australia and such other parts of the world as have been studied. In South Africa the Bushveld norite complex is famous geologically and of commercial interest for its platinum and chromite ores; and the "great dike" of Southern Rhodesia has similar rocks. Titaniferous magnetites occur characteristically in gabbro or anorthosite masses.

Phanerites of the Pyroxenite and Peridotite Clans

Mineralogic Composition, Varieties. — The gabbros pass insensibly, by the decrease of plagioclase, into the pyroxenites and peridotites, and in any great gabbro area all these are usually present. At a few places the darker rocks occur also as independent masses. Many pyroxenites are nearly all pyroxene with only small traces of other minerals. There is some variety, according as the rock contains one or several of the following: enstatite, bronzite, hypersthene, diallage or augite; but with the unassisted eye, it is seldom that one can be sure of these distinctions, unless the orthorhombic pyroxenes have a bronze luster. Hornblende, magnetite, and pyrrhotite may be associated with one or more of the minerals cited for pyroxenites. At the extreme of peridotites we have nearly pure olivine rocks, called *dunites,* ranging from pale green to dark greenish brown. They are named after Dun Mountain in New Zealand and are well known in North Carolina and elsewhere. Much magnetite may be associated with peridotite; indeed at Cumberland Hill, Rhode Island, there is enough to make the rock almost an ore. Chromite, too, is a common associate. Peridotites with a porphyritic texture are called *kimberlite,* and are famous the world over as the mother rock of diamonds. Black hornblende is common in both pyroxenites and peridotites, and may even form a rock itself, *hornblendite.* This may result from differentiation from hornblendic magmas of several clans, granite to gabbro; or from the alteration of a pyroxenite, under conditions that change augite to hornblende. Dark brown biotite is also common. Pegmatites which are known in all the preceding clans are practically lacking in pyroxenites and peridotites, although some rocks in these families are coarse-grained.

Some writers have regarded the pyroxenites and even peridotites as of doubtful igneous origin and have placed them with metamorphic rocks; but where they are associated with gabbro, or in independent dikes, there is no good reason to doubt their truly igneous nature.

Alteration.—Pyroxenites and hornblendites resist alteration very well, but dynamic stresses produce hornblende-schists or amphibolites. Peridotites are commonly changed to masses of serpentine, and near granite intrusives there may be important asbestos veins. Some commercial magnesite also may result from the alteration of highly magnesian peridotites.

Distribution.—Pyroxenites occur as subordinate members of the gabbro areas, as for example near Baltimore. Hornblendites are not rare as border facies of hornblende-granite and hornblende syenite in the batholiths of the Canadian Shield. Peridotites are in similar subordinate relations in the Cordlandt series, in the Baltimore area and in North Carolina. They are known also on

Little Deer Island, Maine; at Cumberland Hill, Rhode Island; in dikes near Syracuse, New York; at Presqu' Isle, near Marquette, Michigan; in Kentucky; in California, and elsewhere in the West. When outlying dikes are met, far from any visible parent mass of igneous rocks and in sedimentary walls, many prove to be peridotite. A significant concentration of olivine occurs near the base of the Palisade diabase opposite New York City, and there is a peridotite near the base of the Duluth gabbro at the western edge of the city of Duluth, Minnesota. Abroad there are stock-like masses in the gabbros of the Ural Mountains and of the Bushveld complex. The kimberlite of the diamond-bearing pipes is best known in South Africa.

Aphanites of the Basalt-Gabbro Clan

General Description. — The basalts are noticeably more basic than the preceding clans. The dark colored silicates are here about half the rock and, with the feldspar darker than in andesites, they give the chief characters to the rock. Augite and olivine are abundant, and hornblende and biotite are scarce or lacking. Magnetite can be detected by testing a little of the powdered rock even if the grains are too small to recognize otherwise. The prevailing colors are dark grays and black. Red and green rocks of this clan indicate alteration. Compact glassy varieties are rare though slaggy crusts and scorias are not uncommon.

Basalts proper are felsitic or show only a few small phenocrysts. In this clan felsitic textures are more common than porphyritic. Most of the abundant basalt lava flows are *cellular basalts* or *scorias* because of the separation of dissolved vapors. The cells are most abundant and form thicker zones at the tops of flows, but occur also for a few inches at the base where the lava chilled before the bubbles rose into the hot central part. There is a gradation from the cellular upper and lower zones to central dense zones. Central zones may be coarse and resist weathering much better than the cellular crusts. The cells or cavities are commonly filled with secondary calcite, quartz, chlorite, epidote, and zeolites, from water solution. These fillings are amygdules and the rock is called amygdaloidal, from the Greek word for an almond, whose outlines they closely resemble (Fig. 12). In the Lake Superior region *amygdaloidal basalts* attain decided prominence because they have furnished a place of deposition of copper. Several features of the flows may have been involved in the formation of the commercial ores. In the first place the porosity of the cellular lava and its partial crushing produced a channel for the solutions. The precipitation of copper seems to have resulted

FIG. 26.—Basalt breccia, Pine County, Minnesota. The aa flows produce amygdaloidal fragments in a matrix of finer fragments. About one-half natural size. Courtesy of the McGraw-Hill Book Company.

from a reaction of copper and sulphur solutions with the red oxidized parts of the flows.[1] It happens that the tops of flows are at the same time porous and favorable places for the oxidation of the iron of basalts—the ropy tops called pahoehoe (page 91) are very commonly red. The iron is not only oxidized by the reaction with air, but concentrated in the tops by the gases rising through the lava.[2]

[1] R. C. Wells, in the report by Butler and Burbank, *The Copper Deposits of Michigan*. U. S. Geological Survey, Professional Paper 144, page 141, 1929.

[2] T. M. Broderick: *Differentiation in Lavas of the Michigan Keweenawan*. Bull. Geological Society of America, volume 36, page 353, 1935.

Most basalts are dense and felsitic in texture, dark colored and heavy. These characters appear in rocks of considerable variety in composition, but all the rocks are included in the Basalt Group (page 46), and in work without the microscope are called basalt (or "trap," a non-committal term for dark felsitic rocks). The basalt group includes the common *olivine-basalt, augitite,* and *limburgite* as well as the basalt more strictly defined as a member of the family of gabbros. It should be clearly understood that the term basalt (or trap) is commonly used for a whole group of rocks as well as specifically (by microscopic study) for one member of the group. In the field, and in the study of hand specimens, where phenocrysts are too few and small to be useful, no distinction is attempted between the several families of the basalt group, just as there is no attempt to distinguish the members of the light felsitic rocks in the felsite group. In the group of rocks with felsitic textures, felsite is a name for the light rocks, and basalt is a name for the dark rocks.

FIG. 27. — Cellular basalt.

Basalts are the most abundant of all lava flows and in the field and even in hand specimens certain varieties can be distinguished. In the great lava fields most flows have spread widely in thin sheets, though some may be locally thick where filling up depressions in the earlier surfaces. The fine-grained dense rocks have a conchoidal fracture almost like chert, but the coarser ones grade into dolerite (pages 79 and 85) and have a hackly fracture.

At central volcanic cones, two other varieties are distinguished, the *aa* flow, which breaks up at its advancing front into blocks of scoria, and the *pahoehoe,* which flows with a ropy surface (Fig. 28) ; both names based on Hawaiian terms. The blocks of vesicular lava may be rolled into the advancing liquid lava or may be later cemented by the fine debris of the basalt forming *"amygdaloid con-glomerates"* as they are called in Michigan, though the rocks are

(*a*)

(*b*)

Fig. 28.— (*a*) Ropy surface of recent pahoehoe flow, Hawaiian Islands. About one-half natural size. (*b*) Keweenawan flow, Schroeder, Minnesota.

more like breccias (see Fig. 26). Many flows after cooling and erosion show *pillow structures* or *ellipsoids,* indicating that during flow the lava broke up into masses which have vesicular or chilled outer zones, but which were still viscous enough to be packed closely together (Fig. 30). Tabular masses, either flows, sills, or dikes, are commonly broken up by joints into *columnar basalt* (Fig. 29). These may appear in certain flows but not all of a series. Still other details may serve to distinguish one basalt mass from another— slight differences in banding, jointing, color, texture, or the nature of weathering.

Besides the usual gradation from felsitic to porphyritic textures, and in this clan the gradation from very fine grained to doleritic (page 91), there are in the basalt clan certain other textural varieties—first the diabases, and second the spherulites, often called variolites when found in basalt. The diabasic or ophitic fabric in basalts is recognized by the mottling, shown by augite cleavages (luster mottling) on fresh surfaces, and by a color mottling after weathering (Fig. 31 (*c*)).

The chief varieties distinguished among basalts in the Lake Superior copper-bearing district are (1) Ophite, (2) Porphyrite, and (3) Melaphyre; the latter being the basalts without either phenocrysts or ophitic texture. Each of these may have amygdaloidal tops, and there may be "amygdaloidal conglomerates" and associated breccias of each kind of fragments. Melaphyre is a term once used for pre-Tertiary olivine basalt porphyry, but the time significance is no longer recognized.

FIG. 29. — Columnar jointing in a lava, Obsidian Cliff, Yellowstone Park.
(Photo by Balk.)

Alteration attacks different basalts differently so that either hydrothermal action or weathering may develop features that distinguish one basalt from another. Hydrothermal attack develops a variety of green colors, and weathering a variety of reds and browns.

Basalt-porphyries have abundant phenocrysts in a groundmass that is felsitic and dense, and rarely have cellular or amygdaloidal structures. Phenocrysts should include augite and plagioclase to class rocks as basalt-porphyry in the scheme on page 46, but some of these minerals may be inferred from other characters, even where not visible as phenocrysts. If, in a gray groundmass, there are only olivine phenocrysts, or only augite phenocrysts, it is almost certain that the gray color indicates plagioclase and the rock is a basalt-porphyry; for if plagioclase was lacking, the groundmass would be black, as in augitite or limburgite-porphyry.

FIG. 30. — Ellipsoidal basalt, Sioux Lookout, Ontario. (Photo by Pettijohn.)

On the other hand, if olivine is not visible in a porphyritic rock, it is commonly assumed to be absent unless microscopic or chemical work indicates it. Thus a dark rock with only plagioclase phenocrysts (Fig. 32 (*b*)) is best referred to basalt-porphyry and a rock with augite-phenocrysts in a gray groundmass (Fig. 32 (*a*)) is similarly classified, not assuming olivine to be present in either. Hornblende may be associated with the more abundant augite, but can rarely be distinguished in hand specimens. Clusters of phenocrysts may form glomero-porphyries analogous to those of the andesites (page 81).

Attention is called to the fact that some men distinguish basalt-porphyry from augite-andesite porphyry, and gabbro from augite diorite. Here the basalt-gabbro family interlocks with the andesite-diorite family. The distinction on page 46 is based on the nature of the mafic mineral, but some men prefer a distinction based on the percentage of dark mineral, basalts having over 50% mafic material; and others restrict basalts to olivine rocks; and others still restrict basalts to rocks with basic plagioclase—a microscopic or chemical determination being necessary.

In these dark rocks where olivine is common, the quartz and potash feldspars of acidic rocks are not to be expected (page 19). Where quartz is seen in basalts, the first impression is that the rock has been contaminated by fragments of older more acidic rocks. At a few places quartz may be primary in basalts, but such rocks are very rare.

(a)

(b)   (c)

FIG. 31.—Basalt, Pine County, Minnesota. About one-half natural size. (a) Very
fine grain, conchoidal fracture. (b) Medium grain. (c) Mottled as a result of
weathering of a rock with diabasic or ophitic texture. (a) and (b) furnished by
courtesy of McGraw-Hill Book Company.

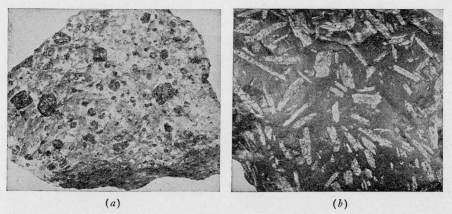

(a)   (b)

FIG. 32.—Basalt porphyries. About natural size. (a) Boggs Creek, Montana: augite
phenocrysts. (b) Boulder with plagioclase phenocrysts. Compare Fig. 33.

The basalt-porphyries constitute the interiors of thick flows and dikes. Yet the interiors of thick flows of these basaltic rocks, do not all become porphyritic, as the more acidic rocks commonly do, but develop coarser and coarser even-textured varieties, the dolerites, which were noted with the granitoid members (page 85).

Where phenocrysts are in marked excess over the groundmass, the rocks are *gabbro-porphyries*. Where the phenocrysts are numerous, they are generally larger and the groundmass between them is slightly coarser than in basalt-porphyry. These rocks occur in deep-seated dikes and thick intrusive sheets.

Synonyms and Relatives. — The name basalt is a very ancient term and has been explained in several ways. Many regard it as a corruption of basanite, a term used by Pliny, although it is uncertain to what rock he applied it. The Greek word for the black touchstone or Lydian stone used by the ancient jewellers is similar to this last form. Others refer it to Basan or Bashan, the kingdom of Og, as mentioned in the Old Testament, Deuteronomy III, 1. Again an Ethiopian word "basal," used by Pliny for an iron-bearing rock, has been suggested. Agricola in the sixteenth century gave it its present signification.

Basalt porphyries as well as andesite porphyries with plagioclase phenocrysts are *porphyrites*. This term was once used for pre-Tertiary porphyritic rocks without olivine, but the time significance is no longer recognized.

A group of dike rocks of dark color and sugary texture, or sugary groundmasses, are distinguished from ordinary basalt dikes by the term, *lamprophyre*. Most of them are more easily altered than basalt dikes and weather to rusty ferruginous outcrops. Most of them are distinguished only by microscopic examination, but a few with biotite or hornblende phenocrysts have been noted in the syenite and diorite clans.

In rare instances nepheline, leucite or melilite are discovered in rocks of basaltic appearance. These can hardly be distinguished without microscopic study, unless perhaps an earlier study has shown that such rocks have locally some peculiarity of structure or of weathering.

The common basalts grade on the one side into andesites and on the other into rocks with little or no feldspar or felspathoid. In felsitic masses these cannot be distinguished without a microscope, and even in the porphyries, if feldspar is not recognized, the distinction is rarely made with certainty. The rocks without feldspar are *augitites,* or if olivine is present, *limburgites.* The porphyries of these families are believed to have a groundmass of glass, or of analcime, more commonly than one of fine grains of the minerals of the phenocrysts. They are rare in this country, but the porphyries with predominant phenocrysts and considerable olivine—the *peridotite porphyries*—are known as *kimberlite,* and have been recognized in several states.

Alteration, Metamorphism. — The olivine of basaltic rocks is the first mineral to alter, and it soon becomes a network of serpentine veinlets enclosing unchanged nuclei. The augite also alters readily into chlorite and finally the feldspar kaolinizes. The prevalence of green, chloritic products suggested the name *greenstone* for old basaltic rocks. After hydrothermal attack the greenstone is hardly distinguishable from propylite, derived from andesite. Many basaltic rocks are thoroughly metamorphosed, and the iron-mining regions around Lake Superior present superb illustrations of the result. Near granite intrusives the augite has a pronounced tendency to change to green hornblende. Under shearing stresses and movements, this change turns basaltic rocks into hornblende-schists, and even chlorite-schists or green-schists, very different rocks. The widespread Catoctin schists of Virginia were derived in this way. The secondary hornblendic rocks are also called amphibolites. Tuffs commonly alter to masses of fine-grained epidote with some secondary quartz.

Tuffs. — Basaltic tuffs, agglomerates, breccias, etc., are well known and accompany many of the massive flows. They mark an explosive stage of eruption before or after the outpouring of lava.

Distribution. — Basalts are known in practically every district in which any kind of igneous rock is abundant, and are of every age from early Archean to the present day. The oldest strata are penetrated by numerous black, igneous dikes, in practically all their exposures. The New England seacoast is especially seamed by them, and hundreds may be met in a short distance. The Adirondacks and the White Mountains, and the Highlands of New York and New Jersey, have many. The intruded sheets of Triassic basaltic rocks, largely diabases, form many of the most prominent landmarks, such as Cape Blomidon, Nova Scotia; Mts. Tom and Holyoke, Massachusetts; and many dikes in the Richmond, Virginia, and Deep River, North Carolina, coal fields. Around Lake Superior, both in the iron and in the copper regions, are great basalt sheets aggregating many thousands of feet thick on Keweenaw Point, and on the north shore. The iron-bearing strata are penetrated by innumerable dikes. The greatest of all American basaltic areas, however, is in the Snake River region of southern Idaho, eastern Oregon and Washington. Many thousands of square miles are covered with the dark lava. In Colorado there are prominent sheets at the Table Mountains, near Golden, at Fisher's Peak, near Trinidad, and at many other points. They are also met in New Mexico, Arizona, and Texas. The volcanoes of the Hawaiian Islands have basaltic flows and a few of them carry nepheline, about the only such rocks known in the area or territories of the United States.

Basalts are equally well known outside of America. The islands off the west coast of Scotland are famous localities. The lavas of Etna are chiefly basaltic. Those of Vesuvius are rich in leucite. In India are the great basalt fields of the Deccan, comparable with those of the Snake River region of northwestern states. Of modern lava flows, one in Iceland comes nearest to spreading over a great area as did those of the Archean, Keweenawan, and Tertiary.

THE DIABASES

The term diabase is a useful one, needed for rocks of basalt-gabbro clan which have a characteristic and peculiar pattern in their texture. In the fine-grained rocks this pattern is seen only by microscopic study, but may be indicated by a luster-mottling, or on a weathered surface by a color mottling (Fig. 31 (c)). In the coarse gabbros, diabases exhibit rods or laths of plagioclase surrounded by coarser augite (Fig. 33), as if the plagioclase had grown early and the augite filled in the interstices.

The student must look closely to distinguish this coarse augite between the plagioclase grains, from a black groundmass (Figs. 32 (*b*) and 33). Two rocks may have plagioclases in similar sizes and abundance, but one having coarse augite between the feldspars is a diabase, the other with black groundmass is a basalt-porphyry.

FIG. 33. — Diabase gabbro with coarse augite, around lath-like plagioclase. Compare Fig. 32.

The basalts with this odd pattern, recognized by their mottled appearance, are *diabase basalts,* or *ophites* (pages 92–3), and the coarse rocks with the same pattern are *diabase gabbros.* The pattern appears in all textures from very fine to very coarse rocks. Strangely enough it is most abundant in rocks of medium grain, with feldspars perhaps .5 to 1 mm. in thickness. Probably 95% of all intrusive sills are diabase, and large parts of them have this medium size of grain. The term diabase without the qualification of basalt or gabbro is usually understood to signify such medium textures. The pattern in such rocks, however, is not so easily recognized as in the ophites and in gabbros. If rods of plagioclase are seen in such rocks, they may be called diabase, but the term *dolerite* is useful here to indicate the intermediate size of grain (page 79) without any implication as to whether the pattern shows needles of plagioclase or more irregular grains.

Scattered in some diabases are large phenocrysts of plagioclase, probably of an earlier generation. These make a *porphyritic diabase*. There are also known some gradations from diabase to rocks of granitic composition. If the diabase is mostly gray, but shows interstitial quartz or red feldspar, it is likely to be a differentiate (or possibly a contaminated rock), and granitic differentiates may be expected as upper zones, or as dikes in aplitic relation to the diabase.

Diabases are well known in many districts where sills intrude sediments. The Palisade of the Hudson River opposite New York City is a noteworthy example. The Triassic sills in New England and the Keweenawan sills north of Lake Superior have been described in detail. The Whin sill in Scotland is exposed over a very extensive area.

The Glasses

Varieties.—The name obsidian is applied to homogeneous glasses with low percentages of water. The word is of classic and ancient origin and is now used for nearly all glasses, with a prefix to indicate the composition, such as *rhyolite-obsidian, basalt-obsidian,* etc. Some glasses appear as independent sheets and dikes, but many more are narrow borders of well-crystallized lava sheets or the outer portions of dikes. Rhyolite obsidian is almost the only glass that makes up large bodies. There is little tendency for basalt to chill to glass, but basalt and andesite lavas are so much more abundant than any others that small masses are the sources of a number of glassy "selvages." The tuffs of the several clans also contain a considerable percentage of glassy fragments, usually very angular and sharp, but these are recognized chiefly by microscopic study.

Obsidians are mostly black, but a black compact glass gives no indication of its composition—it may be rhyolitic or basaltic. The black color probably results from microscopically small black crystals, but is not from an abundance of dark minerals; and the glass is not a mineral. Basalt obsidian may be slightly dull in luster, perhaps from alteration, but not all basaltic glass is dull. If the

glass is magnetic, there are crystals of magnetite of minute size, and these suggest a basic or basaltic composition. The specific gravity of basalt obsidian is about 2.76 and that of rhyolite obsidian about 2.32, so that a test may reveal something of the composition (Fig. 92), but the test is a difficult one to perform accurately on account of the common presence of gas bubbles, many of them so small as to escape notice.

Fig. 34. — Conchoidal fracture and spherulites in obsidian, Yellowstone Park. About one-half natural size.

Any glass that is lighter colored than the usual black, or the rusty red of a basalt scoria, is likely to be rhyolitic in composition. Some glasses are red, green, brown, and various shades of gray.

Almost all the glasses contain dusty, embryonic crystals and gas pores, and some have skeleton crystals of larger growth. *Vitrophyre* has a few phenocrysts, commonly arranged in flow lines and swirling eddies. Almost all large developments of the glasses show dense, stony or lithoidal layers and streaks, which are due to the development of minute crystals of feldspar and quartz, commonly arranged in radiating rosettes, called spherulites (Fig. 34); and in basic rocks, variolites. The individual crystals are rarely large enough to be seen with the unassisted eye. Expanded, bubble-like cavities are also met, many with several concentric walls, on which are perched little well-formed crystals. These cavities are called lithophysae, i.e., stone bubbles. Topaz, quartz, tridymite, feldspars, fayalite, and garnet have been found in beautiful crystals in them. The lithophysae are due to the influence and escape of mineralizers, and may reach a diameter of more than an inch.

Basic glasses are seldom sufficiently free from included crystals to be separable from the porphyritic rocks. Frothy and cellular crusts do, however, appear on lava streams, and are known as *scoria,* and rare, homogeneous basic glasses have been called *tachylyte*.

The structural modifications of rhyolite glasses are *pumice, perlite,* and *pitchstone*. Pumice is an excessively cellular glass, caused by expanding steam bubbles. Perlite is a glass broken into small onion-like, individual masses from contraction in cooling. The concentric cracks form shelly masses between intersecting series of larger straight cracks. The perlites have usually 2–4 per cent of water. The word is also written pearlstone, and was suggested by the fancied resemblance of the concentric shells to the familiar gem. Pitchstone is a homogeneous glass, like obsidian, but contains 5–10 per cent of water. Pitchstones were named when the common pitch of commerce was derived from trees, and are mostly light green to brownish red. They have a more resinous luster than obsidian, but the name is applied more on the basis of color than luster.

Aside from these features and the gradation of glass to a rock of known composition, the best methods of distinguishing different glasses are by the use of a microscope or by chemical analysis.

Alteration. — Glasses resist alteration notably well, but in the long run are subject to decay along cracks and exposed surfaces. They yield quartz, kaolinite and fine, scaly muscovite. In instances they devitrify, as it is called, or break up into aggregates of quartz and feldspar in excessively minute crystals, so that we can trace them back to the original glass only by the flow lines, perlitic cracks, spherulites, and lithophysae that still remain. Such devitrified forms have been called by F. Bascom, *apobsidian*. Petrosilex is an older term applied to these and other similar rocks, and felsite has been also used. There are no Archean glasses, all having been devitrified. Probably some hydration of basic glasses occurs before they lose their glassy appearance. The glassy fragments in tuffs have at certain places been altered, by some peculiar process not well understood, to bentonite, a rock with a large content of montmorillonite, or beidellite, two odd clay minerals.

Distribution. — The glasses are widespread in the West. Obsidian Cliff, in the Yellowstone Park, yields black, red and stony varieties, and has been made famous by the studies of J. P. Iddings. Silver Cliff, Colorado, has furnished some remarkable pitchstones. The extinct volcanoes of New Mexico, Utah, Montana, and California, are well-known localities. Alaska has supplied much from near Fort Wrangel, and in Mexico and Iceland are other prolific sources. Along the Atlantic Coast there are only the devitrified glasses of ancient (pre-Cambrian) volcanoes. These are well developed in New Brunswick, Maine, Massachusetts and Pennsylvania. Abroad the obsidian of the Lipari Islands is a famous one, and the perlites of Hungary supply the specimens in many collections. The best known of all pitchstones are found at Meissen, near Dresden, in Saxony, and on the island of Arran, off the west coast of Scotland.

ULTRABASIC IGNEOUS ROCKS, METEORITES

A few ultra-basic igneous rocks are known in which the silica decreases almost to nil, and in which the bases, especially iron, are correspondingly high. They are in general rather to be considered as basic segregations in a cooling and crystallizing magma than as individual intrusions. The so-called peridotite of Cumberland Hill, Rhode Island, cited above, has very little silica. Titaniferous magnetites have almost none (Fig. 35), but some are rich in alumina. In a few basic igneous rocks metallic iron has been detected suggesting analogies with meteorites. None of these are of commercial value unless the titanium mineral can be concentrated to ore. A more valuable deposit, believed to be a segregation, is the nickeliferous pyrrhotite near the base of the large norite intrusive of Sudbury, Ontario. Several segregated layers rich in chromite have been prospected in the norites of South Africa.

Meteorites are rare and of only scientific interest, but it is extremely suggestive that such silicates as are met in them are chiefly olivine and enstatite, minerals rather characteristic of basic igneous rocks. The metorites most easily recognized are the alloys of iron and nickel, but some rare sulphides occur. The recognition of stony meteorites and their distinction from basic igneous are not always easy. The features expected in meteorites are (1) rocks of basic igneous character with medium grain, (2) a black

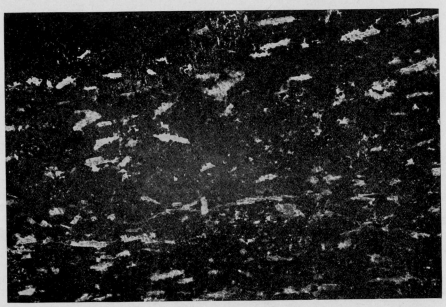

FIG. 35. — Gneissoid structure in titaniferous magnetite, Cook County, Minnesota. The nearly euhedral plagioclase surrounded by ore indicates magmatic segregation. Nearly natural size.

crust about a millimeter thick, (3) a pitted surface almost as if a plastic mass of putty had been handled all over with finger tips, and (4) in about half of the meteorites some metallic iron or alloy.

As filling out the theoretical series we cannot bar out water and ice. There is no reason why they should not be considered igneous rocks of extremely low fusing point, but they are so familiar that a simple reference to them is sufficient.

CHAPTER VI

GENERAL REMARKS ON THE IGNEOUS ROCKS

Chemical Composition. — The chemical compositions of the several clans of igneous rocks range widely, and the study of compositions is complex. Daly has compiled average analyses of a number of igneous rocks, some of which are here given for reference, without any suggestion that tables of analyses should be

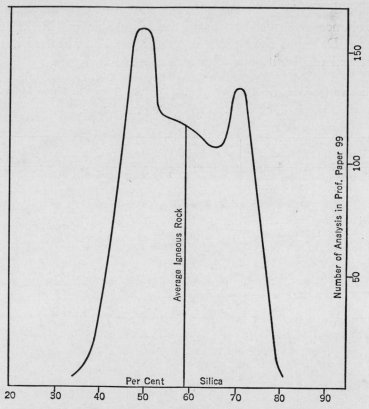

FIG. 36. — Frequency distribution of igneous rocks in U. S. G. S. Professional Paper 99 (omitting diabase and dolerite).

memorized. Johannsen's averages and Robinson's "types" agree well enough to indicate that the estimates are fairly satisfactory.[1] Daly believed that the aphanites in most clans are chemically much like the phanerites, but slightly more alkalic and silicic.

The silica content of igneous rocks ranges from over 80 per cent down to practically none, but few rocks have less than 40 per cent. The extremes appear only in rare facies of intrusives, not in flows. The curve of abundance of rocks at different amounts of silica (Fig. 36) shows two pronounced maxima, one at 48 per cent for the abundant basic lava flows and the other at 70 per cent for abundant granites and grano-diorites. These two groups are clearly dominant in the igneous rocks of the crust.

The dominance of two groups is shown also by an estimate of the volumes of rocks exposed in the mapped areas in the United States. Daly has shown the abundance of andesite and basalt in flows, and of granite and granodiorite in batholiths.

APPROXIMATE QUANTITATIVE DISTRIBUTION OF IGNEOUS ROCKS IN FOLIO MAPS OF THE UNITED STATES GEOLOGICAL SURVEY

(Modified from Daly)

Forms of rock mass	Rock	Sq. miles	Per cent
Batholiths.............	{ Granites	3,836	23
	{ Granodiorites	2,040	12
Sills and dikes............	Gabbro	274	2
	Diabase	268	2—
Extrusive flows............	{ Rhyolite	2,147	13—
	{ Andesite	4,245	25
	{ Basalt	3,209	19
All others.............	....	713	4+
		16,732	100

Alumina is highest in the anorthosites, where it may be 30 per cent, but the clan with the highest average is the nephelite-syenite

[1] R. A. Daly: *Igneous Rocks and Their Origin,* pages 19–36, 1914. A. Johannsen: *Neues Jahrbuch.* B. B. 1931, volume 64A, page 505. H. H. Robinson: *The San Franciscan Volcanic Field.* U. S. Geological Survey, Professional Paper 76, 1913.

TABLE III

AVERAGE COMPOSITIONS (mostly after Daly) *

	Granite of all periods	Syenite includ. alkalic syenite	Nephe-line-Syenite	Quartz-Diorite	Diorite exclud. Quartz-diorite	Gabbro exclud. Olivine-gabbro	Olivine gabbro	Pyrox-enite	Peri-dotite	Ores
Number of analyses	546	50	43	55	70	24	17	10	31	
SiO_2	70.18	60.19	54.63	61.59	56.77	49.50	46.49	51.29	41.09	7.35
TiO_2	.39	.67	.86	.66	.84	.84	1.17	.58	1.16	23.01
Al_2O_3	14.47	16.28+	19.89	16.21	16.67	18.00	17.73	3.52	4.80	3.81
Fe_2O_3	1.57	2.74—	3.37	2.54	3.16	2.80	3.66	1.82	3.96	30.59
FeO	1.78	3.28	2.20	3.77	4.40	5.80	6.17	6.00	7.12	24.05
MnO	.12	.14	.35	.10	.13	.12	.17	.13	.10	.22
MgO	.88	2.49—	.87	2.80	4.17	6.62	8.86	21.06	32.25	3.06
CaO	1.99	4.30—	2.51	5.38	6.74	10.64	11.48	13.88	4.42	4.74
Na_2O	3.48	3.98	8.26	3.37	3.39	2.82	2.16	.30	.49	.12
K_2O	4.11	4.49	5.46	2.10	2.12	.98	.78	.16	.96	.13
H_2O	.84	1.16—	1.35	1.22	1.36	1.60	1.04	1.20	3.53	.67
P_2O_5	.19	.28	.25	.26	.25	.28	.29	.06	.12	2.51

clan. In the pyroxenites and ores, alumina may be less than one per cent.

Iron oxides are almost lacking in some siliceous aplites, and even in anorthosites, but rise to 20 per cent in basalts and, with other metallic oxides, may be nearly 100 per cent in segregated ores. Lime attains its maximum in pyroxenites and gabbros; magnesia in the peridotites. Each of these is closely related to the mineral concentrations characteristic of the clan mentioned. The three metals, iron, calcium, and magnesium, reach their concentrations, commonly, in the three differentiation products of large bodies of gabbro.

Potash is most abundant in orthoclase and leucite rocks; soda in the nepheline and albite rocks; but the soda is more nearly constant than potash. The combined alkalies are at a maximum near 15 per cent in the nepheline-syenites. It should again be em-

* Most of these averages are by Daly on "Igneous Rocks" . . . and the ores are estimated from 24 analyses in J. P. Iddings, Igneous Rocks, vol. 2, pp. 340–341 and 13 analyses in Johannsen's Vol. IV, p. 468.

phasized that orthoclase rocks have commonly much associated albite, but most gabbros have plagioclase with only negligible amounts of orthoclase. Water in quantities over 1 per cent suggests alteration, but in certain glasses primary water may range from 1 to 8 per cent.

For each of the clans the average mineral composition has been roughly estimated, and if these estimates can be fixed in mind (perhaps assisted by the tables and diagrams in the next section) it is possible to estimate fairly closely the analysis of igneous rocks by a simple calculation from mineral compositions. Illustrative calculations are given in Chapter XIII and the estimates usually fall very close to the data of Tables III, IV, and V. It is much easier to make these simple calculations than to remember tables.

Johannsen[2] has selected analyses on a different basis from those selected by Daly for averages, and Table IV is taken from his discussion of granites. Since it shows that the two averages are very much alike, the corresponding tables for other clans are not

TABLE IV

COMPOSITION OF GRANITE (after Johannsen)

	Average of 23	Daly's average of 236	Range found	Range calculated
SiO_2	69.35	69.92	77.47–58.46	80.70–49.67
TiO_2	.35	.39	.85– —	
Al_2O_3	14.27	14.78	16.49–10.88	
Fe_2O_3	1.22	1.62	3.75– .10	
FeO	2.33	1.67	6.67– .79	
MnO	.07	.13	.36– .00	
MgO	1.13	.97	3.67– .13	
CaO	2.18	2.07	5.24– .47	
Na_2O	2.98	3.28	4.38– 1.08 ⎫	15.53– 2.85
K_2O	5.36	4.07	8.36– 2.84 ⎭	
H_2O	.55	.78	2.03–	
P_2O_5	.17	.24	.61–	
BaO	.03	.06	.27	
SrO	.01	.02	.10	
FeS_2	.01	—	.18	
	99.98	100.00		

[2] Op. cit.

quoted. The student should note, however, that the *range* of values is very wide. For example in granites the silica content may be as low as 60%, or as high as 77% or more. Naturally this appears in the rock as a low percentage of quartz in one and a high percentage in the other.

One more chemical analysis is useful for reference. Table V gives the estimated composition of the average igneous rock of the earth's outer 10 miles, the crust.[3] It resembles syenites and quartz diorites, and perhaps is closest to the intermediate rock known as quartz-monzonite.

TABLE V

AVERAGE IGNEOUS ROCK OF THE EARTH'S CRUST

	Per cent		Per cent
SiO_2	59.12	S	0.052
Al_2O_3	15.34	F	0.030
Fe_2O_3	3.08	$(Ce, Y)_2O_3$	0.020
FeO	3.80	Cr_2O_3	0.055
MgO	3.49	V_2O_3	0.026
CaO	5.08	MnO	0.124
Na_2O	3.84	NiO	0.025
K_2O	3.13	BaO	0.055
H_2O+	1.15	SrO	0.022
CO_2	0.102	Li_2O	0.007
TiO_2	1.050	Cu	0.010
ZrO_2	0.039	Zn	0.004
P_2O_5	0.299	Pb	0.002
Cl	0.048		
			100.000

Textures. — All of the typical textures are easily recognized in characteristic development, but the glassy rocks shade insensibly into the felsitic, the felsitic into the porphyritic, and the porphyritic into the granitoid. There are, therefore, intermediate forms that are difficult to classify. Yet on the whole the four textures are the most satisfactory basis for classification and study. Chemical composition being the same, texture is a result of the physical con-

[3] F. W. Clarke and H. S. Washington: *The Composition of the Earth's Crust.* U. S. Geological Survey, Professional Paper 127, page 16, 1924.

ditions surrounding the magma at the time of crystallization and of the presence of mineralizers.

The glasses range in composition through all the clans from rhyolite to limburgite, but little is done with them except by advanced chemical and microscopic methods (pages 100 to 103).

The fragmental igneous rocks form a group transitional from igneous to sedimentary rocks and deserve a further remark as to varieties and names. The best variety names are formed by prefixing to the terms tuff or breccia, the names of the felsitic rocks of the same mineral compositions; but many fragmental rocks are mixtures of fragments of different compositions, for which we have no good term but *mixed tuff*, or *mixed breccia*.

There is a further chance to add detailed variety names indicating the sizes of fragments, as in the sediments (page 152).[4] Fragments over 32 mm. in diameter are bombs, blocks, or driblets.

Fig. 37. — Intrusive breccia of anorthosite in diabase. Nicado, Minnesota.
Courtesy of the McGraw-Hill Book Company.

[4] Wentworth, C. K.: *The Classification and Terminology of the Pyroclastic Rocks.* Bull. National Research Council, No. 89, pages 19–53, 1932.

Their cemented equivalents are breccias or volcanic rubble if made of blocks, or agglomerates if made of bombs, both more or less mixed with finer volcanic debris. Fragments from 4 to 32 mm. in diameter are lapilli, and those of smaller sizes make up volcanic ash, or dust. When cemented they are tuffs.

Breccias consisting of coarse fragments may originate in several distinguishable ways. The common ones result from violent explosions, shattering an already built volcano. A second kind is the result of blocky, broken aa fragments at the front of a scoriaceous flow. A third kind results when a flow has a chilled crust which collapses and the fragments drop into the lava or into the caves from which lava has drained out. There are finally a great many breccias related to violent intrusion underground rather than to volcanoes—they have ordinarily a cement of granitoid rock and fragments of wall rock (Fig. 37).

Specific Gravity. — Holmes has compiled the data on specific gravities of the igneous rocks of several clans, and shows the number in each clan that have a certain specific gravity. The figures show considerable range for each rock, but those dominant are:

Granites	2.66	Rhyolite	2.49
(Rhyolite porphyry	2.62)	(Obsidian	2.29)
Syenite	2.69	Trachite	2.56
Nepheline-syenite	2.62		
Monzonite	2.83		
Granodiorite	2.73		
Quartz-diorite	2.80		
Diorite	2.87	Andesite	2.65
Gabbro	2.97	Basalt	2.87
Anorthosite	2.75		
Olivine-gabbro	3.00	Olivine basalt	2.95
Pyroxenite	3.23		
Hornblendite	3.18		
Peridotite	3.21		
Ores	4.13		

Average igneous rock of the crust 2.79

The lowest density noted is around 2.2 for an acidic glass, and the highest around 5.0 for segregated ores.

Mineralogy. — Figures 38 (*a*) and (*b*), with a reasonable approximation to the truth, illustrate the quantitative mineralogy of the igneous rocks. A section cut through the charts at any one point expresses the relative amounts as well as kinds of the several minerals in the rocks whose names are along the top lines, and whose percentages of silica are approximately shown. No mention is made of texture.

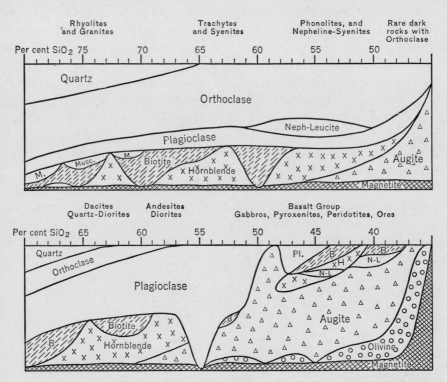

FIG. 38. — Diagram of the mineralogical composition of igneous rocks. The numbers indicate percentages of silica. The upper diagram is for rocks that have orthoclase as chief feldspar; the lower, the plagioclase and non-feldspathic rocks.

In the orthoclase rocks quartz disappears at about 65% SiO_2, while orthoclase continues to the end; plagioclase in small amount is constantly present throughout the series. Nepheline and leucite come in as indicated. Muscovite appears only in the more acidic granites. Biotite and hornblende range widely, but toward the basic end both yield to augite. The continuation of the orthoclase series to a basic extreme is a fact that was not appreciated until recent years. The rocks at the basic end are chiefly those discovered by Weed and Pirsson in Montana, by Iddings in the Yellowstone Park and by Lawson in the Rainy Lake region.

In the plagioclase and non-feldspathic rocks quartz and orthoclase soon run out, so far as any notable or regular amount is concerned. Plagioclase holds along to about 45% SiO_2, and at about 55% SiO_2 may in the anorthosites be the only silicate present. Olivine begins to appear at 55% and increases with occasional lapses almost to the end, where it may be the chief mineral. The ores increase so as to be the only minerals in the rock, forming thus the theoretical, basic limit. The diagrams also emphasize the fact that igneous rocks shade into one another by imperceptible gradations, and this is true of the orthoclase and plagioclase groups themselves, although not suggested by the separation of the two in the drawings.

A careful scrutiny of analyses and mineralogical composition leads to the conclusion that practically the same magma may, under

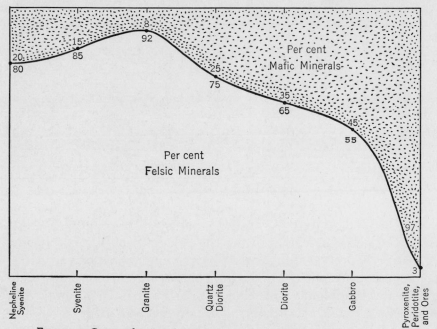

FIG. 39. — Curve of approximate proportions of mafic to felsic minerals in the igneous rock clans.

different physical conditions of crystallization, afford mineralogic aggregates that differ considerably in the proportions of the several minerals—now yielding more hornblende, again more augite, and even affording quartz in a basalt. Hence, analyses in different groups overlap more or less, and the difficulty of drawing sharp lines of distinction is very great. Yet, allowing for this variation, chemical composition largely determines the resulting mineralogical aggregate and is fairly characteristic.

Through the clans there are noteworthy changes in abundance of minerals and mineral groups as well as changes in the minerals on the basis of which the rock is named. Roughly estimated for a tabular resumé they are as follows:

Rock family	Mafic mineral	per cent	Felsic mineral	per cent
Granite	Biotite	10—	Orthoclase Albite Quartz	45 15+ 30
Syenite	Hornblende	15	Orthoclase Albite Others	60 20 5
Nepheline-syenite	Acmite } Biotite }	20	Nepheline Orthoclase Albite	20 40 20
Quartz-diorite	Hornblende, etc.	25	Plagioclase Orthoclase Quartz	55 5 15
Diorite	Hornblende	35	Plagioclase	65
Gabbro	Augite Olivine Magnetite	45	Plagioclase	55
Pyroxenite, peridotite and ores		97		3

Figure 39 shows the changes in the average color ratio, light to dark minerals, through the clans distinguished on page 46. This emphasizes the dominance of light minerals, chiefly feldspar through all the clans but the last three, which are not abundant.

Igneous Rock Series. — If all igneous rocks are compiled in a diagram or plot of almost any sort, it is apparent that there is no break between one kind and another but a complete gradation from each rock to all others. In world-wide studies of such rocks there may be regions in which the rocks all have some small peculiarity of composition. The data suggest such terms as "petrographic provinces," "comagmatic regions," and "consanguinity" of the rocks of a region. Professor Niggli of Switzerland has emphasized the idea that the magmatic character of a province may be related to its dynamic history, whether in orogenic zones, or bordering the zones, or in older Shield areas.

More definitely it is known that a variety of different rocks are genetically related, because they can be found in outcrops to grade from one family or clan to another. A batholith may be partly diorite and partly granite, and the change through quartz-diorite, granodiorite, and quartz monzonite may be so gradual that it is quite impossible to draw a line along the contacts. Another batholith may grade in a single outcrop from hornblende granite to a dark hornblende syenite and then to hornblendite. The thick sills and lopoliths also show a series of rocks in genetic relation, most of the series being in gravitative arrangement—with the lighter rocks near the tops of the sills. In the logical development of igneous theory, these masses that are exposed from top to bottom give us our best evidence as to the behavior of magmas during injection and crystallization.

Lava flows from volcanic centers are less definite in their relationship, but it is easy to believe that two flows from a single crater have some sort of genetic connection. Daly has compiled the series from many examples, and there are commonly acidic, medium, and basic rocks, but no uniform order, or cycle. A rather large number are dominated by basalt and rhyolite in irregular alternation.

Where rock series are thus related it is common to study them by graphic methods. One of the simplest plots of a series shows the minerals of each rock quantitatively by bars, and a composite of the series, by a series of adjacent bars (Fig. 40). A more valuable plot is based on chemical data if available. There are several methods of showing how the chemical constituents differ in the different members of a series. Perhaps the best makes use of the locations of the specimens as abscissas, and the amounts of a certain oxide as ordinates and draws a curve through the points so

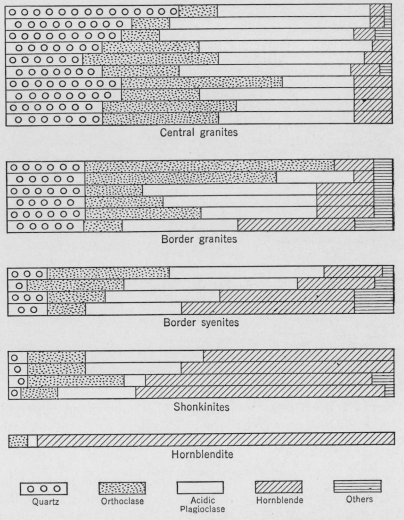

FIG. 40. — Diagram of the modes of several facies of the Saganaga batholith in Minnesota and Ontario. The central granites constitute 85–90% of the exposures.

located (Figs. 41 and 42). This is a so-called "variation diagram," and presents very clearly the nature of a series. Where the locations are not known or where they give less regular curves, it is common to plot the silica contents as abscissas and the contents

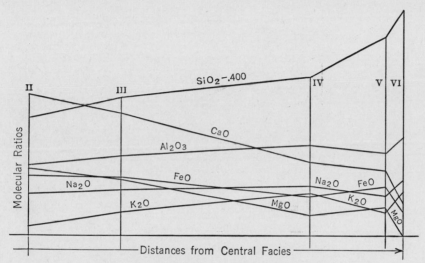

FIG. 41.— Variation diagram for rocks at Magnet Cove, Arkansas. (After H. S. Washington.)

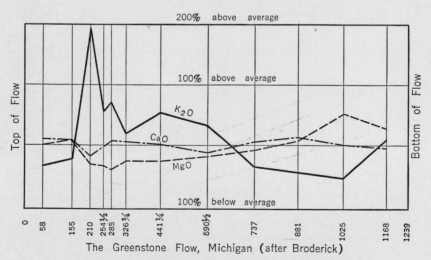

FIG. 42.— Variation diagram of the "greenstone flow," Michigan. (Modified from T. M. Broderick.)

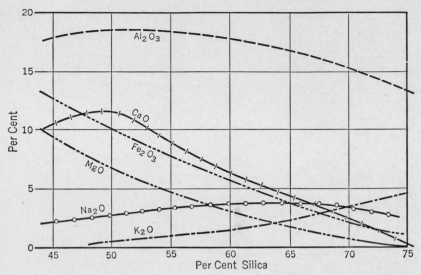

FIG. 43.— Variation diagram of the rocks at Lassen Peak, California.   (After Harker.)

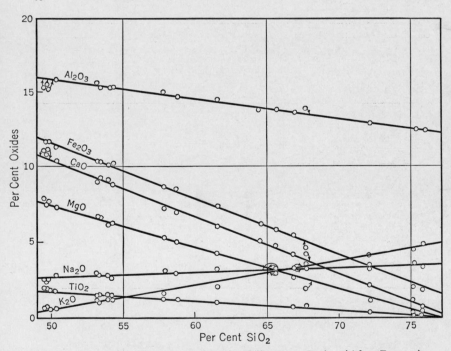

FIG. 44.— Variation diagram of flows in Yellowstone Park.   (After Fenner.)

of other oxides as ordinates. Many such diagrams have been made in reports on areas where chemical work has been available (Figs. 43 and 44). The student should study these variation diagrams to see the nature of rock series as actually developed in the earth. A simple plot of silica and alkalies on two coordinates serves to show that there are series of different kinds (Fig. 45).

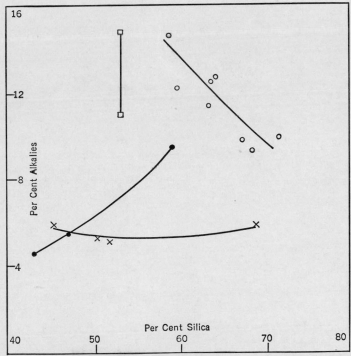

FIG. 45. — Curves of the differentiation series in four districts, showing that the trends of differentiation are different. Squares, Igaliko batholith, Greenland. Circles, Essex County, Massachusetts, alkalic. Crosses, the same, subalkalic. Spots, Väkkerö, Norway.

It is possible to show more than the two constituents, silica and alkalies, by using a triangular plot. Several such have been suggested.[5] Perhaps one of the most valuable is a plot by von Wolff

[5] A. Holmes: *Petrographic Methods and Calculations,* pages 227–8 and 472–90, 1921.

A. Johannsen: *A Descriptive Petrography of the Igneous Rocks,* volume I, pages 100–139, 1931.

which shows the trend of a series of rocks very well on a triangle with quartz at the apex, feldspar at the left and augite at the right, and extensions below for deficiencies of silica (Fig. 46).

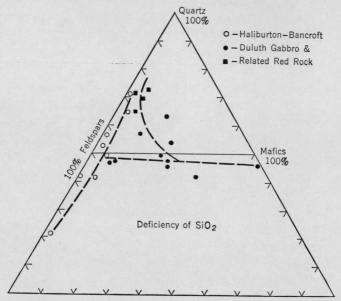

FIG. 46.— Diagram by the method of Von Wolff, for two differentiated series.

Economic Interest in Igneous Rocks. — Some of the most prominent uses of igneous rocks have been mentioned in the descriptions of the rocks. A review with certain additions will emphasize the value of rock study, commercially.

The important features of building stones are strength and durability, widely spaced joints in the quarry, popular color, and workability. Stiny has listed in detail some 39 properties of stone which can be tested in determining its adaptability. Interest centers in the structure, texture, and minerals. Flow structures in unaltered igneous rocks are not especially injurious for building materials unless they are actually openings as in some lavas. The fine-grained rocks are commonly more closely jointed than is desirable in good building material, but when blocks can be obtained of good size the fine rocks prove as serviceable as coarse. In any grain size, a mosaic fabric shows less strength than a sutured or interlocking one, but this is seldom observed without a microscope.

The minerals listed on pages 11 to 17 as essential are all sufficiently strong and weather-resistant to be satisfactory in a building stone. Nepheline and olivine are most soluble and on polished surfaces might soon weather forming discolored pits. Micas especially when in clots or aggregates are so soft that they are not easily polished. Much more objectionable than these are the introduced pyrite and the secondary kaolinite. Pyrite, especially in small disseminated grains, oxidizes rapidly on exposure, stains the rock brown, and generates sulphuric acid which attacks other minerals, weakening the stone and producing sulphate salts that form unsightly efflorescences. Kaolinite in feldspar greatly weakens the grains.

Granites are probably used in more buildings than other igneous rocks, but in the market all granitoid rocks and some gneisses are sold under the trade name, granite. A "black granite" is probably a gabbro, and although dark rocks may be too somber for a whole building, they may be attractive in combination with others. The demand for stones of special kinds runs in cycles and is based on popular fads.

Several igneous rocks, especially granites, are used for monuments and ornamental stones. For concrete aggregate, any igneous rock is excellent unless the grain has been loosened by weathering. For macadam roads, trap rock is best, but several others are satisfactory. Volcanic ash and pumice are excellent abrasives produced in Nebraska, Kansas, and California. Certain tuffs can be mixed with lime to make cement.

The coarse grains of pegmatites make it possible to sort out pure minerals by hand and several are so produced commercially. Quartz, orthoclase, muscovite, and apatite are most common in granites, but the cost of separation of small grains is great, and such minerals are produced almost wholly from pegmatites. These rocks are also the sources of several gems, such as tourmaline and topaz; and of several metallic ores.

The ores of most metals are deposited in some relation to igneous rocks, and the kind of rock is an important guide for the prospector. These broad relations have been given detailed discussion by Buddington in the Lindgren Volume on Ore Deposits of Western States. Certain metals form segregations in basic rocks; and a very different group of metals occur in veins near the contacts of intermediate or siliceous igneous rocks. Finally there are igneous rocks, which are "protores," from which ores may be formed by weathering and enrichment. It is well known that some bauxite ores of aluminum are derived by weathering of nepheline-syenites. Iron ores are largely products of weathering, and partly from original iron-rich igneous rocks such as peridotite. The peridotites have other valuable alteration products as well, asbestos, magnesite, and the nickel silicate ores.

The characteristic segregations in basic rocks are titaniferous-magnetite, nickeliferous-pyrrhotite, chromite, and some ores of copper and platinum. Diamonds are commonly related to kimberlite.

The lode deposits related to granites and similar batholiths and stocks seem to have formed by emanation from the magma into its roof and walls, or into its already solidified upper parts—its hood. Professor Kemp early observed the zonal arrangement of the metals deposited around an igneous center.[6] The facts in some specific districts had been noted, and he called attention to the generality of the relation. Near the igneous source and in pegmatites that are themselves igneous, are cassiterite, molybdenite, and minerals of radium and uranium, and lithium. With some overlapping or telescoping, the sequence away from the source includes iron, arsenic, tungsten, copper, gold, zinc, lead, silver, antimony, and mercury. Intermediate rocks, diorite and syenite, may have lodes with zones of metallic ores, but the sequence is less extensive.

[6] J. J. Kemp: *The Zonal Distribution of Ores Around Igneous Centers.* Economic Geology, volume 16, page 474, 1921, and volume 17, page 46, 1922.

CHAPTER VII

GENERALITIES REGARDING SEDIMENTATION

INTRODUCTION

Sediments are deposits of solid material (or material in transportation that may be deposited as solid) formed on the surface or in the outer crust of the earth under normal temperatures.

The members of this, the second grand division of rocks, are as a rule much easier to identify and understand than are the igneous rocks. They form a large part of the rocks exposed at the surface and their common members are familiar objects in everyday life. Every student of general geology recognizes typical clays, shales, sandstones and limestones, and these make up nearly 99 per cent of the sediments. The minor sediments, however, are of some commercial value and nearly all deserve attention because their recognition may serve to indicate structure or to indicate conditions of formation not indicated by the more abundant rocks. For the common types, details of structure and composition should be studied as a basis for further classification and varietal names.

Materials that have been carried by moving water make up a large part of the group of sediments, but some have been moved by wind or by ice. Associated with the rocks that are formed by the accumulation of materials carried mechanically, are other rocks formed from solution in water, deposited either chemically or by action of organisms. We thus distinguish the main processes of sedimentation. (1) True clastic or fragmental sediments are carried by mechanical processes such as form glacial till, conglomerates, sandstones, and clays. (2) Precipitates from solution are associated with sediments by (a) chemical processes, such as form some iron ores, salt, and gypsum, or by (b) organic processes, such as form diatomaceous earth, coal, and limestone. Along with these are included, in the discussion in this book, certain residual deposits from weathering, chiefly clays and soils, which resemble mechanically deposited clays so closely that they are not readily distinguished.

The student should be on guard not to confuse the origin of the rock with the origin of the mineral in it. A quartz sand may have derived its quartz from a granite, in which the minerals are of igneous origin, but the sand derived from it has been transported and deposited, probably by water, and is therefore a clastic rock formed as an aqueous mechanical sediment. Again, weathering may attack a feldspar chemically altering it to kaolinite, which is so fine-grained that it is easily carried by streams and deposited as clay; and this also is an aqueous mechanical sediment, in spite of the fact that the kaolinite resulted from chemical action on the feldspar.

The occurrence of sediments in the earth is almost universal in the upper, visible parts of the crust, but in mountainous regions, or in former mountainous areas worn down by erosion, sediments are sparse and in large areas may be absent. In the plains of great river valleys sediments may be the only rocks exposed.

The study of sedimentation has been very active in recent years. A committee of the National Research Council under the leadership of Dr. W. H. Twenhofel has issued a valuable compilation of studies under the title a Treatise on Sedimentation, and this has been followed in 1939 by his Principles of Sedimentation.

SOURCES OF MATERIALS

The chief sources of sediments may be grouped as (1) debris of earlier rocks, broken up mechanically; (2) residues from leaching of earlier rocks; (3) solutions formed by leaching; (4) solutions from igneous emanations, notably HCl and CO_2. Minor sources include (5) cosmic dust, which forms part of the deep-sea red clay; and (6) the atmosphere, which supplies snow and some of the carbonaceous matter of organisms. The igneous emanations contributed to sediments are the same as those already described as igneous effects (page 36). The minor red clay of the deep sea, and the snow from the atmosphere, need no comment here. The hydrocarbon compounds produced from the carbonic

acid of the atmosphere are well understood to depend on plant
life. The three important sources involve the process of weathering.

Weathering

Weathering is a process of alteration of rocks near the earth's
surface, chiefly by air, water, and water solutions. It is partly a
mechanical breaking down and partly a chemical change into new
minerals and solutions. The mechanical processes may produce
fragmental material almost without mineral change or transportation, but in most sediments some of the minerals are at least partly
decomposed, and nearly all are transported. "Insoluble" minerals
are only relatively less soluble than others. It is probable that
there is no constituent of rocks that may not be chemically attacked
by some of the reagents involved in weathering. Many minerals
are attacked so slowly as to be common in weathered residues, and
the chief among these is quartz. The most stable decomposition
products are hydrous compounds of aluminum and iron.

It is a matter of common observation that outcrops of rocks
and loose boulders are always more or less decomposed and broken
down or "weathered" for a greater or less distance below their
surfaces. This may not be serious enough to prevent the accurate

Fig. 47. — Spheroidal weathering, diabase sill on north shore of Lake Superior.

recognition of the rock, and usually within the area once covered by the great ice sheet of the Glacial Period it is not, because the moving ice has ploughed away all loose and decomposed materials. But south of the terminal moraine decomposition is excessive and may reach to a depth of a hundred feet or more producing a mass of alteration products that give slight, if any, clue to their originals. This is a common experience in the Southern States and in the tropics, where the indefinite character of the surface rock throws great difficulties in the way of accurate geological mapping.

The search for signs of the original rock should include an examination of the usually soft, argillaceous residue for unweathered cores of fresh rock, an examination of the texture in place, the colors, and the minerals. Locally some conclusions may be drawn from the topography, the depth to ground water, or the nature of the vegetation. Very fragile angular quartz grains in a clay derived from weathering, suggest an original granite or quartz diorite, whereas rounded quartzes indicate a transported sediment. Traces of original textures, porphyritic, diabasic, amygdaloidal, pebbly, gneissic, schistose, and others may be seen long after weathering has completely changed the mineral nature of the rock. The colors of deeply weathered rocks are commonly red, but degrees of redness can be distinguished. The strongest reds suggest a basic igneous original, such as basalt, but bright red clays also develop from limestone and are especially strong evidence of that rock if the clay contains chert. Lighter reds are mostly from sediments other than limestone, or from intermediate rock; and the white, gray, and yellow soils are mostly from granite or rhyolite. Greenish micaceous residues suggest basic rocks. These color effects are modified by climatic conditions, for red soils are much more common in tropical lowlands than in temperate or cold areas, where soils are light gray below humus. A sedimentary clay remains as clay after weathering and may be hard to distinguish from other residual clays, but residual clays are rarely plastic. Bentonite, which swells enormously in water, is a sign of original volcanic ash. If none of these signs serve, it may be necessary to test some of the weathered rock by panning off the finer parts and studying the coarser heavier residues for odd features (page 199).

If they are not easily recognized, it may be advisable to have microscopic stud!es made, for it is expensive to sink deep test pits to determine the nature of the formation, as has been done in some tropical explorations.

Products of weathering are so widespread and so individual that special names for them have been suggested at various times, such as laterite and saprolite (page 157). The U. S. Geological Survey employs the term *surficial* as a general designation for these untransported products of decomposition. Many of them are residual clays.

FIG. 48. — Granite with diagonal joints, weathering, south of Butte, Montana. (Photo by Balk.)

Mechanical Processes. — Mechanical processes include action by air, water and ice, action by organisms such as growing roots of plants, and volume changes resulting from temperature changes, or from chemical action. Rocks are worn or broken by air and water chiefly through sand and gravel carried against the solid rock by winds, streams and waves. These are the cutting tools by which air and water carve solid rock. Similarly, but perhaps in a more striking way, ice carves rocks by means of the boulders frozen in at the borders of the moving ice.

The change of volume by reason of daily or seasonal temperature change is probably small in comparison with the change at times of forest fires, though the alternations are more numerous and may have some effect in a period of years. Chips are forced off from rocks by the expansion of water freezing in crevices. The spalling produced by a single forest fire is probably comparable to the effects of sun and frost for 1,000 years, though the great effect of a fire may be partly a result of previous loosening of grains by sun, frost and other agencies. Deep weathering to residual boulder-like masses cannot be considered a result of forest fires. Commonly spheroidal structures result (Fig. 47). This is not a sign of altitude, or of desert conditions, but rather of a moist situation, where the hydration of feldspars and other minerals causes exfoliation. The effects of temperature change may be subordinate to the mechanical effects of hydration.[1]

Gravel is produced chiefly subaerially, though the pressure of ice may break some weak rocks, and even wave action may develop a force of a kilogram per square centimeter and break off fragments of shore cliffs. Norton has discussed the criteria of origin of sedimentary breccias (page 159).

Most erosive action is exerted on the surfaces of land masses of wide area rather than on coast lines, so that the source of a sediment is seldom the nearest cliff of rock exposed. The sediments from river and rain erosion are probably fifty to one hundred times more abundant than those from marine erosion of shores. Sediments transported for great distances usually receive minerals from a variety of rock sources. All the rocks produced by mechanical breaking of earlier rocks are called fragmental or clastic rocks.

Chemical Processes. — The solutions formed by the leaching of rocks pass into ground water and in large part into the rivers, so that analyses of the river waters show the main results of leaching in a broad way. In mountainous regions the dissolved metals are Ca, Na, and Mg, and the acid radicles are CO_3, SO_4, Cl, and SiO_2, in the order given. On the plains Na and SO_4 become more important, either by precipitation of early solutions

[1] Eliot Blackwelder discusses these processes in two papers in the Journal of Geology, volume 33, pages 793–806, 1925, and volume 35, pages 134–140, 1927.

or by additions from the rocks of the plains. Note that K and SiO_2 are not largely carried in solution and that the CO_2 is largely from the atmosphere.

TABLE VI

ORDER OF RATE OF LOSS BY WEATHERING, ASSUMING ALUMINA CONSTANT

S. S. Goldich, Journal of Geology, volume 46, page 54, 1938.

		Goldich		
Steidtmann	Leith and Mead acid igneous rocks	Morton gneiss	Medford diabase	Black Hills amphibolite
CaO	CaO	Na_2O	CaO	CaO
MgO	Na_2O	CaO	MgO	Na_2O
Na_2O	MgO	MgO	K_2O	MgO
K_2O	K_2O	K_2O	Na_2O	Fe oxides
SiO_2	SiO_2	SiO_2	SiO_2	SiO_2
Fe oxides	Fe oxides	Al_2O_3	Al_2O_3	Al_2O_3
Al_2O_3	Al_2O_3	Fe gain	Fe gain	K_2O gain
		H_2O gain	H_2O gain	H_2O gain

The losses indicated by analyses of fresh and weathered rocks are similar (Table VI), and examples of some results are shown in Figs. 49 and 50.

Goldich has suggested that there is a "stability series" in the attack of common rock minerals, strikingly like the reaction series of Bowen (page 38), indicating that minerals near the top of that series are more rapidly attacked by average weathering than those

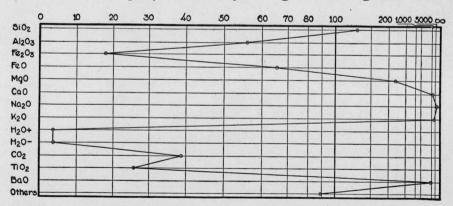

FIG. 49.—Straight line diagram of the weathering of granite gneiss, Morton, Minnesota. (After Goldich.) See Table VII, page 130.

TABLE VII
FRESH AND WEATHERED GNEISS, MORTON, MINNESOTA

	Fresh	Most weathered	$\dfrac{\text{Fresh}}{\text{Weathered}} \times 100$
SiO_2	71.54	55.07	129.1
Al_2O_3	14.62	26.14	55.6
Fe_2O_3	.69	3.72	18.4
FeO	1.64	2.53	64.6
MgO	.77	.33	233.3
CaO	2.08	.16	1300.0
Na_2O	3.84	.05	7680.0
K_2O	3.92	.14	2800.0
H_2O+	.30	9.75	3.1
H_2O-	.02	.64	3.1
CO_2	.14	.36	38.9
TiO_2	.26	1.03	25.0
BaO	.09	.01	900.0
Others	.16	.18	88.8
	100.07	100.11	

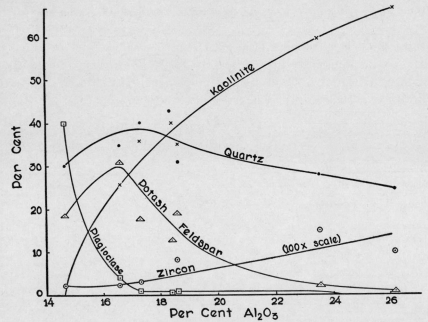

FIG. 50. — Curves of changing mineral content on weathering of gneiss, at Morton, Minn. (After Goldich.)

TABLE VIII
ALTERATION OF COMMON MINERALS (Modified from Holmes)

Deep-seated minerals	Hydrothermal alteration products	Weathering products		Minerals deposited from solution
		Secondary minerals	Removed in solution*	
Quartz	....	....	SiO_2	Quartz, opal chalcedony
Feldspars				
Orthoclase Plagioclase	Sericite Clay minerals Zeolites Epidote Paragonite Clay minerals	Kaolinite Other clay minerals Bauxite	K_2CO_3 SiO_2 Na_2CO_3 $CaH_2(CO_3)_2$	Salts Calcite Gypsum Glauconite, etc.
Feldspathoid	Zeolites Sericite	Kaolinite Bauxite	Na_2CO_3 K_2CO_3 SiO_2	Salts
Muscovite	Sericite	Hydromicas clay, etc.	K_2CO_3 SiO_2	Salts
Biotite	Chlorite	Limonite, clay, etc.	$(Mg.Fe)H_2(CO_3)_2$	Siderite Glauconite, etc.
Augite	Hornblende Biotite Chlorite	Limonite Clay minerals	SiO_2 $CaH_2(CO_3)_2$ $MgH_2(CO_3)_2$ $FeH_2(CO_3)_2$	Calcite Dolomite Siderite
Hornblende	Biotite Chlorite			
Enstatite and Olivine	Serpentine Talc Iron oxides	Limonite Hematite	SiO_2 $MgH_2(CO_3)_2$ $FeH_2(CO_3)_2$	Siderite Magnesite Limonite
Magnetite	Pyrite	Limonite	$FeH_2(CO_3)_2$	Limonite
Pyrite	Pyrite	Limonite	$FeSO_4$ H_2SO_4	Limonite Gypsum
Ilmenite	Leucoxene Rutile	Leucoxene Limonite, etc.	$FeH_2(CO_3)_2$	Limonite
Garnet	Chlorite	Limonite Clay minerals	Bicarbonates	Limonite Carbonates
Apatite	....	....	$Ca_3(PO_4)_2$	Phosphorite, etc.

* SiO_2 in solution is probably colloidal. Carbonates derive CO_2 from the air. The H_2SO_4 from pyrite turns much of the carbonate to sulphate.

below.   Several generalizations have been attempted also to show the order of attack of the minor accessory minerals,[2] but these usually need the microscope for identification.   The least soluble constituents, Al_2O_3 and Fe_2O_3, are rather readily dissolved in the presence of organic matter.   Crusts of bauxite and iron oxide at the surface are therefore formed mostly where humus is rapidly destroyed by bacterial action.

Conditions and Results of Weathering. — It will be noted that the conditions that favor weathering are varied.   Rocks are most weathered above the water table, in warm moist climates, where the topography favors considerable circulation of water.   The rocks most rapidly weathered are the porous, fine-grained rocks containing soluble minerals, notably the carbonates, basic silicates, pyrite, or volcanic ash.   The porosity may be primary, as in a fragmental rock or in an amygdaloid, or secondary, in sheared metamorphic rocks.   Probably acid northern soils lose a good deal of alumina and iron[3] leaving silica concentrated, in contrast to the alkaline soils of warm moist areas, in which practically no iron and alumina are lost.

The whole discussion emphasizes the variety of materials available to be worked over into sediments—fragments of the original rocks, products of their alteration by hot water and by weathering, and the solutions formed by their decomposition.

The results of weathering commonly include a series of zones[4] or horizons from the surface down to fresh rock at depth—the soil profile.   Those horizons from which material has been removed—eluviated—are called A horizons; those enriched by material added from A—illuviated—are B horizons; the undifferentiated parent materials are the C horizons.   Results depend on climate and ground water conditions as much as on original rock.

[2] A. B. Cozzens: *Rates of Wear of Common Minerals.*   Wash. University Studies, Science & Technology, No. 5, pp. 71–80, 1931.

G. A. Thiel: *Sedimentary and Petrographic Analysis of the St. Peter Sandstone.*   Bull. Geological Society of America, volume 46, pages 592–600, 1935.

[3] A. Salminen: *On the Weathering of Rocks and the Composition of Clays.*   Agric. Experiment Station of Finland, 1935.

[4] G. W. Robinson: *Soils,* 2d Ed., 1932.

SAMPLE SOIL PROFILES

(1) Typical	(2) Limestone of Southern United States	(3) Lateritic, tropical

A₁ Amorphous peat soil
A₂ Ash gray, leached of sesqui-
  oxides
B₁ Black layer. Humus stain
  on gravel
B₂ Brown layer of sesquioxide
  coating on gravel
C. Gray parent glacial till
	A. Light brown clay
	
	B. Reddish brown
	
	C. Gray limestone
		B. Ferruginous crust
		A. Leached zone
		
		Decomposed zone
		
		C. Basic igneous rock

TRANSPORTATION

The discussion of mechanical transportation by water may be divided into three parts on the basis of sizes of grains. Sand and gravel are carried by rapid streams, and the size of particle carried varies with the sixth power of the velocity. Thus if we have a current of proper velocity to move a cube of one cubic inch, and then double the velocity, the faster current can move a cube of $(2)^6$ or 64 cubic inches—a cube 4 inches on the edge. An appreciation of this law makes the size of boulders moved by many streams at times of flood, less surprising. See the problems of Chapter XIII. This simple law is, of course, much modified by other factors, such as the smoothness of stream bed, the slope, and the shapes and specific gravities of the grains. A convenient average figure to remember as a basis for calculation is that a quartz grain 1 mm. in diameter is moved by a stream flowing about 150 cm. per second, or 3½ miles per hour—water flowing about as fast as a man walks.

With smaller grains the method of transport is different. Particles smaller than coarse sand require much higher velocities than indicated by the sixth power law.[5] The velocity of a stream at the sides and bed is not as great as near the center, and a thin layer of water near the bottom has "laminar" rather than "turbu-

[5] W. W. Rubey: *The Force Required to Move Particles on a Stream Bed.* U. S. Geological Survey, Prof. Paper 189 (E), pages 120–140, 1938.

lent" flow. At the base of a granule resting on the bottom, the water velocity is zero, but at the top it may be high. The pressure difference tends to lift the particle into suspension. For small grains this factor is more important than the sixth power law.

With grains below .001 mm. in diameter the suspension grades into colloidal solution. Such grains attach to themselves electrical charges, and repell each other so that there is little tendency to settle in pure water. A suspension of fine clay may remain cloudy for years. Nevertheless it is noteworthy that most sea water is not muddy, even where ocean currents keep it agitated. Clearly the sea water has caused a coagulation or flocculation of the clay so that larger particles form and settle. This is because the sea water contains electrolytes in solution. They are ionized with abundant positive and negative charges. The colloidal particles with their charges, when mixed with electrolytes, attract the charged ions of opposite sign, and then no longer repell each other. They group themselves into aggregates which settle rapidly. When, therefore, a sediment-laden stream flows into the sea or into a salt lake, even the finest part of its load speedily settles out.

While we may state thus simply the laws of sedimentation, we must not expect in Nature such well-sorted and differentiated results as would at first thought appear to be the rule. Of rivers and shore currents—the two great transporting agents—the former are subject to floods and freshets, giving enormously increased efficiency for limited periods, and again to droughts, with the same at a minimum, so that different sediments overlap and are involved together. Eddies and quiet portions in the streams themselves contribute further confusion, and an intermingling of coarse and fine materials. Shore currents have parallel increases of violence at times of wind storms.

One further mode of transport may be referred to as "mass movement." It covers such a variety of things as landslides, rock slides, the "creep" of wet muds and soils down slopes, and the movement of large layers of freshly deposited muds on deltas, either from later loads of sediment or by slipping down the foreset slopes.

Transportation by air produces deposits of sand and silt, but the air carries relatively little coarse material, and it sorts the material closely into grains of one size in a single bed. Glacial ice on the contrary carries grains of all sizes and deposits them together in confusion.

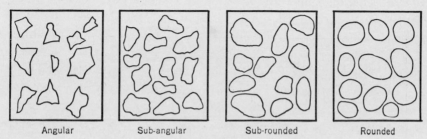

Angular   Sub-angular   Sub-rounded   Rounded

FIG. 51.— Shapes of fragments in sediments.

Transportation tends to wear down the mechanical sediments to smaller sizes but, depending on the original sizes, hardness and other factors, some pebbles may be transported by water 500 to 2,000 miles before being entirely reduced to sands.

This same wearing down by transportation tends to round the corners of grains, so that the shapes of grains are of importance in interpretation. Sharp angular grains indicate either a short transport or glacial action. In a study of pebbles and to some extent of sands, the student can distinguish about four grades in the progress of wear (Fig. 51)—angular, sub-angular, sub-rounded and rounded.[6] The sands along beaches may be transported several hundred miles before becoming rounded. Grains .5 to 1 mm. in diameter seem to become rounded before grains of much smaller sizes. Possibly rounding is accomplished more promptly by wind than by water currents because the grains are not cushioned from each other by water films. The well-rounded sands have probably been transported more than once.

[6] More accurate research methods distinguish "sphericity" (in three dimensions) and use calculations to obtain numerical values to show the changes in form. H. Wadell: *Volume, Shape and Roundness of Rock Particles.* Journal of Geology, volume 40, pages 443–451, 1932; *Sphericity and roundness of rock particles,* Journal of Geology, volume 41, pages 310–314, 1933.

The student may note as additional features (Fig. 52) some scratched facets on glacial boulders, the sharp ridges and polished facets on the ventifacts—pebbles cut by wind-blown sand—and the disc-like forms common in beach gravel. Small grains of single minerals, such as quartz in common sands, may show secondary growths of crystal faces, developed at some time after the deposition of the more or less worn grains.

FIG. 52.—Shapes of pebbles of different origins. A, rounded; B, sub-rounded; C, angular; D, discoid; E, faceted and striated glacial pebbles; F, Dreikanter, faceted by wind-blown sand. About one-fourth natural size. Courtesy of the McGraw-Hill Book Company.

The surfaces of grains are also noteworthy. Water worn sands are better polished than wind blown grains, which commonly show a surface resembling ground glass—called "frosted" or, if the depressions are visible, "pitted."

Transportation works together with deposition—discussed in the following section—to separate or sort out grains of certain character or size from others. The common rule is that heavy and soft minerals concentrate in finer sizes, and light and hard minerals in coarser sizes.[7] Most of the sorting, however, is dominated by the separation of the sand, silt, and clay sizes, thus normally separating the quartz of sand from the aluminous silicates of the clay sizes.

Transportation in water solution requires no special comment (see page 131).

DEPOSITION

Most sediments, having been transported by water, are deposited as bedded or stratified deposits. Beds or strata differ from one another in texture or composition or both (Figs. 53 and 60). The thinner divisions within a bed of considerable thickness are called laminae. Many of them differ from each other only in

FIG. 53.— Stratified rocks. A sandstone quarry at Sandstone, Minnesota.
Courtesy of the McGraw-Hill Book Company.

[7] W. W. Rubey: *The Size Distribution of Heavy Minerals Within a Water-laid Sandstone.* Journal of Sedimentary Petrology, volume 3, page 4, 1933.

color, though others may differ in texture and composition also. Laminae are rarely more than half an inch thick (Fig. 54). Thicker bands by general usage are called beds or strata, and they are commonly separated from the beds above and below them by bedding planes along which there is little cohesion. A group of beds of similar material constitutes a formation. These several structures may be very smooth and uniform over great distances, as in some clays and chemical and organic sediments, but in sand-

FIG. 54. — Varved clay and sand, of pre-Cambrian, Lake County, Minnesota.

stones and mechanical sediments the beds are likely to be very irregular. Practically all beds ultimately grade into other materials laterally, or pinch out so that in a large or small way they are lens-shaped. If a standstone wedges out between impermeable beds, it makes a trap for petroleum as serviceable as an anticline. Not uncommonly beds can be traced laterally over very many miles, and large areas. Some have been deposited on continents and others on ocean floors at various depths. The deltas of great rivers are transitional from marine to terrestrial.

The structures of sediments are objects of a most interesting and valuable study, but involve so many details as to constitute a separate course of study which can be only briefly abstracted in these pages devoted mostly to identification and classification.

The major structures of the great accumulations of sediments result from the filling of subsiding basins called geosynclines. The total accumulations of shallow sediments may be as much as 50,000 feet thick. In any particular period the sequence of sediments in the geosyncline is normally (1) conglomerate, (2) sandstone, (3) shale, and (4) limestone. Minor rock species may fit in at definite places in some such series. If, on occasion, there is a reversal of the normal sinking of the geosyncline or if there are minor oscillations the sequence is reversed. Corresponding to the crustal sinking the shores of the basin of deposition migrate to produce a normal *overlap* of higher sediments over greater areas than the lower. Where oscillation occurs there is the contrasted shore effect of *offlap*. If sediments are carried by streams to the sea shore where water is deep and quiet, there is a tendency for the sediment to deposit almost at once. If the sea is shallow, however, and the currents and waves are active, the sediment is not only carried far out to sea, but it acts as a cutting tool to carve the rocks on the floor of the shallow sea. Between these two conditions there must be at places a gently sloping sea floor, where neither erosion nor deposition is active. Such a slope is a "profile of equilibrium." There is a constant tendency at any shore with stationary crust conditions, to build up or cut down to such a profile. Where sedimentation builds up the sea floor to the profile of equilibrium any further supply brought in by streams will be carried across the deposited sediments, without further deposition till it reaches deeper water, below "wave-base."

With all the possible complexities of the process, the result is that the geosyncline is filled with sedimentary formations, grading both laterally and vertically one into another, with unconformities marking chiefly the beginning and end of the period of sedimentation. The repetition of conditions of sedimentation in a succeeding period, or in the minor oscillations of a developing geosyncline, results in cycles of deposition which have proved economically in-

teresting at places, such as the coal basins in Illinois.   A series of
beds resulting from such changing conditions constitute a cyclothem.
Cyclothems may resemble each other so closely that, if only one
is exposed, it cannot be identified, but certain peculiarities commonly
distinguish one from another.[8]   Cycles commonly involve different
rates of deposition and different kinds of sediment.   In some cycles
of sedimentation the deposition not only becomes slower but actually ceases, and for a time the freshly deposited sediment may
be so near to the surface of the sea that it is subjected to erosion.
If the break in deposition is very inconspicuous it is a "diastem"
rather than a disconformity, the latter term indicating a more important erosion interval.   Similar cycles may occur during limestone deposition, with times of active deposition grading into others
when deposition is retarded or wholly stopped.   If it stops with
freshly deposited calcite standing in shallow water, the calcite may

FIG. 55.—The contact of two limestone formations, St. Paul, Minnesota. The lower
one is corroded and blackened, but not tilted or eroded.

[8] H. R. Wanless: *Pennsylvanian Correlations in the Eastern Interior and
Appalachian Coal Fields.*   Geological Society of America, Special Paper 17,
pages 8–9, 1939.

be partly redissolved, and the residual fragments may be rolled by the waves. This commonly results in corroded flat pebbles of limestone. After the deposition of limestone begins again, the interval of non-deposition, the diastem, is marked by the pebbles and the corrosion zone (Fig. 55). Evidently some sedimentary beds may be deposited rather rapidly, but where they are part of a cycle, the whole formation, including gaps and erosion, may have taken very great lengths of time to be completed.

In the next smaller unit, the formation, structures of interest are bedding, with gradations and interfingering, crossbedding, lamination, and all the interesting phenomena of beaches and stream bottoms, such as ripple marks, worm borings, mud cracks, and rain prints. The clays of several formations, notably those of the Pleistocene lake beds, show a "varved" character, a gradation in each lamina from a coarse-grained base to a much finer top, with an abrupt change to the coarse base of the next lamina, formed in similar sequence the following year (Fig. 54). These probably result from sedimentation in glacial lakes, where the supply of water from melting ice varied with the seasons—spring and summer floods bringing coarse sands, and the cold winters with little water, permitting the finer sediment to settle before the next flood. Several of these structural features may persist through metamorphism and folding and determine the original position of deformed or overturned beds.[9]

Sediments that are porous as deposited may enclose in their pores some of the water in which they settled, called connate water. Where such sediments are enclosed in other beds with low permeability, the connate water may remain through geologic periods, and there is evidence of such connate waters associated with petroleum in some fields. It is perhaps less surprising to find evidence that water remains so long unchanged when it is recalled that petroleum has evidently remained in certain beds since Ordovician time.

Organic deposition may occur in three ways: where the functioning organic material is accumulated, as in coal; where the hard parts, skeleton or shell, are accumulated, as in coral reefs or dia-

[9] T. L. Tanton: *Determination of Age Relations in Folded Rocks.* Geological Magazine, volume 67, pages 73–76, 1930.

tomaceous earths; and where the organism causes a reaction which precipitates some substance from the solution around it, as in algal precipitation of $CaCO_3$ or limonite. These processes may be interwoven with mechanical action which reworks the deposit almost as soon as deposited.

Chemical deposition from solution is chiefly by evaporation, but iron minerals may be precipitated by oxidation and hydrolysis.

On evaporation of sea water a series of minerals precipitate. When the volume is reduced to about 50 per cent of the original, the only precipitates are (1) Fe_2O_3 and (2) $CaCO_3$. When eight-tenths to nine-tenths of the water is removed, some (3) gypsum precipitates; (4) salt, NaCl, precipitates only after the volume is reduced to about one-tenth of the original. These several precipitates overlap a little, but some beds may be formed of fairly pure minerals, with only a small gradation zone to the next mineral. After the beginning of salt precipitation (5) anhydrite forms rather than gypsum, and there is commonly some alternation. Later there are precipitated (6) magnesium sulphate, (7) the double sulphate of magnesium and potassium, (8) magnesium bromide, (9) the double chloride of magnesium and potassium, (10) a hydrous magnesium chloride. The sequence may be interrupted at any stage by drainage or by the addition of fresh water, so that the complete series is deposited at very few places.

Cementation and Diagenesis

The division between sedimentary and metamorphic rocks is arbitrary. Processes of change may begin in sediments as soon as they are deposited. If the change is great, and especially if it has taken place under high temperature and pressure, we call the rock metamorphic, but if slight we still class the rock as sedimentary. Certain changes that occur before the succeeding beds of sediments (more or less uncertain as to volume) are deposited, are classed as primary changes or processes of diagenesis, and are included in sedimentary processes. These include concretionary effects, cementation, and even a certain amount of dehydration (clays), recrystallization (limestone) and replacement (dolomite). By definition *diagenesis* denotes physical or chemical changes in sediments before consolidation; consolidation, however, as applied to sediments is not a very definite term.

Induration usually involves the introduction of some cementing material. Those constituents of a sedimentary rock that have formed or solidified elsewhere and been brought from another place are *allogenic;* those formed within the sediment by changes subsequent to rock deposition are *authigenic.* The cementing minerals are partly allogenic and partly authigenic. Diagenetic cementation is commonly effected by water solutions.

The cements are chiefly carbonates, iron oxides, iron sulphides, and silica in various forms; less commonly there are cements of hydrothermal minerals. The main locations of deposition of sands —the bottoms of shallow seas—are probably not very favorable to cementation, for there is little circulation through them. The amount of ground water in the rocks of the crust is much less than was once supposed. The source of the cement may be local or distant. Many of the calcareous cements may be produced by the recrystallization of shells almost as soon as they are deposited. Feldspars may be altered to form argillaceous cement. The porosity of sediments as deposited may be 30% or more, but cementation may reduce this to less than 5%.

Meteoric waters probably cause some cementation during artesian circulation through long periods of time, but studies in deep mines indicate that their effectiveness is slight except at shallow depths. The whole of the liquid in an artesian reservoir moves, but the motion is most vigorous in a direct route, and slower in the deeper, longer routes. In general the movement is first down, then laterally and finally upward. The upward movement into zones of reduced temperature and pressure favors deposition of cement.

In clays the exact nature of the induration is not certain; it may be a sort of pressure cohesion, or welding. Pressure brings the grains into close contact and may be the main factor involved. There are in most clays, however, certain colloids, which may serve as binders, and microscopic studies indicate that early in the consolidation of clays there is some recrystallization. Clay hardened by pressure may also serve as a cement for coarse fragments. Some detailed studies have been made of the stages of hardening of shales. The progress of change appears in specific gravity, porosity (page 191), hardness, fissility, crushing strength, slaking, weather resistance, and luster.

Recrystallization as a process of diagenesis affects mostly the more soluble rocks like limestone. When the growth of a shell bed is not so rapid as to cover the shells at once with other shells, sea water stands in contact with the shells so long that a readjustment occurs within the bed. Small grains disappear, and large grains grow larger in accord with the usual physico-chemical rules. By such a process a primary bed of shells may lose most of its porosity and develop crystals about as coarse as those in common marble, yet have no signs of deformation in the enclosed fossils. The widely used brown Tennessee "marble" is a striking example. Recrystallization like cementation may largely modify the porosity of a sediment. Limestones recrystallize so easily that porosities range widely. Some lose their porosity promptly and almost completely; others are leached and have their pores greatly enlarged.[10]

Replacements of one mineral by another are partly diagenetic. The "dolomite reaction" (page 271) may occur before a shell limestone is buried by other sediments. It might produce a porosity of 12% in a rock that had little before, and there are many suggestions that dolomites are more porous than the limestones from which they formed.

A replacement of limestone by hematite produces iron ores of the Clinton type. Concretions of several kinds are at least partly diagenetic.

Field and Laboratory Methods on Sediments [11]

There is a growing recognition of the fact that field methods in sedimentary rocks have not always been successful and adequate to the requirements of scientific study. For each station occupied, or for each formational unit, a series of observations should be made. For detailed work an outline may be carried in a notebook and consulted as often as needed to avoid overlooking essential

[10] W. V. Howard and Max W. Davis: *Development of Porosity in Limestones.* Bull. A. A. P. G., volume 20, pages 1389–1412, 1936.

[11] W. C. Krumbein and F. J. Pettijohn have recently issued a *Manual of Sedimentary Petrography,* 1938, giving methods in detail.

facts. If such a sheet is not available it is at least possible for the geologist in a sedimentary field to memorize a list of 13 items that should serve to avoid any gross omissions.

1. Location.
2. Name of rock.
3. Size and shape and topographic development.
4. Bedding features and large structures.
5. Color when fresh.
6. Luster.
7. Composition; size and shape of grain and minerals.
8. Hardness under a hammer.
9. Fossils.
10. Concretions.
11. Variation.
12. Weathering.
13. Specimens collected.

The method of collection of material may be governed by its purpose [12]—(1) petrographic description, (2) suitability of the material for economic use, (3) the environment of deposition, or (4) correlation, by similarities with samples from other places. It is always a problem for the field worker to determine how much of a sediment to include as a unit in sampling. Otto has suggested that the sedimentation unit at any point of sampling is that thickness of sediment that was deposited under essentially constant physical condition. (See page 7.)

Most sedimentary rocks are classed as shale, sandstone, or limestone in the field with no great difficulty. When rare varieties or unexpected rare sediments are met, and when the ordinary classification is not enough to be a safe basis for correlations, samples are taken for more detailed work. Probably most of the careful laboratory work on sediments in recent years has been done in the effort to correlate sediments encountered in prospecting for oil. The work in practice at a drill rig advances logically from the simple easy observations and tests to the more difficult ones, but does not usually require a petrographic microscope. Fossils,

[12] G. H. Otto: *The Sedimentation Unit and its Field Sampling*. Journal of Geology, volume 46, pages 569–582, 1938.

SCHEDULE FOR FIELD DESCRIPTION OF SEDIMENTARY ROCKS

(after *Goldman and Hewett*)

Note. — Define all terms that might be at all uncertain. Use metric units if possible. Describe first the largest units recognized, then those of the next order, and so on down to the smallest.

A. **External form of the rock unit.** Lenticular, persistent, very regular in thickness, etc.; dimensions.

B. **Color.** Color of unit as a whole, wet or dry, according to Ridgway or Munsell color system.

C. **Bedding.**

1. How manifested: Sharp, by partings, by difference in texture, color, etc.; transitional; shaly.

2. Shape of bedding surfaces: Plane, undulating, ripple-marked, etc.; irregular; if not plane, give details of form and dimensions of features.

3. Thickness of beds: Comparative thicknesses; different orders. Relation of thicknesses; rhythmic; random. If variable, relation between thickness and composition, bedding, etc.

4. Attitude and direction of bedding surfaces: Horizontal, inclined, curved. Relation to each other: Parallel, interesecting, tangential; angles between different attitudes and directions; dips, strikes; dimensions; relation of size, composition, shape, etc., to attitude and direction; relation of composition to different types of bedding.

5. Markings of bedding surfaces: Mud cracks, rain prints, bubble impressions, ice-crystal impressions, trails, footprints, etc.

6. Disturbances of bedding: Edgewise or intraformational conglomerates, folding or crumpling of individual beds before consolidation, etc.

D. **Composition.**

1. Inorganic constituents.

   a. Mineralogy or lithology of principal constituents in %.

   b. Size: Prevailing size if fairly uniform; range in sizes if not; proportions of different sizes; distribution of sizes with relation to minerals and other features; vertical and lateral variations in size.

   c. Shape: Crystalline, angular, subangular, subrounded, rounded, %; relation of shape to size, material, position in beds, etc. For quantitative results on pebbles, etc., estimate radius of curvature of sharpest edge, mean radius, and maximum and minimum diameter.

d. Character of surface: Glossy, smooth, mat, pitted, chatter marked, etc.

e. Orientation: If not equidimensional, direction of greater dimensions with respect to bedding, to each other, etc.

f. Chemical and internal physical condition: Fresh, weathered, decomposed, cracked, etc.

g. Packing: Closeness and manner.

h. Pore space.

i. Cement: Present or absent; proportion; composition; differences in composition vertically and laterally and in relation to other characters; disposition with respect to bedding, fractures, etc.

j. Color: Wet or dry; location, inherent or as a stain in constituents or cement; variations and their relation to other factors, as composition, porosity, bedding, fracturing, fossils.

2. Organic constituents.

a. Kinds.

b. Size: Does the distribution of sizes show effects of mechanical deposition?

c. Condition: Entire, fragmented, degree of wear or rounding, partly dissolved, etc.   Relation to kinds.

d. Distribution: With respect to character of beds, kinds of organisms, bedding, evidence of burrowing, etc.

e. Orientation: With respect to bedding; with respect to life habits, possible manner of death, etc.

E. Concretions.

1. Form, size, color, composition, and uniformity or lack of it.

2. Internal structure: central nucleus organic or inorganic; central hollow; homogeneous; banded horizontally, concentrically, etc.; radial; compact; vesicular; septaria.

3. Boundary against country rock: Sharp, transitional with or without change in character.

4. Relation of bedding to concretions: Continuous through concretions; deflected above, below, or both; thinned above, below, etc.

5. Distribution: Random or regular; if regular, intervals between groups (layers), vertically and horizontally; differences between characters of concretions in different groups (layers).   Relation of distribution to other characters, as mechanical, chemical, or organic composition of country rock; jointing, fissuring, folding, etc., of country rock; topography; ground-water level; etc.

especially micro-fossils, are of great value in correlation, and the petrographer should be constantly observing and collecting such materials, but their classification requires another course of study.

The following procedure is given as if it was to be carried out in greatest detail. In practical work, of course, the procedure is interrupted as soon as the data obtained are sufficient for the purpose in mind—say for correlation.

Rotary drills produce "core" and "sludge," and churn drills produce chiefly "cuttings" below ¼ inch in diameter. Observations begin at once as material comes from the well. Even before that, the geologist should know what sort of sludge is being circulated past the tools, and how long it takes to bring bottom cuttings up to the surface. He should also know what formations have been encountered at higher levels in the wells, for fragments of them are to be expected as "ravel," contaminating the cuttings or sludge produced at the bottom. Good samples should have less than 20% of ravel. Sands and shales may in some fields be correlated by their tendency to "heave," or squeeze into the well, interfering with the drilling. The geologist may well consult the expert driller; he can tell much about the rock from the "feel" of the drill and the behavior of the pumps and the engine. Sticky clays slow up the pump.

1. Cuttings coming from a well to a settling trough can be deflected into a sampling pail for the study of the contained rock fragments. The first step is to wash out, with clear water, the sludge and very fine cuttings that conceal the sands and fragments of rock. If the formation is shaly there is danger here of loss of the whole sample, but most shales yield lumps in addition to fines.

2. As soon as cuttings are visible, or a core of the rock is obtained, note whether the wet rock is "slaking" as shales do, or dissolving as salts do. If salt is indicated, clean the surface and check by the taste. See also item 9 of this procedure.

3. Test at least part of the washed sample with dilute HCl for effervescence, and the amount of soluble material. The amount easily soluble is commonly considered "carbonates." After this is estimated, record for the sample the approximate percentages of sand, limestone, shale, gypsum, and others.

4. Note the color wet and after drying, and the luster. For accurate work use Ridgway's color chart or the two-page abstract by the National Research Council.

5. Estimate the hardness or firmness of the rock, its porosity, and whether it has a notably high or low specific gravity. The cohesion of a rock or of cuttings is not usually estimated, as is the hardness of a mineral, but a geologist can estimate about four grades by the use of a hammer and a knife. Such tests are perhaps as much dependent on brittleness as on true hardness (page 8).

6. Test for magnetic grains (distinguish the iron ore minerals from metallic iron fragments left by the abrasion of iron tools and casings).

7. Heat some of the rock to note odors of oil or carbonaceous matter. In a closed tube hydrous minerals give off water, and most hydrocarbons form deposits on the walls. Tests for petroleum in a rock outcrop may be unreliable if the rock is much weathered. A positive test may be obtained from some fresh rock a few inches or few feet down, even when the surface rock gives no sign of petroleum.

Another test for oil is useful if any doubt arises in the closed tube. Cover the dry rock in a test tube with acetone, shake and filter, allowing the filtrate to run into clear water. A cloudiness or milkiness indicates oil in the rock.

8. If the original sample or residue from acid is of sandy or granular texture, it is well to pan off the lighter minerals to see whether the heavy minerals are abundant or peculiar.

9. At all stages of the work, from the first sampling to the acid treatment and panning, the "mass characters" are examined closely, using a pocket lens, and, if available, a binocular microscope. Micro-fossils are detected mostly before acid treatment, but other features may be more easily seen after acid treatment or panning. A great variety of peculiar features may be discovered in such examinations (page 199). After the monotony of hundreds of feet of common gray sand, shale, and limestone, it is noteworthy to find grains of *odd* minerals, or forms, or textures, or colors, or lusters, and such discoveries may supply a key-bed or horizon marker as useful as a fossil.

10. If material is wanted for a file or needed for more detailed petrographic work, a sample is collected. Further laboratory work on the sample includes the separation of grains by size (screening or elutriation) and the separation of heavy minerals by use of bromoform and the identification of minerals by the petrographic microscope.[13] These are not usually done at the drill rig. The more accurate data may be shown by diagrams, and the student should be familiar with the several kinds (Chapter XIII).

11. At the well the record of observations is commonly kept in a notebook, from which a graphic log may be constructed. See pages 202 to 206.

[13] The methods of work with heavy liquids may be qualitative for some rough comparisons. The accurate counts of several hundred grains are time consuming and not usually justified unless all the preliminary work of sampling and separation is done with more care and standardized methods than usual. R. D. Reed and J. P. Bailey: *Subsurface Correlation by Means of Heavy Minerals*. Bull. A. A. P. G., volume 11, p. 367, 1927.

CHAPTER VIII

THE SEDIMENTARY ROCKS

INTRODUCTION

The classification of sediments here used is mineralogical and serves as a basis for description. Probably 99 per cent of our sedimentary rocks consist of clay, sandstone, limestone, and mixtures of these. The clays probably make over 50 per cent and sandstones are clearly more abundant than limestones in the remainder. Those sandy textured rocks in which the grains are calcite are most conveniently treated as limestones. Many minor sediments have special names, which characterize them with reasonable exactness. They are best learned by a study of labelled specimens. The abundant sands, clays, and limestones show such a wide range of varieties that it is best to subdivide such groups. There are needed in the first place some qualifying adjectives.

Clay is an argillaceous rock.

Sandstone is an arenaceous rock.

Limestone is a calcareous rock.

Coal is a carbonaceous rock.

Iron ore is a ferruginous rock.

Salt is a saline rock.

Various other adjectives refer to less common rocks.

The terms are used mostly to describe mixtures. We seldom say "argillaceous rock" when we mean clay, but if a sandstone contains some clay, it is an argillaceous sandstone. Most of the terms are clearly mineralogical, but "arenaceous" may be textural—usually it implies quartz as well as sand sizes of grain.

Some attempts have been made to apply a uniform system to all sediments, but none has been accepted as of general application. Several of the proposed terms are widely used, however, and a few are here listed, as possibly serviceable in distinguishing varieties of the common sediments, especially in emphasizing the chief agent in their genesis.

151

Hydrogenic, mostly precipitated from water.

Biogenic, shells, skeletons, and plant remains.

Anemoclastic, broken by wind erosion.

Hydroclastic broken by water erosion.

Bioclastic broken by man or other living things.

It may be logical to make main divisions of sedimentary rocks on the basis of origin, under three heads—clastic sediments, chemical precipitates, and organic remains—with subdivisions indicating where or how the deposits accumulated. Such a system, however, seems to have few practical advantages.

TABLE IX

Grade Sizes of Fragmental Grains *

Size limits	Pieces	Aggregates	Cemented rock
256 mm.	Rounded: boulders Angular: blocks	Gravel	Conglomerate Breccia
64 mm.	Rounded: cobbles Angular: blocks	Gravel	Conglomerate Breccia
4 mm.	Rounded: pebbles Angular: blocks	Gravel	Conglomerate Breccia
2 mm.	Rounded granules Angular	Gravel (Grit)	Conglomerate (Grit)
1 mm.	Very coarse sand grains	Very coarse sand	Very coarse sandstone
1/2 mm.	Coarse sand grains	Coarse sand	Coarse sandstone
1/4 mm.	Medium sand grains	Medium sand	Medium sandstone
1/8 mm.	Fine sand grains	Fine sand	Fine sandstone
1/16 mm.	Very fine sand grains	Very fine sand	Very fine sandstone
1/256 mm.	Silt particles	Silt	Siltstone ⎱⎰ shale, mudstone and argillite
	Clay particles including colloids	Clay	Claystone

* Modified from Wentworth. Journal of Geology, volume 30, p. 377, 1922.

Sizes of Grain Sediments

In common practice sediments are largely defined by the sizes of their grains, and in the interest of uniformity it is desirable to follow standard usage. The suggested form much used by geologists is shown in Table IX.

A sieve with 9 openings to the inch catches gravel, not sand.
A sieve with 230 openings to the inch catches sand, not silt or clay.
35-mesh sieve openings are 1/2 mm.
60-mesh sieve openings are 1/4 mm.
120-mesh sieve openings are 1/8 mm.

I. Clays and Shales and Weathered Residues

Definitions. — Clays are commonly defined as the natural earths that become plastic when wet, but include some non-plastic earths that are largely composed of hydrous compounds of alumina and silica. Some petrographers would base the definition on size of grain, specifying those disperse forms of mineral grains in which particles smaller than 0.002 mm. predominate; but many commercial clays have only a small proportion of such fine particles. It would be nearer average to use as the upper limit of the clay size 1/256 mm., about 0.004 mm. Some of the properties of clay, especially plasticity, are related to the fineness of grain, many grains being so fine as to be classed as colloidal. Most clays have an earthy odor.

Twenhofel insists[1] that to be called clay, the rock should have such a proportion (more than 50%) of fine particles, largely clay minerals, as to mask rather completely the particles larger than "clay-size." Many commercial "brick clays" have less than this proportion and may well be technically classed as argillaceous silts, though popular usage will no doubt continue to include them with clays. Under this definition origin is not emphasized. Some clays are residual from the weathering of feldspathic rocks though most are transported and deposited by water.

Shale is typically a hardened laminated clay, or mixture of silt and clay. Some shales, however, may lack one of these two

[1] W. H. Twenhofel, in Report of Committee on Sedimentation. National Research Council 1936–7, Terminology of the Fine-grained Sediments, pages 81–104, 1937.

characteristics; they may be hard and not laminated; or they may be laminated and soft. Most shales are formations that have been buried under other sediments; recent surface deposits are not called shale. The lamination is commonly detected by the ease of parting or cleavage parallel to the bedding and is supposed to be due to slight differences in the texture of successive very thin layers, but may be due to some process of sedimentation, more or less obscure.

It will be noted that the definition of clay referred to hydrous compounds of alumina and silica without giving mineral names. There are several of the so-called clay minerals and some have different proportions of silica and water, as well as structures and optical properties different from the common kaolinite; dickite, nacrite, allophane, beidellite, montmorillonite, and halloysite.[2] A sericite-like mineral occurs in many shales, probably formed by recrystallization after deposition. These are not easily distinguished in rock study, but need advanced optical, chemical, and X-ray methods.

Mineralogic Composition, Varieties. — The clays and shales have varieties chiefly as they contain impurities. Pure deposits of clay minerals are mostly white and a white kaolinite is given the rock name *kaolin.* Colors indicate some impurities, and as the clay becomes mixed with coarser debris it has textural varieties grading to other sediments.

The colors of clays are white, gray, blue, green, yellow, brown, red, black, and intermediate colors. These bear some relation to composition, for the reds and yellows almost always indicate ferric oxides. The color is not always reliable, however, for clays of essentially the same composition may have different colors and *vice versa.*

The admixture of other sediments gives *ferruginous clays, carbonaceous* or *bituminous clays,*[3] *calcareous clays, gypsiferous clays,*

---

[2] See Paul Kerr, *A Decade of Research on the Nature of Clay.* Transactions of the American Ceramic Society, volume 21, pages 267–286, 1938. There is an odd clay mineral or mixture in Illinois, for which the name "illite" has been suggested.

[3] Twenhofel's Treatise distinguishes carbonaceous shale as mixed with organic matter like coal, and bituminous shale as mixed with marine organic matter from which material like petroleum may be distilled.

glauconitic clays, pyritic clays, and *siliceous*—usually *sandy*—*clays.*
Less common are *bauxitic clays, diaspore clays, bentonitic clays,
diatomaceous* and *radiolarian clays,* and *tuffaceous clays.*

For each of these varieties it is desirable to be quantitative
as soon as information is available, and even the field observer can
distinguish a highly sandy from a slightly sandy clay. As the
impurity becomes dominant, the classification changes—a highly
sandy clay grades into argillaceous sand. The calcareous clays
may become about as hard as limestone with even less than 50 per
cent of carbonate.

Beside the common sandy clays, there are *silty clays,* and much
less commonly the *boulder clays* characteristic of *glacial till,* or if
well-cemented, *tillite.* Clays with concretions are mostly calcareous, but may bear a variety of concretionary materials. *Concretionary clay* has the clay mineral itself in concentric structures.
Fossiliferous clays are also chiefly calcareous. *Bentonite* is a clay
derived from volcanic ash, and composed chiefly of montmorillonite

FIG. 56.—Two equal blocks of bentonite, one wet with water and the other remaining
dry. Courtesy of the McGraw-Hall Book Company.

or beidellite—recognized by its enormous swelling when wet (Fig.
56) and its tendency to make a milky suspension in water.[4] Most
of the *bleaching clays* that absorb color from various oils are those
that contain montmorillonite or beidellite. *Gouge* is a term for
clay made of the crushed material along a fault or vein.

[4] Recent use of bentonite for decolorizing oils has led some writers to
include under the term bentonite, other clays that serve that purpose, formerly
known as fullers earth. The mineralogic definition is best. Bleaching clays
are said to be acid in reaction, but a practical test is only means of recognition.
See Bull. A. A. P. G., volume 19, page 1050, 1935. A suspension of bentonite
is used commercially to inject into earth dams to make them water-tight.

Many terms prefixed to clay indicate physical characters with only very indefinite relation to the composition and other properties—*plastic clay, flint clay* (non-plastic and hard), *fire clay* (refractory), and others.

Many clays have been given names indicating origin, but few of these names have definite petrographic significance. It is hard to tell an alluvial or lacustrine clay from a marine clay. Some glacial clay is boulder clay; and *varved* clays, having bedding or lamination with gradation upward from silt to clay in each bed, suggest deposition in cold fresh water (Fig. 54).

There remain a series of variety terms applied to clays based on uses—brick clay, pottery clay, slip clay, etc. These tell very little about texture or minerals, but most fire clays are relatively pure hydrous aluminum silicate and are refractory. Variety terms based on age show equally little of the nature of the rock.

The processes of diagenesis and later metamorphism make a series of distinguisable varieties of clay. Twenhofel suggests a tabulation:

Unindurated............................ $\left\{ \begin{matrix} \text{Silt} \\ \text{Clay} \end{matrix} \right\rangle + H_2O = \text{mud}$

Indurated.............................. $\left\{ \begin{matrix} \text{Siltstone} \\ \text{Claystone} \end{matrix} \right\rangle + \text{fissility} = \text{shale, or mudstone}$

After incipient metamorphism, no secondary cleavage....Argillite.
Moderate metamorphism, secondary cleavage....Slate.

A few terms of local or special significance are noteworthy. *Adobe,* in the semi-arid districts of southwestern states and Mexico, is a clay or silt deposit, used for sun-dried bricks. *Pipestone* (catlinite) is a hard red shale used by the Dakota Indians for making pipes (it contains pyrophyllite and diaspore). *Fullers earth* is an acid clay that decolorizes oil. *Gumbo* is a sticky surface clay. *Loess* is a silt with some clay, largely windblown. *Marl* is an earthy mixture that may contain clay. *Loam* is a soil or earth with about equal parts of sand, silt, and clay.

Residual clays and earths formed by weathering make up a group with a nomenclature that requires further comment, especially because some are not clays, though associated with clays and listed in this group. The oldest term and one still current is *laterite*. This is probably best defined as a porous, residual deposit derived by the tropical weathering of basic rocks *in situ*, to form hard surface crusts characterized by ferruginous or aluminous concretionary masses, and at places by secondary silicates.[5] The concretionary concentration occurs in ground waters, where evaporation is greater than precipitation. Highly aluminous light-colored laterites contain gibbsite, are called *bauxite*, and are ores of aluminum, but there are other laterites that are high in quartz. Acidic rocks do not weather directly to laterite even in the tropics, but form clays which, if very porous, may later be leached to bauxite. Weathering in a desert or in temperate climates does not form laterite. Some residual products like bauxite may be transported a short distance, becoming bedded deposits but still retaining most of the residual characters. There may thus be stratified bauxite rocks.

Commercially important iron ores are largely residual from weathering, and certain residual manganese deposits and phosphates may be noted here, though so small that their inclusion with rocks is questionable. Some especially ferruginous clays are called *ocher*, and are used as pigments, grading from red to yellow colors according to the hydration of the ferric oxide.

In 1895, Becker of the United States Geological Survey proposed the name *saprolite*, a word meaning literally rotten rock, as a general name for "thoroughly decomposed, earthy, but untransported rock." This term applies well to the plastic red clay soils of southeastern states, but they are essentially residual clays and a special term is hardly needed. See the section above on recognition of original rocks by the study of weathered residues (pages 126 and 127).

Metamorphism. — Clays have formed largely by weathering and are but little affected by more weathering. By metamorphism shales are compacted, hardened and ultimately recrystallized grading through slates to schists. Slates have a secondary cleavage

[5] J. B. Harrison: *The Katamorphism of Igneous Rocks under Humid Tropical Conditions*. Imp. Bureau of Soil Science. Rothamsted Experiment Station, Harpenden, 1933.

independent of the bedding and are so much more altered than shales that they are commonly distinguished without trouble. Shales should not be called slates (page 225).

Distribution.— Shales and clays are such common members of extended geological sections that particular localities deserve no special mention.   Many are more than a thousand feet thick and cover great areas.   High grade clay for ceramic purposes is well known in southeastern states, in Ohio, in Illinois, and elsewhere. Diaspore clay is important in Missouri.   Bleaching clays are produced at places from Georgia to California.   Bentonite is produced in South Dakota and Wyoming.   Pipestone is a Minnesota product.   Loess is prominent in the states along the Missouri River. The marl that is a calcareous earth has been the basis of a large cement industry in Michigan.

II. Sands and Other Mechanical Sediments
(not clay or limestone)

This group is subdivided in a series from coarse to fine, as in the Table on page 152.   The rocks with grains over 2 mm. in diameter are breccias and conglomerates.   Sand grains range from 2 mm. to 1/16 mm. and silts from 1/16 to 1/256 mm.   Minor varieties are associated with these major groups in the text.

Breccias

The word *breccia* is of Italian origin and is used to describe aggregates of angular fragments cemented together into a coherent mass.   The breccias cannot all be properly considered sedimentary, for some have already been described as igneous rocks.   Many resemble conglomerates, but, unless formed of fragments of some soluble rock, whose edges have become rounded by solution, there is no difficulty in distinguishing them.   Breccias may have angular fragments of the same materials as interstitial filling, or they may have different ones.   We may distinguish *Friction breccias* (Fault breccias), *Talus breccias,* and for the sake of completeness, may also mention here *Eruptive breccias* (page 34).   The methods of distinction of several breccias are noted on page 195.

Friction breccias are formed during earth-movements by the rubbing of the walls of a fault on each other, and by the consequent crushing of the rock. The crushed material of finest grade fills in the interstices between the coarser angular fragments, and all the aggregate is soon cemented together by circulating mineral waters. Such breccias occur in all kinds of rocks and supply many ores, which are introduced into the interstices by infiltrating solutions. Quartz and calcite are the commonest cements (Fig. 57). Breccias resulting from crushing a rock in place are spoken of as autoclastic or cataclastic.

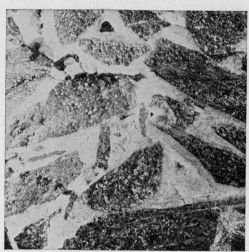

Talus breccia consists of the angular debris that falls at the foot of a cliff and becomes cemented by circulating waters, chiefly those charged with lime. We often speak of breccias as "brecciated limestone," "brecciated gneiss," or some other rock, thus making prominent the character of the original. When the fragments and the cement are contrasted in color, very beautiful ornamental stones result, which may be susceptible of a high

FIG. 57.— Friction breccia of rhyolite porphyry fragments and quartz and chalcedony cement. North shore of Lake Superior. About one-half natural size.

polish. Uncemented angular grains are called blocks, chips, flakes, or slabs, rather than boulders or pebbles. Residual clays at places contain enough angular chert fragments to constitute breccias. These probably developed angular fragments by slumping, but differ notably from talus.

Norton [6] has given a discussion of breccias from different points of view. As to movement of fragments he suggests: *crackle* breccia, fragments little displaced, *mosaic* breccia, largely but not wholly replaced, and *rubble* breccia,

[6] W. H. Norton: *A Classification of Breccias.* Journal of Geology, volume 25, page 160, 1917.

retaining no initial planes of rupture.   As to origin there are (a) subaerial, (b) subaqueous, and (c) endolithic breccias.   The endolithic group include the fault breccias, fold breccias, and the collapse of the roofs of caverns.   A moment's consideration will convince the student that breccias, except as formed by volcanic eruptions, are of very limited occurrence.

Gravels and Conglomerates

Loose aggregates of rounded and water-worn pebbles and boulders are called *gravels,* and when they become cemented into coherent rocks they form *conglomerates* (Fig. 58).   Sand almost always occupies the interstices.   Silica, calcite, and limonite are the commonest cements.   The component pebbles, cobbles or boulders, as tabulated on page 152, are of all sorts of rock depending on the ledges that have supplied them, hard rocks of course predominating.   Rounded fragments of vein quartz are especially abundant.   A series of adjectives may be prefixed to show the

Fig. 58. — Conglomerate.   About one-half natural size.   Courtesy of the McGraw-Hill Book Company.

nature of the fragments and the nature of the cement (see page 166).

Conglomerates are almost entirely aqueous. Gravels and conglomerates, if of limited extent, indicate the former presence of swift streams; if of wide area, they suggest the former existence of sea beaches and the advance of the sea over the land. It is possible that conglomerates of great thickness, say more than 100 feet, are rarely accumulated except by streams—they are dominantly terrestrial rather than marine; but the criterion needs further study because some marine conglomerates are thick.[7]

The component pebbles of a conglomerate are of course older than the conglomerate itself, and if igneous, they prove that the intrusion is older than the conglomerate. Fossiliferous boulders prove that the conglomerate is younger than the strata which supplied the boulders. Under favorable circumstances gravels may be cemented to conglomerates in a comparatively few years.

A number of special varieties of conglomerates have been named. Gravels and conglomerates graduate by imperceptible stages into *pebbly sands* and sandstones, and these into typical sands and sandstones. Notably unsorted aggregates of relatively large and more or less angular boulders in fine sands or clay suggest glacial *till;* if solidified they yield *tillites,* distinguished from other bouldery clays chiefly by an occasional striated pebble. Pebbly beds in the midst of limestones, and other soluble rocks, especially where the rocks above and below the pebbly bed are much alike, are *intraformational conglomerates* (Fig. 59). Pebbles of such beds are usually flat and rather irregular as if from corrosion. *"Flat-pebble conglomerates"* are not all from corrosion, however, for many beach pebbles are disc-shaped. They make up a gravel called *shingle*. *"Edgewise"* conglomerates have disc-shaped pebbles with their planes transverse to the bedding, probably oriented largely by running water. A *fanglomerate* is a pebbly or bouldery deposit in an alluvial fan. *Hard-pan* is a term commonly applied to placer gravel cemented by limonite.[8]

[7] W. H. Twenhofel: *Marine Unconformities, Marine Conglomerates and Thicknesses of Strata.* Bull. American Association of Petroleum Geologists, volume 20, pages 677–703, 1936.

[8] Also used for wet clays that are tough and hard to excavate.

Under dynamic stresses, especially under high pressure and shearing, the pebbles of a conglomerate are commonly flattened into lenses. If the pebbles are feldspathic as is the case in those from granite ledges, and if the interstitial filling is aluminous and not purely quartzose, conglomerates may be granulated and recrystallized into augen-gneisses with their characteristic "augen" or "eyes" of feldspar and quartz, which but faintly suggest their original character. Excessive metamorphism may recrystallize conglomerates into rocks, simulating granite, forming thus the so-called "recomposed granite" of the Lake Superior region.

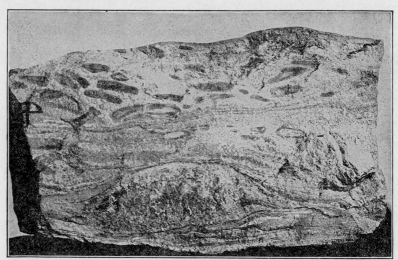

FIG. 59.—Intraformational (flat-pebble) conglomerate in ferruginous chert of Mesabi Range, Minnesota. About one-half natural size. Courtesy of the McGraw-Hill Book Company.

Gravels are too familiar to require further reference. Conglomerates are met in all extended sedimentary series. Our greatest one lies at the base of the productive Coal Measures of Pennsylvania and adjacent States. It is properly called the "Great Conglomerate." Remarkable conglomerates of pre-Cambrian age are valuable guides to the structure and history throughout the Canadian Shield and its extension into the Lake Superior Region and New England. In Central Massachusetts there is an augen-gneiss derived from a Cambrian conglomerate. It has been quarried at Munson and widely used as a building stone under the name of granite.

Sands and Sandstones and Silts

Mineralogic Composition, Varieties. — The mechanical sediments whose predominant particles are finer than gravel and coarser than clay are grouped here, as *sand* and *silt* if loose and uncemented, and as *sandstone* and *siltstone* if cemented, and as *quartzite* if well cemented with silica. Some old sandstones still poorly cemented are *friable sandstones.* *"Quick sands"* are uncemented sands well lubricated by water. The textures range from coarse sand to silt as shown in the table on page 152, and there are gradations on one side through *pebbly sandstones* to conglomerates, and on the other through *shaly sandstones* to shales. A very coarse sand, especially one with angular grains, is called *grit.* Various structural features may be added as qualifiers to the names—bedded, cross-bedded (Fig. 60), concretionary, ripple-marked, etc. For medium and fine sands the shapes can hardly be seen without a lens. It is common to find mixed sands, with the coarse grains more rounded than the fine grains. No term indicates the shapes of grain in sandstones, but a phrase is commonly added to describe them. It is not to be expected that single names can ever replace the descriptive terms prefixed to the standard names indicating textures and minerals.

Sandstones generally have well-marked bedding, some in very thick beds and others thin. A somewhat shaly sandstone with thin beds is called *"flagstone."* A mixture of nearly equal amounts of sand, silt, and clay is called *loam.*

Wind blown sands are not usually very coarse. The finer silts blown by the wind afford a surface deposit called *"loess,"* which may lack all stratification, and which commonly stands in vertical walls where partly eroded. More or less water-transported material and surface vegetation may be intermingled making the term a difficult one to define sharply. The mixed character makes its origin a puzzle at many places. Much of it is "rock flour," which is a silt derived from rock minerals without much decomposition, and contrasted with "rock rot," the result of decomposition to

Fig. 60. — Cross-bedded sandstone under a basalt lava flow, Grand Portage, Minnesota. Courtesy of the McGraw-Hill Book Company.

abundant clay minerals. Loess is buff to brown and is always loose-textured but feels harsh compared with clay, when rubbed between the fingers. It is important in its relations to agriculture.

Quartz is much the commonest mineral of the grains of sand as it is the most resistant of the common rock-making minerals. In river sands the grains may be angular, but after long and repeated transportation, they become rounded. *Ganister* is a fairly pure quartzitic sandstone used as a refractory material. *Feldspathic sands* are perhaps second in abundance after quartz sands, and sands with notable feldspar [9] are called *arkose,* formed where mechanical disintegration of granite and gneiss is more rapid than chemical attack.   This occurs mostly where the climate is rigorous, either arid or very cold.   A similar attack on basic igneous rock or slate produces *graywacke,* with enough gray and black grains to make the rock look gray.   *"Blacksand"* technically indicates that magnetite-ilmenite grains are abundant.   *"Greensand"* indicates glauconite or other green ferruginous silicates, commonly formed on the sea floor, about where sands grade into muds.   Other resistant minerals such as garnet, zircon, tourmaline, and apatite are widely distributed in small amounts and may locally be concentrated.   Many others are known by microscopic study of heavy mineral separates but are rarely abundant enough to afford variety names.   Tuffs of igneous origin may grade through *tuffaceous sands* to ordinary sands.   Earthy mixtures of sand, with clay, limy material, glauconite and other materials, are called *marl.*   The term is somewhat loosely used, but the greensand marls of the Atlantic coastal plain are valuable as fertilizers.

The cements of sandstones are *siliceous, calcareous, argillaceous, ferruginous,* and less commonly a variety of others.   Sandstones with silica cement, either opal, chalcedony, or quartz, are very durable stone.   If the cement is quartz, the rocks grade into *quartzites,* which are commonly considered metamorphic rocks, though there is a great difference between sand cemented by quartz and a thoroughly recrystallized quartzite.   It has been very definitely shown that many quartzites are derived from sands, and there is an increasing tendency in recent work to list them as parts of a sedimentary series.   The ferruginous cements give *brown, yellow, green,* and *red sandstones.*   The characteristic *"red beds"* of the Permian and Triassic are red shaly sandstones and sandy shales.   Commonly red beds have scattered, nearly spherical spots, bleached greenish white, probably by reduction of the iron oxide or possibly as a result of some vanadium or other local material. The calcareous and argillaceous sands grade into limestones and

---

[9] The recognition of light-colored sand minerals is not easy without optical work with a microscope, but some staining methods may help.   See R. D. Russell, *Frequency Percentage Determination* . . . , Journal of Sedimentary Petrology, volume 5, page 109, 1935.

clays respectively. Exceptionally coarse calcite cement may assume crystal forms, with enclosed sand, and later weather out as *"sand calcites."* Some other cements behave similarly. Sandstones formed of calcareous fragments are known but are described under limestone. *Flexible sandstone (itacolumite)* is a friable sandstone, said to have a micaceous cement. *Case-hardened sandstones* are blocks with a surficial cement or desert varnish formed by evaporating solutions. Concretionary deposits may replace or cement the sandstones locally (see page 189). The porosity of sandstones is largely influenced by the amount of cement between the grains. Good reservoir rocks for petroleum or for artesian water have 15 to 30 per cent of space in large connected pores (see page 191).

Terms indicating origin give very little indication of the character of sands. Aqueous, eolian and glacial sands may be much alike, whereas those in one group may show great variety; marine and terrestrial sands are distinguished with difficulty. Terms showing the age are also of little value in rock classification.

To distinguish the prefixes that show the nature of clastic fragments from the prefixes that show the cement, two schemes have been proposed, but it cannot be said that either is widely adopted. In fact they conflict with each other, because one uses the ordinary adjectives to show cement, the other to show the fragments.

Grout recommends the adjectival form for cement, and the rock or mineral name as a prefix for the nature of the fragment; thus, calcareous quartz sandstones, and ferruginous granite conglomerate. Wentworth (Allen) [10] recommends a new form of adjective "——inate" for cement, and uses rock name, mineral name, or adjectival terms indiscriminately for composition of fragments; thus, calcarinate quartz sandstone, silicinate granite conglomerate, and ferruginate siliceous sandstone.

Metamorphism. — The purer sandstones in metamorphism yield quartzites which are denser and harder than their originals because, by deposition of the cementing quartz, the fragmental

[10] Allen credits Wentworth with the suggestion as to compound nomenclature on page 40 of a report of the Committee on Sedimentation, National Research Council for 1935–6, Exhibit B on the Terminology of Medium-grained Sediments, 1936.

grains are very firmly bound together. Less pure sandstones yield quartz-schists by the development of mica scales.

Distribution. — Sandstones are so common in all extended geo-logical sections as to deserve slight special mention. Next to limestones they are the most widely used of sedimentary rocks as building stone. The Potsdam sandstone of Cambrian age in New York and on the south shore of Lake Superior is extensively quarried. Other prominent sandstones are the Medina of New York, the Berea grit of Ohio; and the red and brown Triassic sandstones of the Atlantic seaboard and the Rocky Mountains.

The windblown loess is common in the Mississippi and Mis-souri Valleys, and in Europe. In China it contributes the yellow sediment from which the names of Yellow River and Yellow Sea are derived.

III. LIMESTONES

Limestone is a sedimentary rock composed principally of cal-cium carbonate, or of that with dolomite, the calcium-magnesium carbonate.

Origin. — Much the greater number of important limestones are of organic origin and the organisms are mostly marine forms, but there are several well-known fresh water formations. The principal sources of the materials of limestone are the calcareous remains of algae, foraminifera, corals and molluscs. These and other organisms secrete from the sea or from lakes, the calcite or aragonite of original deposits, as shells or skeletons. The algae may cause precipitation by using up the CO_2 which holds the carbonate in solution.

A study of the present distribution of such organisms, and of the nature of our most extensive limestone formations, indicates that such organisms probably grow along low flat shores where no great amount of mud is washed into the sea. The original shells are worked over by waves and currents and become thoroughly comminuted to calcareous sands and slimes before final deposition. The solubility of the carbonate facilitates its recrystallization and works with the mechanical processes to efface most of the organic structures. Nevertheless, organisms of the same species continue to grow while the earlier shells are being broken and recrystallized, and the result is that waves and storms scatter some shells in local beds and concentrations in a matrix of much finer grain. After cementation the rock is a fossiliferous limestone, and is commonly given a variety name based on the fossils still visible, even where only a small per cent of the rock is in recognizable forms.

Shell sands accumulate on or near the immediate shore, and may even be heaped up by the wind. They show all the ordinary structures of sands, such as bedding and cross-bedding. The finer slimes are carried farther into quiet water, to form calcareous ooze.

As a different explanation of the fine matrix around shells it might be suggested that innumerable microscopic organisms grew at the same time and in the same general location as the larger shells. Such microscopic fossils make up almost the whole of the "chalk" formations. It is hardly likely that they form the matrix of a common limestone, however, because traces of their forms can be seen in the chalks and should be visible in the limestones if they were originally present. It is also possible but not very probable that some of the fine parts of limestones are chemical precipitates in the sea where shells grew.

Although this outline of origin from shell beds along a rela- tively flat shore is believed to apply to most limestones, certain modifications are well known. If, by reason of a protected shore line, the shells are not broken so vigorously, the limestone will be a mass of unbroken shells; but shell-limestones without a matrix of sandy grains or calcareous slimes are neither thick nor abundant in the geologic column. Again if the organisms grow in colonies on a muddy bottom, or in reefs along a shore line, the geologic relations are modified. Figure 61 shows a coral reef which grew persistently.[11] While such a reef grows, the waves break up

[11] At Funafuti, a coral island which was explored by drilling, and prob- ably at most "coral reefs," most of the material is secreted by organisms other than corals. In order of reef-building importance, there are:

1. Lithothamnium (algae, commonly called "nullipores").
2. Halimeda (algae).
3. Foraminifera.
4. Corals.

See reference to M. A. Howe, page 170.

FIG. 61. — Cross section of ancient coral reef at Alpena, Michigan, showing coral in fan-shaped pattern, with fragments grading into slimes at a distance. (Modified from A. W. Grabau, Am. Rept. Mich. State Geologist, 1901, page 176.)

FIG. 62. — Shell limestone or coquina from Florida.

fragments to sands which are scattered on the flanks of the reef. The gentle slopes are favorable to the growth of various mollusca whose hard parts contribute additional material to the growing limestones.[12] The finer material is transported to a greater distance and gradually settles out as slimes which afford dense, thin-bedded limestones. The conditions of deposition of slimes are

[12] R. R. Shrock: *Wisconsin Silurian Bioherms* (*Organic Reefs*). Bull. Geological Society of America, volume 50, pages 529–562, 1929. About 18 bioherms are known in a limestone area 200 miles long and 25 miles wide.

not favorable for organic life, and commonly the resulting limestones have few fossils except in the vicinity of the old reef.

The agency of microscopic algae in depositing calcium carbonate, especially in hot and cold springs, has long been recognized. The extensive deposits of travertine in Yellowstone National Park are precipitated when algae (or their chlorophyll) use up the carbon dioxide of the water and reduce the amount of calcium that can be held in solution.[13]

It is also known that calcium carbonate may be chemically precipitated in parts of the sea by evaporation and loss of carbon dioxide. The atmosphere has about 3 parts of CO_2 in 10,000, and this largely determines the amount of CO_2 in bodies of water standing in equilibrium with the air. The amount of CO_2 in the water, in turn, determines the amount of $CaCO_3$ that will be dissolved at any particular temperature. Hence as the CO_2 in the air changes, the solubility changes. At 16° C., if the CO_2 content of the air was increased to 4 parts in 10,000, water might dissolve 69 parts of $CaCO_3$ per million; if reduced to 2 parts in 10,000, only 55 parts $CaCO_3$.[14]

Limestones pass by insensible gradations through more and more impure varieties into calcareous shales, but, as a rule, they are deposited in deeper water than the shales and sandstones. This conception must not be applied too strictly, because, beyond question, a depth of a few feet may suffice, and too much emphasis has been placed upon the depth regarded as necessary for limestones.

Mineralogic Composition, Varieties. — These various methods of formation result in limestones with textural varieties very different from those of mechanical sediments. The calcareous deposits of organic origin range from very coarse to microscopically fine as originally deposited. These are described as organic limestones, *coarse, medium,* or *fine.* The particular organism may be

[13] M. A. Howe: *The Geologic Importance of the Lime-Secreting Algae.* U. S. Geological Survey, Professional Paper 170 E, 1932.

[14] J. Johnston and E. D. Williamson: *The Role of Inorganic Agencies in the Deposition of Calcium Carbonate.* Journal of Geology, volume 24, page 732, 1916.

used in naming; as in *crinoidal, coralline, fusilina,* or *bryozoan* limestone. A common shell limestone is known as *coquina* (Fig. 62). An aggregate of very fine shells, globigerina and others, is *chalk,* with a good deal of porosity and absorbed water. A lake deposit of fine shells and algal (chara) precipitates, especially if mixed with clay and of earthy character, is *marl.* The coarser remains may be transported as indicated in Fig. 61, breaking

FIG. 63. — Fossiliferous limestone, Minnesota.

up into limy sands which consolidate to *sandy textured limestone,* and eventually to *fine-grained limestone,* or, if especially fine and uniform, *"lithographic stone."* The limestones with fine grain and only scattered shells are best called *fossiliferous limestones* (Fig. 63). Those in which the matrix has recrystallized to coarse calcite without much deformation are called *crystalline limestones.* Some of them are quarried commercially as marble, though they contain undeformed fossils and are really not much metamorphosed. There is a strong tendency to record as sedimentary rocks on geological maps all the *marbles* that are definitely known to have originated as limestones. During diagenetic recrystallization there may be solution along bedding planes and channels, with a concentration of the insoluble clays and iron oxides of the rock. If these channels are later closed by the load of overlying rock, the layers marked by the irregular amounts of dark insoluble earth may be very much distorted and even suggest intense crumpling. The structures are known as stylolites (Fig. 65).

FIG. 64. — Travertine, Minneapolis, Minnesota.

Another series of textural varieties of limestones result from chemical deposition. *Oölitic, pisolitic,* and *concretionary limestones* have concentric layers in fine, medium and coarse aggregates, respectively. The precipitates from waters on plants form *travertine*[15] (Fig. 64), on a flat surface form the layered *Mexican onyx,* and on dripping surfaces in a cave form *stalactites* and *stalagmites.* Ground-waters bearing calcium carbonate may evaporate at the surface in semi-arid regions leaving a limestone crust known as calcareous *caliche* (see page 184), more or less contaminated with soil. This has also been called *"calcrete"* from

[15] *Calcareous tufa* and *calcareous sinter* are synonyms.

its resemblance to concrete. Since it is a surface formation and resembles limestones of different origin, it has been a source of confusion in stratigraphy.[16]

Calcite is the chief mineral of limestone though it may be so fine-grained that it does not show the rhombic forms of characteristic cleavage pieces. Some shells are aragonite, but the distinction of aragonite from calcite is not usually attempted in rock study. Dolomite and siderite accompany or replace calcite in

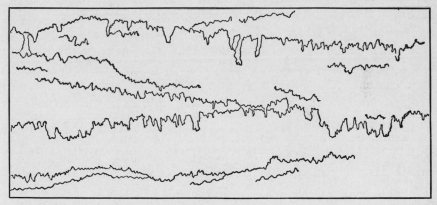

FIG. 65. — Stylolites in Tennessee "marble," a crystalline limestone.
About one-half natural size.

many limestones; so many in fact that *dolomite limestone* is the chief mineralogic variety after the common calcite limestone. There is little isomorphous mixture of iron or magnesium with calcium of calcite, but dolomite and calcite grains occur together, or in local concentrations. The dolomite is commonly slightly ferruginous and weathers darker than the calcite. Limestones with 5–15 per cent MgO are called *magnesian limestones,* and those near 20 per cent, *dolomite limestones.* The sources of magnesia in dolomites are the subjects of several speculations, but it is significant that some coral islands in warm seas show a high per cent of $MgCO_3$ at a depth of a few hundred feet, and that limestones older than Carboniferous have a much higher

[16] W. A. Price: *Reynosa Problem of South Texas, and Origin of Caliche.* Bull. A. A. P. G., volume 17, page 518, 1933.

average content of magnesia than younger limestones. It is thus evident that some dolomites result from a reaction of calcite with magnesian solutions (page 271). The shells of organisms commonly have only a little magnesia as secreted, but Clarke has shown that some have 3 to 7 per cent of MgO, so that a selective leaching of calcite might leave dolomite. Such a residual dolomite might be even more porous than one formed by replacement.

The other common sediments are likely to be mixed with limestones. *Argillaceous* or *shaly limestones* are especially common, several being so valuable as cement material that they are called *hydraulic limestone* or *"cement rock."* *Sandy* or *arenaceous limestones* are well known, but less common. *Carbonaceous limestones* are likely to be black and some are used for their asphalt or bitumen content. Phosphatic shells mixed in with carbonate shells produce *phosphatic limestones,* but they are distinguished only by testing.

The highly *ferruginous limestones* grade into *"clay ironstone"* and *"black band iron ores."* The Clinton type of iron ore has calcite largely replaced by hematite. *Cherty limestone* is very common and the cherts are largely in nodules or concretions. Other noteworthy mineral varieties have glauconite or pyrite. Several of these varieties are classed as diagenetic because the minerals form soon after deposition. A diagenetic textural effect gives intraformational conglomerates, which are *limestone conglomerates.*

Variety terms indicating age or conditions of deposition of limestones are of little value in rock study.

Metamorphism. — Limestones under deforming stresses, probably accompanied by elevation of temperature, are affected by metamorphism with exceptional readiness. In the presence of water, or along the contacts with intruded dikes and sheets of igneous rocks, they lose their sedimentary characteristics, such as bedding-planes and fossils, and change into crystalline marbles. The contained bituminous matter becomes graphite; the alumina and silica unite with the lime, magnesia and iron to give various silicates. Other oxides together with the bituminous ingredients contribute to the various colorations. Mechanical effects are manifested in flow lines, brecciation and other familiar features of many that are cut and polished for ornamental stones. Impure limestones which undergo these metamorphic changes are the most prolific of all rocks in variety and beauty of minerals. Arendal, Norway, and the crystalline limestone belt from Sparta, N. J., north through Franklin Furnace are good illustrations. The crystalline limestones will be again mentioned under the metamorphic rocks.

Distribution. — Limestones are too common to deserve much special mention as regards occurrence, but the Trenton limestone of the Ordovician, the Niagara of the Silurian and the Subcarboniferous limestones are worthy of note. Oölites are growing in Salt Lake, and travertine is forming in Yellowstone Park. Chalks form prominent cliffs in western Europe, and are known in several southern states of America.

IV. Remains of Organisms not Limestones

Calcareous remains are much the most important of the contributions made by organisms to rocks, but there are others, respectively siliceous, ferruginous and carbonaceous, which deserve mention. The sulphur deposits (page 183) may result largely from bacterial action on sedimentary sulphates.

Siliceous Organic Rocks

The principal members of this group are *siliceous earths; siliceous sinters;* and *cherts* and *flints*. In the group of siliceous earths, *diatomite* consists of the abandoned frustules of diatoms, which are microscopic organisms belonging to the vegetable kingdom; other earths consist of the hard parts of radiolaria, which are microscopic animals. *Kieselguhr* is a common term for any of these earths. Though not common rocks, they are met in series of sedimentary strata, both freshwater and marine, with sufficient frequency to justify their mention. They are usually distinguished by their high porosity which makes a hand specimen remarkably light. They lack plasticity and feel harsh between the fingers when compared with common clay. Both kinds of organisms float in the large bodies of water and may live far from shore where little mechanical sediment is deposited. At such places the siliceous earths may be nearly pure, but nearer the shores they are mixed with other earthy minerals. The mineralogy of the siliceous earths can be stated less definitely than the chemical composition. The individual diatoms are very minute, but the analyses indicate both opaline and chalcedonic silica.

The *siliceous sinters* are extracted from hot springs by algae which, as shown by W. H. Weed, are capable of living and secreting silica in waters up to 185° F. They are far less important geologically than the siliceous earths. In the sinters and cherts, when the latter can be shown to be organic, opal and chalcedony are associated with various amounts of calcite. *Siliceous sinters* are often called *geyserite*. They are cellular crusts and fancifully shaped masses which closely resemble calcareous tufas, but which are readily distinguished by their lack of effervescence.

Chert is a rock consisting of fine grained silica minerals, quartz, chalcedony or opal, or mixtures of these. It is common in limestones, either as entire beds, or as isolated, included masses. It may have druses with quartz crystals, and may contain microscopic fossils. Cherts not provided with these organic remains may be regarded with great reason as chemical precipitates, and as many American varieties lack them, the cherts receive more extended mention under the chemical precipitates (page 184). Chert is dense, hard and homogeneous, and of white, gray or yellowish color. It readily strikes fire with steel, and when it breaks has a splintery or conchoidal fracture. On weathering it decomposes to powdery silica called *"tripoli,"* used for various practical purposes.

Siliceous earths are abundant near Richmond, Va., and on Chesapeake Bay, at Dunkirk, and Pope's Mills, Md. Beds deposited in evanescent ponds or lakes are also well known in states farther north. In the West, the Tertiary strata have them in thick beds in Nevada. In California and Oregon there are great beds of diatomaceous earth, up to 5,000 feet thick. They have probably contained organic material when first deposited and may have contributed petroleum to some associated beds. There is considerable production of such earths for polishing powder and insulation, not only in this country, but in Mexico and Germany.

Siliceous sinters produced by algae are extensive in Yellowstone Park, and similar deposits, perhaps caused by the same agent, are found in many regions of hot springs.   The most important occurrences of chert are all mentioned together on page 186.

Ferruginous Organic Rocks

Bog iron ores are commonly attributed largely to secretion by bacteria, algae and fungi.[17]   The great cherty iron-bearing formations of the Lake Superior region have traces of organic structures, but these are so rare that it is probable that organic precipitation was not the most important factor in the deposition of iron.   In black band iron ores, the iron carbonate is associated with organic matter, which probably keeps it from changing to iron oxide, but it is not certain that living organisms caused the precipitation of the carbonate.

Organic Phosphate Rocks

Commercial phosphate rock (phosphorite) so resembles limestone that much of it cannot be recognized except by a chemical test—strong nitric acid and a little white ammonium molybdate produce on the phosphate rock an intense canary yellow.   The remains of various organisms have some phosphate, but most good phosphate rock has had the phosphate concentrated by some process after the growth of the hard parts of organisms.

PERCENTAGE OF $Ca_3(PO_4)_2$ IN REMAINS OF VARIOUS ORGANISMS
(After Clarke)

Lingulas	91.74
Discinisca	75.17
Alcyonarian	8:57
Crabs about	15.00
Shrimps about	30.00

[17] E. C. Harder: *Iron Depositing Bacteria and their Geologic Relations.* U. S. Geological Survey, Professional Paper 113 (1919).   A similar group of organisms precipitate manganese oxides; G. A. Thiel: *Precipitation of Manganese from Meteoric Solution.* American Journal of Science, volume 7, pages 457–472 (1924).

Chemical leaching and enrichment may separate the carbonate, usually associated with phosphate in shells, leaving a rich phosphate rock. Commonly the shell fragments thus altered are peculiarly blackened so that some phosphate rock is recognized by its gray color and black granules; but these colors are not strictly diagnostic —the phosphates have many colors.

The bones of vertebrates, and the guano deposits from birds on oceanic islands, are rich in phosphate as deposited.

Commercial production comes from southeastern states from Tennessee to Florida, but there are large deposits in northwestern states, and much is produced in northern Africa, Russia and Oceania.

Carbonaceous Organic Rocks

When plant tissue accumulates under a protecting layer of water which prevents too rapid oxidation, new accessions may more than compensate for loss by decay so that extensive deposits result. There is such a perfect gradation from plant tissues to coal that it is generally agreed that coal is of vegetable origin. Chemical and physical changes produce a series of products, peat, lignite, sub-bituminous coal, bituminous coal, semi-bituminous coal, semi-anthracite, anthracite, and graphite (Fig. 66). The chemical differences in the organic materials are shown by Clarke (U. S. G. S. Bulletin 770, p. 773).

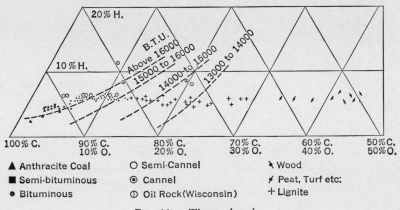

FIG. 66. — The coal series.

AVERAGE COMPOSITION OF CERTAIN FUELS

	C	H	N	O
Wood	49.65	6.23	.92	43.20
Peat	55.44	6.28	1.72	36.56
Lignite	72.95	5.24	1.31	20.50
Bituminous coal	84.24	5.55	1.52	8.69
Anthracite	93.50	2.81	.97	2.72

Peat is formed by the growth and partial decay of grasses, moss, and other plants in moist places. Most of it is brown, shows shreds of plant tissue, and is very porous, with the pores well filled with water until artificially dried. Similar material, more altered, after burial under other sediments is *lignite*, a *brown coal* which burns with a long smoky flame. In the fire, or on weathering, it falls to pieces, or "slakes."

FIG. 67.— Bituminous coal, Colorado. Bright and dull layers. Woody structure conspicuous in bright layers. About one-half natural size. Courtesy of the McGraw-Hill Book Company.

When alteration has gone far enough to turn the material black, it is coal. The coal of lowest rank, *sub-bituminous,* resembles lignite in slaking in the fire or on exposure to weather (Fig. 69). Most *bituminous coal, soft coal,* is denser and shows less of the vegetable tissue (but see Fig. 67), and burns with a long flame

and much smoke.   Some bituminous coals melt in a hot fire and
form coke.   *Cannel coal,* made up largely of microscopic spores,
is a non-coking bituminous coal of dull luster, and massive structure.
It burns with an especially long flame.   *Anthracite, hard coal,* may
still show bright and dull bands representing masses of vegetation,
flattened by pressure.   It burns, if heated, with a short blue flame.
Graphite occurs at places in such association with metamorphic
rocks that it seems to have resulted from metamorphism of coal.

Coals are classified as to "rank," in this series, anthracite being
the coal of highest rank.[18]   The "grade" refers to the impurities,
high ash and moisture making a coal of low grade.

The student should recognize peat and lignite and cannel by
their appearance; bituminous coal is distinguished from anthracite
by its behavior in the fire, so that even field geologists can estimate
the value of newly discovered coal beds.   Tests show that the

FIG. 68.—Mineral charcoal or "mother of coal," Colorado. Usually very thin
layers in bituminous coal.

[18] The rank of coal serves as a guide to the prospects for petroleum, because
none is found with coals highly metamorphosed.   David White: *Metamor-*
phism of Organic Sediments and Derived Oils.   Bull. A. A. P. G., volume 19,
pages 592–609, 1935.

coals increase in hardness and specific gravity as the rank increases, but the differences are so slight as to elude the beginner.

More accurate tests in a crucible give what is called a proximate analysis, determining 1. Moisture, 2. Volatile matter, 3. Fixed carbon, and 4. Ash. There is progressively more fixed carbon and less volatile matter in proportion as the rank increases from peat to graphite. Fixed carbon increases from around 30% to over 99% of the ash-free dry coal. The methods of driving out moisture and volatile matter are standardized and unless the standard is strictly followed erratic results will be obtained.[19]

Other recognizable varieties of coal are the thin layers of *mineral charcoal* or mother-of-coal, looking like wood charcoal (Fig. 68), and *bone-coal*, the lean sandy or shaly partings in some coal beds, which contain too much ash to be good fuel.

Oil shales from which shale oil is distilled, especially in Scotland, seem to contain organic materials intermediate between coal and petroleum, but probably closer to coal, because little oil can be extracted except by destructive distillation. Some oil shales, with their fine grain, con-

Fig. 69. — Lignite, Texas. After exposure to air, it checks (net work of irregular cracks) and slakes badly. Courtesy of the McGraw-Hill Book Company.

choidal fracture, and a little more hardness than common shales, might be confused with flints, but are really much softer than flint.

[19] U. S. Bureau of Mines Technical Papers 8 (revised) and 76, and Bull. 22.

Oil, asphalt, and *waxes* in various natural occurrences are hardly abundant enough to be rocks, and need no more than passing mention. They occur as minor constituents in other rocks and locally in commercial masses.

Peat favors cool and moist latitudes in all parts of the world, and is chiefly of fresh water origin. Lignites are best developed in the Cretaceous strata of Texas, the Dakotas, and western states. They are used, as in Germany, where bituminous coal is not cheap. Bituminous coal is the chief world coal at present, and large quantities are mined in several continents. In the United States, the eastern and interior fields are highly productive. Anthracite which is cleaner for use in house heating is produced chiefly in Wales and in eastern Pennsylvania, but in small amounts at many other places. Oil shales are abundant in Colorado and Kentucky, and probably could supply oil as well as those of Scotland, if there was not an abundant supply of petroleum.

V. CHEMICAL PRECIPITATES

Bearing in mind that a rock should form a large mass in the earth, it is evident that the only natural solvent abundant enough to yield precipitated rocks is water. The precipitated varieties of limestone have already been described, and others are here noted.

Salts. — Evaporation of sea water, especially in lagoons fed by sea water in arid regions, results in thick deposits of the sea salts. The sequence of deposits is outlined on page 142. The large bodies of rock are salt and gypsum. The gypsum, having

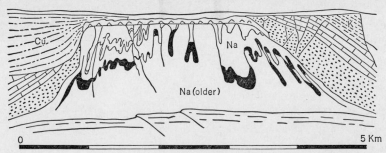

FIG. 70. — Structural sketch in cross section of German salt-dome.
(After Stille and Seidl.)

precipitated before salt, may occur without salt, but salt is rarely deposited without the earlier sulphates. In the presence of sodium chloride at any temperature above 25° C. (above 42° C. in water without salt) anhydrite forms rather than gypsum, but much of the anhydrite may later be altered to gypsum by groundwaters and by weathering.

Salt beds are recognized by their luster, softness, solubility, taste, and the fact that they rarely outcrop. Many are red or brown from iron oxides. *Gypsum rock* forms white, gray, or black earthy beds which outcrop much as limestone does, but which are more likely to be deeply furrowed by running water. A test of the hardness, especially by the characteristic lack of grit between the teeth, serves to distinguish it, even when acid is not available to show that it fails to effervesce. *Anhydrite rock* is more like limestone, with a hardness of 3 to 3.5, but it fails to effervesce.

All three of these rocks are easily deformed and in many occurrences the bedding, marked by differences in color, has been remarkably contorted by rock flow. The beds of salt are locally thickened and thrust up into great "salt domes" (Fig. 70), with a "cap rock" of anhydrite—probably not a normal sediment, but an accumulation of insoluble material left when some of the upper part of the salt dissolved.[20] Sulphur and the sulphate rocks, gypsum and anhydrite, are partly syngenetic, but some sulphur is believed to result from an organic reduction of the sulphate, giving calcium carbonate as a by-product.[21] The association of these minerals in a sedimentary series aids in their identification.[22] Although the sulphur is a mineral of the rock, it is hardly in large enough masses to be classed as a rock of itself. The sulphur produced in states along the Gulf of Mexico is disseminated in limestones that appear to be derived from anhydrite in the cap-rocks of salt domes. Some sulphur occurs in shales also.

[20] R. E. Taylor: *Origin of the Cap Rock of Louisiana Salt Domes.* Louisiana Geol. Survey, Bull 11, 1938.

[21] The salt domes were discussed in considerable detail at a meeting of the Amer. Assoc. Petroleum Geologists. See their Bulletin, volume 9, 1925; also volume 15, page 511, and volume 17, pages 1025–1083.

[22] E. S. Bastin: *The Problem of the Natural Reduction of Sulphates.* Bull. A. A. P. G., volume 10, pages 1270–99, 1926.

Salts deposited in lake beds, as distinct from those in arms of the sea, have much smaller volume, but include sodium carbonate so commonly that it distinguishes them from sea salts. Sodium sulphate, borax, and related borates, and the nitrates are common lake salts. The nitrates that crystallized in the soil, from solution in ground waters, are called *caliche*, and are produced in commercial quantities in Chile.

Large bodies of salt occur in New York, Michigan, southwest to the Gulf of Mexico and in other states, and there are several in north central Europe. The potash salts resulting from extreme concentration of brines are famous at Stassfurt, Germany, and other foreign localities. Since 1918 there has been a new development in Texas and New Mexico.

Siliceous Precipitates. — The visible siliceous precipitates are *siliceous sinter* (*geyserite*) and some gelatinous silica masses in the bottom of the sea. Some geyserite, having formed in water so hot that organic life is not expected, is attributed to chemical reaction. By far the greater volumes of siliceous precipitates are the cherts.

Chert is fine-grained, dense, precipitated silica with conchoidal fracture. The term is used in hand specimen and field work, and is not at all definite as to minerals, which may be opal, quartz, or chalcedony, or mixtures. Many cherts are contaminated with carbonates, and many have fossil forms or oölites, indicating that the chert replaced a carbonate, but others show no relation to carbonate.

Flints and *jaspers* are closely related to cherts, in fact so closely related that some men consider them varieties of the more general broad family of chert. Flints are gray to black, and jaspers are red or dark brown. The more ordinary cherts are light gray, white, yellow, or similar colors. The term flint is almost universally applied by anthropologists to the material of siliceous implements made by early men; and by almost everyone to the siliceous rocks used in striking sparks for making fire. Many of these are true flints by the definition here given, but there are some cherts and other rocks. Cherts are more abundant than flints in the limestones and iron-bearing rocks of the United States, but flints are not rare.   Many flints are imported from the chalks of western Europe as abrasive materials for ball-mills.   Jasper and other cherts are abundant in the iron-bearing rocks of the Lake Superior and other regions.   They are products of precipitation in shallow water, alternating with iron carbonate or, on the Mesabi range, with an iron silicate.   The siliceous protores of many iron ranges are *ferruginous cherts,* but some are banded red jasper and black hematite called *jaspilite,* and others granular like the Mesabi range rocks called *taconite* (Figs. 59 and 71).

Fig. 71.— Joint systems in ferruginous chert, taconite, Mesabi Range.

Locally some limestones containing sulphide ores have been silicified so thoroughly that they resemble chert, and the red and brown varieties are called *jasperoid.*

Novaculite is a very uniform bedded cherty rock with conchoidal fracture, highly siliceous and translucent on thin edges. It was deposited in the sea with other sediments, and was probably a precipitate,[23] but is now folded and somewhat altered.

[23] H. D. Miser and A. H. Purdue: U. S. Geological Survey, Bull. 808, pages 49–59, 1929.

As noted on page 176, cherts commonly weather to soft powdery earthy masses of silica called *tripoli*. This may be a superficial layer on concretions or, in extreme cases, large beds completely changed. Tripoli, or "soft silica," is produced commercially as an abrasive, defined as porous microcrystalline siliceous sediment.

The weathering of cherty limestone leaves a red clay with chert fragments. This is so characteristic that it may be recognized even in drill cuttings, locating a weathered zone in the sub-surface rocks —probably an unconformity. The weathering of ferruginous cherts probably formed most of our iron ores. By high-temperature metamorphism cherty limestones form lime-silicate minerals, and ferruginous cherts become banded amphibole-quartz-magnetite rocks. The common amphibole is a ferruginous actinolite, but locally a variety of other ferromagnesian minerals result.

Aside from the occurrences of cherty iron-bearing rocks in the pre-Cambrian rocks around Lake Superior, cherts are common in the Paleozoic limestones both east and west. Fractured cherts are the chief gangue of the zinc ores of southwest Missouri. Novaculite is best known in Arkansas, but similar beds occur in Tennessee and elsewhere. Tripoli is produced in the same states and in Illinois, Oklahoma, and Missouri.

Ferruginous Precipitates. — In spite of the organic precipitates of iron minerals (page 177) many iron-bearing formations show little sign that the iron minerals were precipitated by living organisms. The chemical reactions which form some precipitates are well understood, but some rare iron-bearing minerals have never been made synthetically.

The igneous, metamorphic and older sedimentary rocks contribute iron to the ground waters (page 131) and may even yield weathered ferruginous residues for mechanical sediments. Oxidation and hydrolysis of the solutions tend to precipitate the iron oxides from the solutions, but if there is any lack of oxygen or excess water, the iron solution may be transported great distances.

The precipitation of iron carbonate from the bicarbonate solution is analogous to the chemical deposition of calcium carbonate. It results from a loss of CO_2. Such deposits may form veins, concretions or beds. If the iron carbonate is mixed with clay and

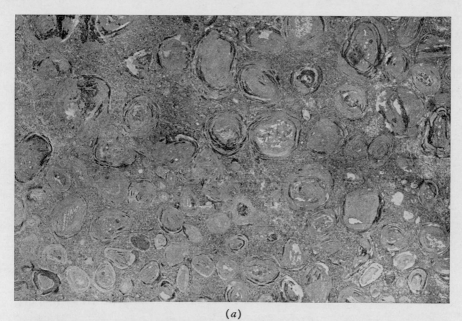

(*a*)

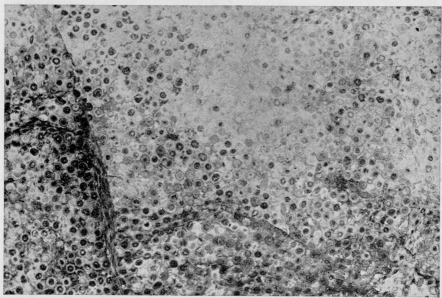

(*b*)

FIG. 72. — Concretionary structures.   (*a*) Pisolitic iron ore, Pretoria, South Africa.
(*b*) Oölitic chert, Minnesota.

organic matter, it forms *black band ores* and *clay ironstone*. Several pre-Cambrian iron-bearing districts have exposures of sideritic slate, or *slaty iron carbonate*. Most of the protores of the Lake Superior region are cherty and many have iron minerals and chert in alternating thin layers. These are the *ferruginous chert* and *cherty iron carbonate*. In the Animikie ores the ferruginous chert appears to have been largely precipitated as greenalite—a hydrous iron silicate—instead of as siderite. Similar green silicates are known in other districts. In all these, there may be thin beds of original iron oxides, but the best ores result from a later enrichment, by a leaching of the silica. Certain beds of ore have concretionary or pisolitic textures (Fig. 72).

General Remarks on Sediments

Mixed Rocks and Structures of Precipitates

The main groups of sediments outlined above are not sharply separated but overlap and grade into each other in very complex fashion. Even the three main divisions of origin, mechanical, chemical, and organic, are not clearly separable, for organic sediments may be transported mechanically, and many precipitates may form both chemically and organically, so that the origin of a particular precipitate may not be shown in the result. It is noteworthy that in recent years the evidence is indicating that a substance that can be precipitated both chemically and organically, is precipitated more rapidly and more completely by organisms. For this reason there is a growing tendency to attribute cherts, protores of iron, and sulphur deposits to organic agents.

The common transitions between sandstone, shale, and limestone probably need no further comment, except that the mollusca are the chief organisms that grow in an environment where mud and sand are being deposited. Some of the carbonate of the mechanical sediments, however, may be transported.

The precipitates have a remarkable variety of forms and structures. The main listing of these is in the discussion of precipitated limestones—beds, onyx, concretions, pisolites, oölites (Figs. 72 (*a*) and (*b*)), stalactites, stalagmites, travertine or sinter, caliche, veins, and replacements. The same structures may form in precipitates of many other minerals, but some are so small in volume that they need not be listed here. Several, however, are such widespread features in other rocks as to deserve description.

Concretions are usually nodular to rounded masses from an inch to a few feet across, differing in chemical and mineral nature from the enclosing rock, and commonly with a concentric structure indicating growth by deposition of successive layers. There are the chert or flint in limestone, the calcite, pyrite, siderite, or limonite in clays, and the pyrite, hematite, or calcite in sandstones. Most of them are smooth on the outside, but internally many are cracked irregularly as if by shrinkage, after which they may be healed with vein matter forming "septaria." A hollow concretion lined with crystals pointing inward is called a geode. Most concretions are given variety names based on mineral composition. In porous rocks, the cement may be deposited in concretionary layers and gradually replace some of the original minerals. A concretionary banding in sandstones is perhaps more common than the replacement of the sand by solid masses of the concretionary deposit.

FIG. 73.—Dendrites, branching crystalline forms, largely manganese oxides, that grow commonly in the joint spaces of fine-grained uniform rocks. About natural size. Courtesy of the McGraw-Hill Book Company.

Replacements commonly form pseudomorphs, and structures may be retained as well as forms. No mineral seems to be so insoluble that it cannot be replaced by another. Limestone may be silicified, and siliceous fossils may be carbonated. Petrified wood forms a particularly striking replacement, with opal, chalcedony, quartz, or pyrite retaining the structure of cells, and canals.

Another common and very striking precipitate forms in joints in fine-grained rocks, such as rhyolite or fine limestone. In such joints crystals grow flat and branch, like frost crystals on windows —they are called *dendrites,* and if they are dark materials, commonly black manganese oxides, they resemble vegetable growths on the light rocks (Fig. 73).

Mineral Association in Sediments

The rules of association in sediments are very different from those in igneous rocks, in which minerals melted together react chemically. In sediments the bases of association are (1) hardness, (2) stability under weathering conditions and (3) the place or conditions of deposition. Clays being soft are mechanically broken up to finer grains and largely sorted away from coarser sands but are associated with iron oxides which are equally fine grained. The weather resistant, hard, sandy minerals, like quartz, tourmaline, zircon, and garnet, are commonly deposited with each other. The deep-sea red clays are not expected with shallow sediments such as conglomerates. Red sands, salt, and gypsum are not expected in association with coal or such sediments as imply humid climates.

Specific Gravity and Porosity

The specific gravity of sedimentary minerals means relatively little because each kind of rock has a variety of different porosities. Porosity is commonly reported in per cent, showing the volume of pores compared to the volume of the rock plus pores. In the following table after Lane, and Barrell, the figures may be a little too high, not allowing enough for porosity; the weight per volume increases as water is eliminated from the minerals.

ESTIMATED SPECIFIC GRAVITIES OF SEDIMENTS

	Specific gravity of mineral mixture without pores	Weight with pores half full, tons per cubic meter
Average igneous rock	2.79	2.8
Shale	2.69	2.51
Sandstone	2.67	2.35
Limestone	2.76	2.64

Somewhat related to the porosity of a sediment is its water-tightness, which governs its usefulness as a cover or base for water-bearing beds, but the sizes of pores and sizes of grains are even more important. A clay may have more water in its pores than a gravel when both are saturated. The clay, however, exerts so much more friction as water circulates through it that it is almost water-tight, in contrast with the gravel which allows rapid circulation.

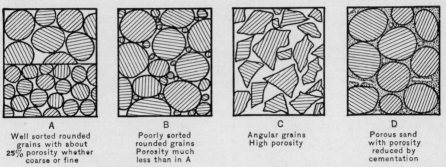

A	B	C	D
Well sorted rounded grains with about 25% porosity whether coarse or fine	Poorly sorted rounded grains Porosity much less than in A	Angular grains High porosity	Porous sand with porosity reduced by cementation

FIG. 74.—Relations of texture and cementation to porosity of sand.

The permeability of a porous rock is defined [24] as the volume of a fluid of unit viscosity passing through a unit cross section of the rock under a unit pressure gradient in a unit time. The accurate determination requires special equipment.[25] The permeability is more related to the sizes of grains and pores than to the per cent porosity. When minerals are mixed with a liquid which wets the grains, thin films are "bound" to the mineral surfaces. If all the pore spaces are small, the liquid which gets into the pores is all so close to the mineral surfaces that it is all bound in the films and cannot move freely. The students of underground circulation commonly refer to "effective porosity" excluding the films and closed pores.

[24] Wyckoff et al.: *Measurement of Permeability of Porous Media.* Bull. A. A. P. G., volume 18, pages 161–190, 1934.

[25] The standard procedure was tentatively established in the A. P. I. Code No. 27, American Petroleum Inst. *Drill and Production*, 1935 (1936), pages 267–273. See also O. E. Meinzer. See U. S. G. S. Water Supply Paper 596, pages 144–176, 1928. A recent paper is by H. C. Pyle and J. E. Sherborne: *Core Analysis*, Tech. Pub. No. 1024, A. I. M. M. E., 1939.

For shales, some detailed studies have been made of the changes in porosity and other properties with increasing overburden.[26] In certain formations with an initial porosity of 50 per cent in the first 100 feet, an overburden of 1,000 feet reduced the porosity to about 30 per cent; 2,000 feet to about 23 per cent; 3,000 feet to about 18 per cent; and 8,000 feet to about 8 per cent. The hardness and resistance to slaking and weathering also increased.

Porosities in sediments range from a fraction of 1 per cent to more than 50 per cent. Closely packed uniform spheres have 25.95 per cent pore space. A mixed sediment, such that the fine grains lie in the spaces between coarse grains, may have much lower porosity (Fig. 74). Cementation (page 143) reduces porosity. Some pore spaces result from joints and even from solution of rock along channels. The determination of porosity may be based on (1) volume and water absorption, or (2) the specific gravities (a) of the rock with pores and (b) of the crushed rock with pores eliminated (page 270). For reservoirs it may be useful to determine the porosity of the rock as it occurs in the ground.

Colors and Compositions

Most of the common sedimentary minerals are white when pure. Colors are added by carbonaceous matter and the oxides of iron, manganese, and others.

Note that certain ratios ordinarily distinguish sediments from igneous rocks (page 253): Al_2O_3 greater than alkalies and lime combined, magnesia greater than lime, potash greater than soda, and other features. These must be used with caution.[27]

[26] L. F. Athy: *Density, Porosity, and Compaction of Sedimentary Rocks.* Amer. Assoc. Petroleum Geologists, Bulletin, volume 14, pages 1–14, 1930.
[27] C. K. Leith and W. J. Mead: *Metamorphic Geology,* 1915, pages 226–240.

TABLE X

ANALYSES OF CERTAIN SEDIMENTS AND SEDIMENTARY MINERALS.

(After Clarke, Leith and Mead, and others)

	Average shale	Kaolin-ite	Average sand-stone	Average lime-stone	Limestone for build-ings	Calcite	Dolo-mite
SiO_2	58.90	46.5	78.64	5.20	14.09		
Al_2O_3	15.63	39.5	4.77	0.81	1.75		
Fe_2O_3	4.07	....	1.08 ⎫	0.54	0.77		
FeO	2.48	....	1.30 ⎭				
MgO	2.47	....	1.17	7.92	4.49	....	21.9
CaO	3.15	....	5.51	42.74	40.60	56.04	30.4
Na_2O	1.32	....	0.45	0.05	0.62		
K_2O	3.28	....	1.32	0.33	0.58		
H_2O+	3.72	14.0	1.33	0.56	0.88		
TiO_2	0.66	....	0.25	0.06	0.08		
P_2O_5	0.17	....	0.08	0.04	0.42		
CO_2	2.67	....	5.03	41.70	35.58	43.96	47.7
Miscellaneous	1.48	....	0.07	0.05	0.48		

The Determination of Sedimentary Rocks

Most sedimentary rocks are easier to identify than igneous rocks. Breccias, conglomerates, sandstones, coal, and fossiliferous limestones are recognized at a glance, as are certain of the minor varieties. Difficulties arise chiefly among the rocks so fine-grained that the minerals cannot be seen as individuals, and for some of these the microscope is needed. In its absence, however, certain distinctions should be made, and a few suggestions may be helpful.

1. *Fine-grained, firm, light-colored rocks* are confusing.

Chert—H = 7. If fresh. Forms concretions and strata.

Felsite—H = 6 $\pm$. Mostly in dikes and flows and may have phenocrysts.

Limestone—H = 3. Effervesces in acid. Stratified.

Shale—H = 1–3. Earthy odor. Stratified.

Weathering may leave the felsites and the outside of cherts much softened so a fresh rock is needed for distinction.

2. *The white or very light-colored earths* look alike.

Volcanic ash—Gritty, sharp.

Kaolin—Plastic when wet.

Marl—Very friable, effervesces.

Chalk—Effervesces.

Siliceous earths—High porosity, light weight, gritty feel.

3. *Black glasses* may be confused with *hard coal.*

Obsidian. $H = 6$. Streak nearly white. Sp. G. $= 2.4$. Massive.

Coal. $H = 3$–4. Streak brown to black. Sp. G. $= 2$. Mostly bedded.

4. *Pebbles* in some odd kinds of cement resemble *amygdules, phenocrysts, concretions, and spherulites.*

Pebbles—Mostly of hard minerals, quartz, feldspars and hard rocks. Mostly rounded grains in sandy matrix. Cemented by quartz, calcite, or iron oxides.

Amygdules—Mostly soft secondary minerals or quartz, in a matrix of dark basaltic rocks. Zeolites commonly radial. Rounded to almond-shaped.

Phenocrysts—Mostly quartz, feldspar, hornblende, augite or olivine, in either light or dark felsitic rocks. Crystal forms.

Concretions—Minerals such as grow from water solution. Structures rounded and commonly concentric. Matrix of common sediments.

Spherulites—Minerals, quartz and orthoclase in light rocks, but plagioclase and others in dark rocks. Structures radial.

5. A buff or gray, loosely cemented *sandstone* of medium grain is much like a buff or gray *dolomite* with crystals of similar sizes. A drop of acid may cause so little effervescence as to be deceptive, and it is always best to use warm acid before deciding whether carbonate is present. Even in the absence of acid, however, the sandstone should be recognized by the hardness of the grains of quartz. These cannot commonly be recognized by testing the hardness of the rock. Loosely cemented quartz rocks can be rubbed to pieces with the fingers, and the rocks are properly said to be soft. The quartz grains in the rock are still hard, and quite capable of scratching either glass or steel. *Reverse the test,* and instead of scratching the rock, see if the grains in the rock will scratch a knife blade.

6. *Phosphate rock* is so much like a *limestone* that a test is needed wherever phosphate is suspected. Otherwise such rocks are called limestone. Put a drop of concentrated nitric acid on the rock and sprinkle on powdered white ammonium molybdate. Good phosphate quickly turns the white powder canary yellow.

7. *A geode* (page 189) somewhat resembles a *miarolitic cavity* (pages 30–31), since the openings are of about the same range of sizes and both are lined with crystals. The common crystals in geodes are quartz, or calcite, and these and all other geodes are minerals deposited from water solution, usually in sedimentary rocks. The common crystals of miarolitic cavities are those of the granitoid igneous rocks in which they occur, with less commonly some "mineralizer" minerals, such as topaz or apatite.

8. *Breccias of several kinds* need some distinguishing criteria. Igneous breccias have fragments chiefly of igneous surface rocks and cements of ash, and opal or calcite.

Talus breccias have fragments from the adjacent cliffs with cements of surface precipitates, such as travertine, opal, or limonite. The fragments may be larger than expected in other breccias.

Friction breccias have fragments of rocks from the adjacent walls of the breccia zone, and cements of vein forming minerals, chiefly vein calcite and vein quartz.

9. A well cemented *arkose* resembles *binary granite,* but is commonly richer in quartz and on close examination may show rounded sand grains.

Economic Importance of Sediments

Sandstones and limestones furnish good building blocks and concrete aggregates, and the deleterious minerals which may occur in some are chiefly pyrite and clay. Limestone is the source of lime for mortar, plaster, and the active constituent of cement. Gypsum rock supplies hard wall plaster. Sand and gravel are the main admixtures in preparing lime and cement for mortar, plaster and concrete. Clays and shales are burned to make brick and tile. Diatomaceous earth is useful for insulation for heat and sound.

The siliceous sediments supply abrasives, and the uses of salt, coal, sulphur, and others are already familiar.

Certain ores, especially of iron, manganese and aluminum, are residual deposits. Placer deposits in sand and gravel include gold, cassiterite, ilmenite, monazite, and diamonds. Other ores may form cements in sandstones, but by far the most favorable host for sulphide ores is limestone, because it is easily replaced by ore-bearing solutions.

The final economic interest in sedimentary rocks depends upon the variety of porosity and permeability shown by common sediments. Contrast the well known permeability of a porous sand or limestone with the water-tightness of shales (pages 191 and 192). This is the basis of several commercial applications of rock study. Porous formations underground may contain important supplies of water, petroleum or natural gas. To confine these underground in artesian basins or oil-bearing anticlines and other structures, there are required some impermeable formations around the permeable. Details of structures favorable to commercial supplies, are the subjects of courses in structural geology and the geology of water supplies and petroleum. Suffice to say that the structure is discovered largely by close observations on sediments at outcrops and in the field where drilling is in progress (pages 197 to 206), and by the correlation of beds.

Rock Study and Sedimentary History

Several geologists have made careful studies of sediments to draw conclusions as to their sources. Even the beginner in rock study can appreciate the fact that boulders in a conglomerate may give a very definite indication that they were derived from some particular underlying formation and thus show the direction of transportation and the slope of the ancient surface. In advanced work many other features are used. The climate of the region at the time of deposition may be estimated, partly from the minerals, structures, colors, and associations, and partly from the organic remains, plant and animal fossils. The ancient tillites are especially clear signs of glaciation.

The direction of the shore line near some marine sediments may be indicated by the lateral gradation in composition of the sediments, and their differences in thickness. The location of shore facies is of great interest to the petroleum geologist, for even a narrow conglomerate or sand, deposited near shore, may have more porosity and permeability than adjacent beds and so constitute a good reservoir. Some "shoestring sands" are of this sort (see page 138).[28]

"The fundamental data of geologic history are: (1) local sequences of formations and (2) the chronologic equivalence of formations in different provinces." Clearly the study of sedimentary rocks is prerequisite to a good record of the sequence of formations. The "chronologic equivalence" also depends in large part on rock study, though fossils are much used to prove the equivalence of groups of formations. The argument between those who map rock formations and those who map groups of equivalent age, is well stated in the Report of a Committee.[29] This leads directly to the methods of correlation.

Correlation of Sedimentary Beds

In districts being explored for oil, gas, or water, rock study serves several purposes. The permeability of good reservoir rock, the lack of permeability in the enclosing formations, and the presence of oil or organic remains that might supply oil, are features to be noted early in the exploration of a district. One of the first steps in further exploration is a determination of the stratigraphic succession of formations in the district. This succession may be known from maps of the surrounding areas, or from records of deep drilling already done in the region,[30] but if not, preliminary mapping or drilling is necessary. Once this is carefully done the problem rapidly becomes a process of correlation of formations seen in outcrop or recovered from drilling, with the known forma-

[28] C. Brewer: *Oil Reservoirs and Shore-line Deposits.* Bull. A. A. P. G., volume 12, pages 597–615, 1928.

[29] *Classification and Nomenclature of Rock Units.* Bull. Geol. Soc. America, volume 44, 1933.

[30] The well logs made by drillers who are not trained in mineralogy and rock study, are often very deceptive. An "oil sand" may prove to be dolomite, or worse.

tions. The student of rocks should be able to guide exploration if he knows what formation is at hand, for that will lead to conclusions as to the underlying formations, and if elevations are also known, it will give structural data of the utmost value—guide the exploration to anticlines and synclines, unconformities and "convergence." It is clear that very serious and expensive errors arise if the student of rocks mistakes one rock formation for another of different horizon.

1. There are a number of significant points to be noted in the field as a basis of correlation, but none is more important than the usual advice to "walk the outcrop." This may be simple in a well-exposed bed with strike easily determined, but is by no means simple where the rocks are largely covered with soil or surface formations. The outcrops may end abruptly, by erosion, by faulting, or by pinching out, and it may not be possible in a reasonable time to decide which.

The correlation based on walking out the beds is not entirely reliable in sandstone formations, for a transgressing sea may deposit sand as a shore formation at progressively higher levels at later times. The method can be used parallel to the shore line but is not good across it. Limestones are rather more constant, but coral reefs may finger out in short distances (Fig. 61).

2. The expert student of rocks next observes with care the details of the formation. Many rocks are mixtures of shale, sand, and limestone, and the percentage of each is estimated and recorded. Marked peculiarities at one horizon—key beds—may be of great value. It is noteworthy that some key beds may be very small, as illustrated by the thin partings in certain coal beds, which persist for many miles. Similar conditions, however, produce similar beds even at widely separated times. Of course, the greater the number of peculiarities noted as identical in two separate exposures or samples, the greater the degree of certainty in correlation.

In sands, well cuttings, and the residues from solution of limestones in acid, the "mass characters" are important.[31] All the

[31] For a good discussion of such work see R. M. Whiteside: *Geologic Interpretation from Rotary Well Cuttings.* Bull. A. A. P. G., volume 16, pages 653–74, 1932.

minerals and rock fragments, and all the structures and textures, should be noted—jointing, bedding, lamination, sorting, nodules, oölites, crystals, twins, secondary growths, firmness of cementation, porphyritic and porphyroblastic spots, chert, coal, rare minerals, porosity, dolocasts, and cavities of other odd shapes,[32] shards, degree of rounding, fossils, fragments of other shapes, zonal growth, peculiarities of surface, color, luster, odor, content of oil or salt water, and many others (see methods, pages 144 to 150). Bentonite beds have been considerably used as key beds.[33]

In some oil fields, where drilling has shown the nature of the formation, correlation can be based on geophysical tests, such as porosity and resistivity, without much need of rock study.[34]

If all other methods fail, the samples may be given detailed petrographic studies of heavy accessory minerals, and the shapes and grade size distribution of minerals. There are only a few examples, however, in which the grade size has been the basis for correlation of such erratic sediments as sands.[35] The points of most value in the laboratory are (1) the distinctive association of minerals, (2) peculiar varieties of minerals and (3) the relative abundance of minerals. Locally, the fusibility of clays has been used in correlation.

3. These two methods, walking the outcrop and comparing the rocks, are greatly reinforced by a third line of evidence which also requires the methods of rock study. This is a sequence of rocks of similar characters and similar thicknesses especially if the sequence is an unusual one. The basic assumption is that, unless too strongly folded, the lower of a series of sedimentary beds is the older. This is very important and may be illustrated by an example.

Suppose a white sandstone with well-rounded medium-sized grains is exposed in nearly horizontal beds in a river valley at only

[32] Compare H. A. Ireland: *Use of Insoluble Residues for Correlation in Oklahoma.* Bull. A. A. P. G., volume 20, pages 1086–1121, 1936.

[33] W. H. Twenhofel et al.: *Treatise on Sedimentation,* 1926, pages 205–9.

[34] H. C. Pyle and J. E. Sherborne: *Core Analysis.* Tech. Pub. No. 1024, A. I. M. M. E., 1939.

[35] For one example see I. I. Gardescu and M. H. Billings: Bull. Am. Assoc. Petroleum Geologists, volume 21, pages 1311–32, 1937.

two places about 10 miles apart.	Correlation is at once suggested, but the evidence given is very weak.	Since the conditions of the problem do not permit "walking out the bed," other evidences are sought.	Above the sandstone at each place there are found first a sandy green shale about two feet thick and next a series of limestone beds about 30 feet thick.	This combination of formations makes correlation very much more satisfactory.	Few men would hesitate to suggest the equivalence of the series.	Abrupt changes in the kinds of rock in a series of beds are much more significant than the total gross character of any single sample.	Nevertheless, the sequence of sand, shale, and limestone is a common one and may be repeated in a higher sequence of beds.	If above the limestone another green shale about 40 feet thick is discovered, the correlation is better not only because of another bed in the sequence but because the sequence in each of the two outcrops includes a shale above limestone—a sequence less common than that of limestone above shale.

In most such examples as this one the careful student of rocks may add to the certainty of correlation by close inspection of the beds within a formation.	Few sandstones and limestones in outcrops 30 feet thick are wholly uniform, and if the sequence of minor changes is the same in two exposures, the correlation may be as definite as if the major sequence is exceptional.	The fossils, the color, the impurities, the surface forms of weathering, the intraformational conglomerates and a host of other features serve to develop such minor sequences.

Attention should be given to any breaks in sequence, such as unconformities, below which the sequence is expected to be different at different places.	Underlying beds may differ from those above in attitude or degree of metamorphism as well as in original materials.

The probable changes in thicknesses of beds, as traced laterally, should always be kept in mind.	Conglomerates and sandstones may thin out rapidly in short distances.	Shales are more uniform, and limestones normally persist to great distances.	Examples are known, however, in which a well-exposed limestone 20 feet thick disappeared from the sequence in less than a mile.[36] This is abnormal for limestones but may be expected in sands. Limestones are especially useful in correlation, both because of this constancy and because they commonly carry fossils.

The student should realize that the complexity of the stratigraphic sequence is very great, and detailed preparation includes studies in sedimentation and stratigraphy in addition to rock study.[37]

4. The topographic expression of a formation is useful in correlation, limestones and hard sandstones forming many cliffs and steep slopes, and shales forming gentle grassy slopes. The harder rocks form ridges, whereas valleys are cut in the soft shales. Fragments of a formation on a steep hillside may be assumed to have come down rather than up the hill unless the country is glaciated. The "float" (fragments in the soil) may commonly be traced in a fairly definite line. Very special features of topography, that prove useful, may be illustrated by "sink-holes," common in limestone.

5. The character of the soil and vegetation (or lack of it) upon a formation may be of much help in poorly exposed districts, but a few exposures must be studied first to determine the nature of the soils and vegetation related to the several formations.

6. The average field geologist uses fossils as he does any other peculiar character in comparing beds, not attempting to name the species or determine their range. In shales and sands the mollusca are expected, and other groups are common in limestone. Age is commonly determined from fossils collected and sent to a paleontologist, who may group formations into systems. The methods of detailed rock study in the laboratory take longer than age determinations by fossils, for a prerequisite to correlation by rocks is the establishment of a type section in the district, whereas the fossil sequence is already nearly world-wide. The advantage of rock study methods is that they are applicable everywhere, even where fossils are absent. The rock detail may also serve to subdivide a group of beds in which fossils are uniform throughout.

[36] G. H. Cox, C. L. Dake and G. A. Muilenburg: *Field Methods in Petroleum Geology*. 1921, page 137.

[37] H. B. Milner, *Sedimentary Petrology,* 2d Ed., 1929, pages 360–451, gives a somewhat more detailed discussion.

7. A certain amount of correlation can be based on ages of rocks, determined by contact relations, or by atomic disintegration, or differences in metamorphism.

The description of a sedimentary *formation,* as distinct from a specimen, covers location, distribution, name, correlation, stratigraphy, thickness, fossils, origin.   In this series the description of the rock, or the several facies of the formation, should probably be placed after the notes on distribution and name.   The points in that description are those covered in Methods of field and laboratory work (pages 144 to 150).[38]

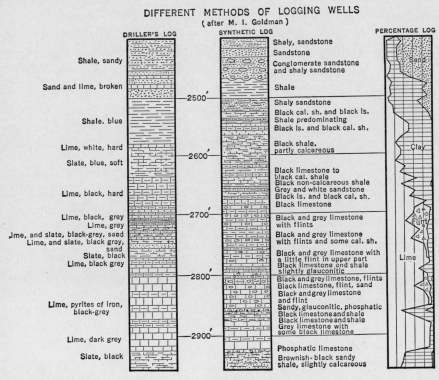

FIG. 75.

[38] A good example of detailed study of a formation is given by G. A. Thiel: *Sedimentary and Petrographic Study of the St. Peter Sandstone.* Bulletin of the Geological Society of America, volume 46, pages 559–614, 1935.

Logging Wells

Logs and records kept by drillers without training in rock study show very little except how hard the rock is. Most large companies now have trained men to log the wells, because they find the record useful—(1) for correlation which determines structure, (2) for planning the casing of the well and hole reduction, and (3) for selecting horizons to plug the well for shallow production. Equipment is carried to the drill rig for almost any desired detail of study of the rock, usually including a binocular microscope and, in important wells, including chemical and a variety of optical equipment.

Every log should distinguish not only the main rocks—shale, sandstone, and limestone—but also dolomite-limestone, chert, gypsum, salt, coal, anhydrite, and others if they are encountered. These main items, once recorded, should next be qualified as to mass characters and results of tests—effervescence, slaking, fusion, presence of oil, etc. (page 199). A blank form for the logs is a convenience and the student may find that such blanks develop habits of observation.

Depth	Principal Material	%	Mass characters Color, luster, acid	Other Materials % %

After a record is made in the notebook for each sample, the final log is compiled to show at what depth changes occur; i.e., the depth of contacts between formations or members is recorded rather than the detailed findings for each sample taken (Figs. 75 and 76).

A log from a rotary drill[39] might be somewhat as follows:

Gypsy Oil Co. Muegge No. 1
Sec. 33, T. 26 N., R. 3 W., Grant County, Oklahoma

Depth in feet	Formation
1520–1530	Red shale
1530–1550	Fine, light, soft, slightly reddish sand
1550–1575	White, porous limestone
1575–1590	Gray, hard subcrystalline limestone
1590–1625	Dark gray shale
1625–1640	Red shale
1640–1670	Dark gray shale
1670–1705	Light, dense limestone
1705–1720	Gray, shaly, thin bedded limestone

Note-taking. — It is good practice in both field and laboratory work to take copious notes, and follow a system or outline so that no essential features are overlooked (see pages 146–147). Under the pressure of commercial work, however, where a large number of exposures or drill samples are to be studied every day, some abbreviations or short cuts are needed, but abbreviation should not be carried so far that the notes are unintelligible. A few suggestions are offered and examples serve to show how they can be used.

For the chief sediments, many are familiar with "*sh, ss, ls, dol, gyp,*" and the same symbols may show an admixture of some of these materials with others, but there are also *arg,* for argillaceous, *aren,* for arenaceous, *calc,* for calcareous, and *carb,* for carbonaceous.

Color records of sediments may be abbreviated to the initial letters of the spectrum colors, *v, i, b, g, y, o, r,* leaving:

bl—black	*bf*—buff	*dk*—dark
br—brown	*pur*—purple	*spec*-- -speckled
gr—gray	*wh*—white	*dap*—dappled
p—pink	*lt*—light	

Color terms for a rock and for the minerals in it may be separated if desirable.

Sizes of grain are referred to the grade-size scale (page 152),

[39] Compare with S. K. Clark, J. I. Daniels and J. T. Richards: *Logging Rotary Wells from Drill Cuttings.* Bull. A. A. P. G., volume 12, 1928, page 73.

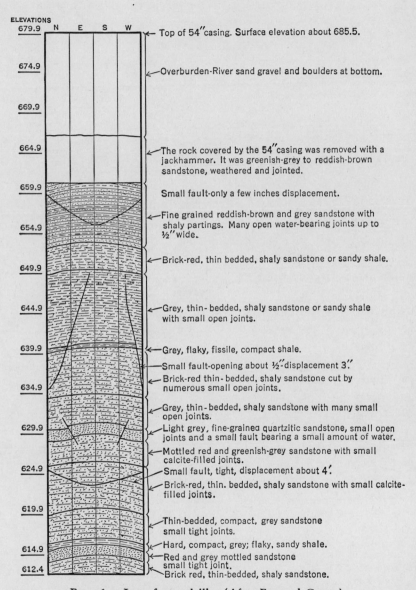

ELEVATIONS

679.9 — Top of 54" casing. Surface elevation about 685.5.

674.9 — Overburden-River sand gravel and boulders at bottom.

669.9

664.9 — The rock covered by the 54" casing was removed with a jackhammer. It was greenish-grey to reddish-brown sandstone, weathered and jointed.

659.9 — Small fault-only a few inches displacement.

— Fine grained reddish-brown and grey sandstone with
654.9 shaly partings. Many open water-bearing joints up to ½" wide.

— Brick-red, thin bedded, shaly sandstone or sandy shale.
649.9

644.9 — Grey, thin- bedded, shaly sandstone or sandy shale with small open joints.

639.9 — Grey, flaky, fissile, compact shale.
— Small fault-opening about ½" displacement 3".
— Brick-red thin- bedded, shaly sandstone cut by
634.9 numerous small open joints.

— Grey, thin- bedded, shaly sandstone with many small open joints.
629.9 — Light grey, fine-grained quartzitic sandstone, small open joints and a small fault bearing a small amount of water.
— Mottled red and greenish-grey sandstone with small calcite-filled joints.
624.9 — Small fault, tight, displacement about 4'.
— Brick-red, thin. bedded, shaly sandstone with small calcite-filled joints.

619.9
— Thin-bedded, compact, grey sandstone small tight joints.

614.9 — Hard, compact, grey; flaky, sandy shale.
— Red and grey mottled sandstone
612.4 small tight joint.
— Brick red, thin-bedded, shaly sandstone.

FIG. 76. — Log of core drill. (After Fox and Grant.)

but grains coarser than sand are met so seldom that they are best named in full. The series of sand sizes are:

V crs
crs
med
fn   Shales may be papery—*pap*
V fn   Dense (limestones)—*ds*

Grain shapes are:

Angular— $\angle r$ oölitic—*ool*
Subangular—*sub $\angle r$*   nodular—*nod*
Subrounded—*sub rdd*   fossiliferous—*fos*
Rounded—*rdd*   cavernous—*cav*
Crystalline—*x*   porous—*por*
Granular—*gran*
Flaky cuttings—*fl*
Spongy—*spgy*
Fibrous—*fib*

Mineral characters and associations, in addition to the terms for the chief sediments, are:

arkosic—*ark*   bituminous—*bit*
micaceous—*mic*   anhydritic—*anhy*
pyritic—*py*   ferruginous—*fer*
cherty—*ch*   manganiferous—*mn*
magnetitic—*mag*   and others that are best
glauconitic—*gl*   spelled out in full

These terms are qualitative only as to the presence or absence of the minerals, and it is best to go farther wherever possible, distinguishing *highly* glauconitic, for example, from *moderately* or *slightly* glauconitic; and so for other minerals.

Other properties such as hardness, cementation, surface characters, and odor should probably be written without much abbreviation.

Sample well logs are given on pages 202, 204 and 205. Goldman gives in parallel columns examples of three kinds of logs that are well worth consideration, although the drillers' log shows only a little of value (Fig. 75).

CHAPTER IX

GENERALITIES ON METAMORPHISM

Outline of Discussion

Definition of metamorphism

Factors of metamorphism

    Forces—heat, pressure (gravity), chemical and crystal forces.
    Agents—air, water and water solutions, magmas and emanations.
    Kind of rock involved.
    Time.

Kinds of metamorphism

    Regional, chief factor pressure.
    Contact, chief factors heat and magmatic emanations.
    Hydrothermal, chief factor hot water solutions.

Processes

    Granulation.
    Recrystallization.
    Injection.
    Replacements, by addition and subtraction and reaction.

Products

    Slates, schists, gneisses, quartzites, marbles, hornfels, and a great variety
of special products, many of which defy ordinary classification and naming.

Definition of Metamorphism

The word metamorphism was first introduced into geological literature by Lyell in 1832, and was used to describe the processes by which rocks undergo alteration. It was particularly applied to those rocks that, from deep burial in the earth, and from the consequent heat and pressure to which they have been subjected, have lost some of their original features and have assumed structures and textures resembling those of the primary or plutonic rocks. In this sense it has been generally employed since, and it implies an increase in crystallization, hardness and those attributes, which are especially associated with the crystalline schists, as contrasted with the unaltered rocks.

The literal meaning of the phrase "the processes by which rocks undergo alteration" is nevertheless somewhat more comprehensive than this, and may be made to include the changes produced by atmospheric agents, which we ordinarily describe by the term weathering. These have already been described under sedimentation because they result largely in the formation of clays and sands. The processes of diagenesis in sediments also involve "alteration," but are considered here under the sedimentary discussion rather than metamorphic, because the changes occur at surface temperatures and pressures. There is no sharp line of separation between the common processes of induration and those of the more thorough transformations that characterize metamorphism. At the two extremes the products are strikingly different, but in the middle ground, the line of separation is arbitrary, and there is room for a difference of opinion. It is sound usage to classify as metamorphic all rocks that have been so much modified that their original structure is largely destroyed, or that have undergone noteworthy changes in mineral character.

The Factors of Metamorphism

Heat.—Temperatures increase with depth in the earth from the average near zero at the surface. The rate ranges widely at different places, from 1° C. in a foot or two, near Recent volcanoes, to 1° C. in over 400 feet in the older Shield areas. The latter figure would probably be normal in the absence of magmatic action. Evidently at a depth of a few miles, especially in regions of batholithic invasion, the temperature is so high that rocks that are stable at the surface may be greatly changed by heat. Water is expelled from many minerals, such as clays, and the carbonates react with silica or other acids losing CO_2.

Heat may at some depths carry metamorphism to the stage of fusion, regenerating igneous rocks, but the evidence that this has occurred in rocks exposed later at the surface is very meager. Such fusion produces igneous magma and should not be classed as metamorphism, but has been referred to by some geologists as "ultrametamorphism." Recently the term "rheomorphism" has been

proposed for a process of at least partial fusion, such that the rock
may be deformed viscously.

Great heat in metamorphism commonly develops a group of
new minerals. This is especially true when the heat acts on a
sedimentary series, for it is hardly to be expected that heat will
greatly modify the minerals formed by cooling from a magma.
Besides regenerating the igneous minerals—quartz, feldspar, and
others—high temperature metamorphism produces new ones such
as garnet, andalusite, sillimanite, cordierite, and graphite, made
from constituents already at hand; and by certain additions of
new constituents produces some very different minerals such as
tourmaline, sulphides, and a variety of "mineralizer minerals."

When stress acts with the heat, the results are very complex.

Pressure. — The most evident condition of pressure is the load
on rocks which are deeply buried in the crust. It is doubtful, however, whether such pressures are the ones most effective in metamorphism. Structural studies indicate that some rocks which are
only slightly metamorphosed have been buried 10 miles or more.
Probably the major forces of metamorphism are related to changes
in volume in the deeper parts of the earth, but partly also to
magmatic injection. The resulting thrusts in the crust of the earth
are directed laterally, and the cleavage that results is steeply
inclined.

In general, uniform pressure increases solubility, and a release
of pressure causes precipitation from water solution. Changes in
pressure thus favor recrystallization.

Non-uniform pressure or stress causes deformation, and if it is
rapidly applied the rock breaks down into smaller grains—is granulated. If more gradually applied and especially if the rock is under
confining pressure, it causes rock flow by internal gliding, twinning,
and probably recrystallization. If one part of a crystal is strained
to a greater degree than another, the strained part is more rapidly
affected by chemical action. It may be dissolved when the rest of
the crystal is not. Thus we find metamorphic rocks with crystals
having elongated forms. The evidences of deformation in the
rocks are noted below in discussion of the processes of meta-

morphism.   It is a safe inference that much more metamorphic recrystallization is due to stress than to uniform pressure.

The results of stress include an orientation of grains, a *schistosity,* which is a parallelism not only of the maximum dimensions of the grains (Fig. 77), but of crystallographic axes.   This orientation may result from granulation and rotation, from gliding internally, or from recrystallization, but the process is still a subject of research (page 218).   Harker lists also the "stress minerals," which form mostly in rocks that give evidence of having been subjected to stress—kyanite, tremolite, actinolite, glaucophane, zoisite, epidote, ottrelite, and staurolite.

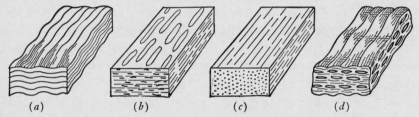

(a)   (b)   (c)   (d)

FIG. 77.— Diagrams of different structures causing schistosity.   (a) Crumpled plates. (b) Platy grains.   (c) Linear grains.   (d) Lenses.

Chemical Affinity. — Chemical reactions are prominent in metamorphic recrystallization.   An impure clay with no biotite is commonly metamorphosed to biotite schist.   The common metamorphic changes are reduction, the removal of water or hydroxyl, the removal of carbonic acid and the formation of silicates.

Crystal Forces. — Where several minerals recrystallize in the same rock some have more tendency to assume good crystal forms than others, apparently because of crystal forces.   Some grow larger than others forming porphyroblasts (Fig. 82).

Water. — The rocks of the earth nearly all have some traces of water, and the porous rocks may have large amounts even at considerable depths.   There is also combined water and hydroxyl, which may become available water when the rocks are metamorphosed by heat.   Probably nearly all rock metamorphism involves some recrystallization by water solution.   Professor Kemp has called attention[1] to the relatively small amount of "pore-water" in this connection, but a little water, even if derived from dehydration of a mineral, may have great metamorphic effects. It dissolves a little of some mineral, allows that to precipitate, and is then available to dissolve more; thus being used over and over.

At shallow depths meteoric water and that chemically combined in the minerals probably dominates reactions, but at greater depths this source of water may be overshadowed by magmatic emanations with their high temperatures, strong solutions of other reagents, and rapid changes as they penetrate cooler rocks.

Magmas. — As agents of metamorphism magmas act largely by their heat—already discussed—and by injection of magma into a rock along fractures or cleavage planes, or even pervasively into intergranular openings, though magma is probably too viscous to penetrate far. Magmas also transmit intrusive stresses to their walls and contribute gaseous emanations which are especially active. Gabbro magmas appear to have been hotter than granite magmas, but have probably contained less water and mineralizer elements than granite magmas.

Gases. — Aside from the action of atmospheric gases, included in weathering (page 125), the chief gases causing metamorphism are the magmatic emanations referred to in the paragraph above. The small emanations from basic magmas carry Cl, Ti, Fe, and Mg; and large volumes from granitic magmas carry water, halogens, sulphur compounds, carbon dioxide, iron, silica, etc. The action of these gases can be observed in fumaroles and solfataras near volcanoes, but their chief metamorphic effects are deep seated. They are perhaps of more interest in connection with ore deposits than in rock study.

Nature of the Rock. — Weak rocks yield more readily than strong rocks to deforming stresses. Soluble rocks recrystallize more rapidly than less soluble rocks. The rocks with secondary cleavage are chiefly those that have such compositions that they are able to recrystallize to form platy minerals. Evidently these

[1] J. F. Kemp: *The Ground Waters.* Trans. Amer. Inst. Min. Eng., volume 45, pages 3–24, 1913.

and other features of the rock have a great influence on the rocks that result from metamorphism.

Time. — The average pre-Cambrian rocks are so much more metamorphosed than the average rocks of any later era, that it seems clear that time is involved in the making of a metamorphic rock.

Summary of Factors. — The tendency of recent years is to emphasize two major groups of factors in metamorphism, first, the lateral thrusts related to orogenic revolutions, and second, the invasions of igneous magmas with their abnormally high temperatures and abundant active emanations.

It is probable that batholith roofs, injected, recrystallized, deformed and almost assimilated, but now exposed by erosion, give the best clues to conditions that prevail widely at depths beyond any possible exploration.

The Kinds of Metamorphism

Each of the factors of metamorphism may be used to distinguish a kind of metamorphism. The student will find in the literature many references to thermal metamorphism, dynamic (or pressure) metamorphism, chemical metamorphism, hydro-metamorphism, etc. None of these, however, is a very satisfactory basis for distinction or classification. There is no metamorphism without heat—that is at absolute zero. There is no metamorphism without at least atmospheric pressure. Practically no rock has been found with so little water that it cannot be detected by the chemists. All metamorphism, therefore, is thermal, all is dynamic and all is "hydro-" in this sense. It seems that the better terms are based on groupings of major or important factors and the terms here used are:

1. **Contact metamorphism,** referring to the contact or near approach of an igneous intrusive, so that in the change of the older rock, heat is a major factor, but gaseous and water solutions, at least locally, have caused great changes in composition.

2. **Regional metamorphism,** in which deep-seated deformation is a major factor, but heat, water, and other factors have considerable influence.

3. **Hydrothermal metamorphism,** in which hot water solutions produce characteristic mineral changes, especially in the walls of veins.

Most general texts on rock study cover chiefly the first two kinds, or these two with weathering as a third kind, in which air and cold water are major factors (page 125). The hydrothermally altered rocks, though very small in total volume, are characteristic wall-rocks of mineral veins, and are almost the only rocks seen by miners who work in ore-deposits that originated as veins.

Van Hise, in a monumental Treatise on Metamorphism,[2] distinguished two major kinds or processes of metamorphism, (1) katamorphism, which breaks rocks down, and (2) anamorphism, which builds up new rocks. He included weathering as katamorphism. The distinction emphasizes a valuable theoretical point, but in common usage, which is followed in this book, the term metamorphism corresponds closely to the anamorphism of Van Hise.

Contact Metamorphism. — Contact metamorphism is the change in the walls of an igneous intrusion or in included fragments of such walls, as a result of the heat, and of materials emanating from the magma. The effects commonly extend for a few feet only, and rarely as much as 2,000 feet.

The igneous rock itself may be notably different near the contact from what it is in the center, and it was formerly the custom to refer to "endomorphic" contact rocks *in* the intrusive, and exomorphic contact rocks *outside*. The present tendency seems to be to use contact metamorphism almost wholly for the wall rocks, using other terms for the rocks within the intrusive— contamination, assimilation, chilled margins, and even autometamorphism.

Widening observation has shown that contact metamorphism is produced by all varieties of igneous rocks. Granites, syenites, nepheline-syenites, diorites, gabbros, and even peridotites have in one place and another proved to be efficient agents. Yet in general the following statements may be said to hold good.

1. Plutonic magmas are more favorable than volcanic flows in causing metamorphism.

[2] C. R. Van Hise: *A Treatise on Metamorphism.* U. S. Geol. Survey, Monograph 47, 1904.

2. Magmas rich in mineralizers are more favorable than those with little vapor in solution. Recall that acidic rocks generally have more abundant mineralizers than basic rocks. Granites are the commonest rocks to have contact metamorphic zones.

3. As regards the walls, different sedimentary rocks possess different susceptibilities. Highly siliceous sandstones and conglomerates, for example, are stubborn subjects, and manifest but slight alteration; but highly aluminous or calcareous beds are favorable to recrystallization, because they contain the alumina, iron, lime, magnesia, and the alkalies which will combine with silica, under metamorphosing influences, to yield copious contact minerals. Of all rocks, impure limestones yield the most varied and interesting results.

4. Chemical changes by introduction are important at some places (pages 218 to 220).

5. The apparent distance to which contact action extends, depends on the angle of emergence of the intrusive. The actual

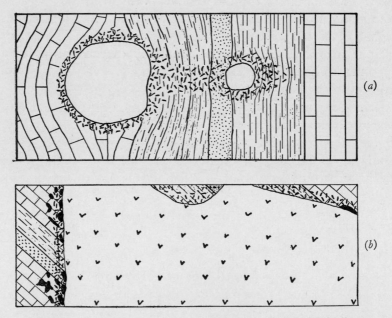

(a)

(b)

Fig. 78.— Diagram of contact zones around intrusive stocks; wider in limestone than in other sediments; wider along the bedding than across it. Outcrop wider where the contact dips at low angles. (a) Map. (b) Section.

distance differs with many factors, being greater in the direction
of structural openings, and in soluble and porous rocks, greater in
shale and limestone than in quartzite or igneous rocks (Fig. 78).

6. Contact effects are strangely small or lacking at some places
where we would naturally expect them.

Regional Metamorphism. — Regional metamorphism takes its
name from its wide distribution. The great pressures and stresses,
which are a major factor, act over great distances simultaneously
and so produce somewhat related effects throughout a region.
Probably most of the action is deep-seated in the earth's crust,
where the temperatures and especially the pressures are high, over
wide areas. These contrast with the narrow zones, very much
higher temperature and moderate pressures of contact action, but
the contrast is not as sharp as it may sound. The heat and solutions involved in regional metamorphism may be derived from a
magma at no very great depth below. Barrell has called attention
to the probability that batholiths may spread widely under the
crust, even where outcrops of igneous rock are very few.[3] The
introduction of such a mineral as tourmaline is highly suggestive
of igneous magma nearby. It is known also that two sediments
buried and folded at about equal depths may be metamorphosed to
very different degrees, so that it seems likely the more altered one
has been affected by a batholithic invasion close below.

Regionally metamorphosed rocks show a wide range of mineral
transformations and structures depending on their original nature
and on the process affecting them, but all are crystalline, with
crystals interlocking so that porosity is at a minimum. Most of
them have become laminated or foliated, independently of original
structures. All have been developed in regions of great disturb-
ance, and most of them at such depths that it has taken a long
period of erosion to bring them to the surface. For this reason
most of them are of ancient geologic age.

Processes of Metamorphism

The new minerals and textures of metamorphic rocks result
from recrystallization, from granulation, and locally from changes

[3] J. Barrell: *The Relation of Igneous Invasion to Regional Metamorphism.*
American Journal of Science, volume 1, pages 1–19 and 174–267, 1921.

of composition.   The pressures involved in regional metamorphism cause rock flowage, a process usually combining granulation and recrystallization, and illustrated in the visible flow of ice in glaciers.

The evidences of deformation are clear in many rocks even without microscopic study.   There are distorted pebbles, amygdules, ellipsoids, fossils, crystals, etc.   The new structures and textures in metamorphic rocks accompany these signs of deformation so regularly that they also become signs of deformation— folds, faults, schistosity, augen structures, etc.

The chief metamorphic deformation of rocks occurs (1) in the deeper parts of earth where effects on the rocks can never be observed, (2) in regions of mountain folds and (3) especially in those mountains invaded by batholiths, so that pressure is reinforced by heat and mineralizers.

Recrystallization. — Recrystallization is the change in texture or mineral make-up produced as material is lost from the boundaries of some crystals and added to others.   In rocks it is commonly believed to involve the solution (or fusion) of some crystals with the practically simultaneous growth of others.   There may, however, be some recrystallization without the intervention of a liquid. No matter how completely reorganized the rock may be, it is supposed to have been at all times a substantially solid rock mass with only minute fractions of the minerals in solution or in process of transformation at any one time.   Recrystallization occurs a little at a time and pervasively throughout the mass.   It is essentially constructive, and minerals are commonly enlarged or new ones are formed by it.   The new crystals may be of the same composition as the original or may be products of reaction.   No change in the total composition of the rock is necessitated, but heat and water are so universal that some changes in hydration are common and more or less addition or loss of other materials is not rare.

Recrystallization is one of the most prominent of metamorphic processes, but the term is not synonymous with metamorphism. The recrystallization that occurs at a late stage of magmatic action is called deuteric, and the recrystallization of a freshly deposited sediment is called diagenetic, rather than metamorphic.

The factors favoring recrystallization are heat, water, and earlier or simultaneous deformation. Water is not an absolute requirement because experimental work on metals in the absence of water shows very great effects at temperatures far below the melting point. Nevertheless practically all rocks contain water, and it is almost certain to be active if recrystallization occurs. There are several examples of metamorphism formerly attributed to dry reaction that are now known to result from water solution. Lime silicates may form in a sandy limestone by a reaction of the lime with introduced silica solutions at a temperature much lower than is needed to make the quartz sand react with calcite.

During recrystallization small grains disappear, and large grains grow larger. This is familiar in the common laboratory practice of boiling a fresh precipitate or letting it stand, to make it coarser-grained so that it will be caught on a filter paper. The process by which shales become phyllites and phyllites become schists is analogous.

Granulation. — Granulation is the crushing of a rock under such conditions that no visible openings result. The fine fractures extend through the minerals, distinguishing granulation from the coarser structures of faulting and jointing. The grains may be reduced to thousands of fragments, but under a confining pressure the minute fragments do not lose their coherence, and the rock remains almost as strong as before.[4]

The factors favoring granulation are largely contrasted with those favoring recrystallization. First and above all others, intense and rapidly applied stress is the dominant factor. The time involved in the deformation must be short, for rocks seem to be deformed without granulation if the stress is moderate but prolonged. A confining pressure usually related to depth is also essential. Finally, the minerals of the rock deformed have a good deal to do with the matter; brittle, hard, insoluble minerals like quartz

---

[4] There is still uncertainty as to the depth at which all openings in rocks are closed by flowage. Rocks may yield abruptly causing earthquakes at very great depths, even if no openings can persist. The zones of fracture and flow are not distinct, but at great depths there is more flowage and less fracturing than near the surface.

and feldspar are granulated more than soft minerals like gypsum. A limestone may be granulated but recrystallizes so readily that the signs of granulation are soon almost lost.

In contrast to the conditions of batholithic roofs where rocks recrystallize, rocks are granulated in zones of shallow deformation farther from igneous intrusives. Both processes may be characteristic of mountain folds, but the granulation is more prominent in the colder, shallower, and drier portions of the folded structure.

Granulation always reduces the grain sizes, forming successively mortar, augen, and mylonite structures. The term cataclastic applies to some. (See page 159.) Commonly if there are grains of different colors, the rocks become banded by a flattening of each grain into a platy or lenticular aggregate.

A process of gliding, or deformation inside as well as between crystals, is best distinguished from granulation, but is seen mostly by microscopic work. Dr. Bruno Sander of Innsbruck, Austria, and his students believe that such pervasive deformation and rotation of grains can explain the crystallographic as well as dimensional orientation of crystals in a schist.[5]

Chemical Changes in Metamorphism. — The clearest of all examples of chemical change in metamorphism is the injection of granite in thin layers along the cleavages of schist. Progressive additions result in a complete gradation from schist through gneisses to granite. The magma being viscous may not be able to penetrate the small cleavage planes of a schist as far as the more fluid volatile emanations from the magma. Van Hise has noted that in the Black Hills of Dakota the more remote dikelets grade into quartz veins.[6] This brings up the matter of contributions to a metamorphic rock which are derived from the nearby magma but are not actually the magma. In contact metamorphism such contributions may be important, but there is much less evidence of magmatic additions in regional metamorphism (page 215).

The mineralizers, noted in the discussion of igneous rocks, have different effects according to the depths at which the igneous rocks

[5] E. B. Knopf and E. Ingerson: *Structural Petrology.* Geological Society of America, Memoir 6, 1938.

[6] Op. cit., page 724, 1904.

solidify. At the surface mineralizers separate from lava flows to form vesicles in the tops of the flows and clouds of vapor rising from the volcanoes. At great depths where batholiths have tight covers, they form hydrous minerals and miarolitic cavities. The metamorphic effects of mineralizers are dominant in that broad zone of earth between the deep batholiths and the surface. In that zone a magma injected from below finds pressure reduced so that gases separate from solution.[7] The gases rise to the top and find the rocks only moderately tight—there are joints and pore spaces which permit the entrance of material. Furthermore at magmatic temperatures gases seem to be able to penetrate a rock even if the pores are sub-microscopic—the entrance is pervasive and affects the whole wall rock for a short distance.

This outline of the action of mineralizers in contact zones has not been agreed upon without long discussion. English, German, and some American students of rocks believed that there was very slight migration of material. Harker described a contact of granite magma on a basic flow, concluding that migration had not exceeded one-twentieth of an inch. But the French and most American geologists found more evidence of chemical change, and in this group Professor Kemp has been a leader. He demonstrated beyond question, by years of study of the garnet zones produced by magmatic invasion of limestones, that a large amount of material was added from the magma.[8] The occurrence of some ores of copper and iron in the contact rocks gave the problem technical as well as scientific importance. The solution involved several steps.

In the first place it was necessary to show that the limestones, though impure at some places, had not been leached of their lime so as to leave a residue that could recrystallize to form garnet. This was done at Tamaulipas, Mexico, by Kemp, and at Morenci, Arizona, by Lindgren, careful analyses showing that the impurities

[7] C. N. Fenner: *Pneumatolytic Processes in the Formation of Minerals and Ores.* Lindgren, Volume, A. I. M. E., pages 58–106, 1933, discusses the evidence that magmatic emanations are gaseous, at least at first.

[8] J. F. Kemp: *Notes on Garnet Zones on the Contact of Intrusive Rocks and Limestones.* Canadian Mining Institute, Trans., volume 15, pages 171–186, 1912.

had not such a composition as to yield the garnet rock.   This was the more impressive because the garnet is commonly andradite, the calcium-iron garnet, rather than grossularite, the aluminous garnet, which might form from shaly limestone.   Such quantities of iron as are indicated by andradite and the associated iron-bearing ore minerals, could not be explained as impurities in limestone.   "Andradite" became a by-word in the argument about contact action. At White Knob, Idaho, Professor Kemp also found evidences that aluminum had migrated with other metals and silica.[9]

In the second place it was necessary to show that the iron and other elements were not added by ordinary ground waters, heated by the intrusive to a point of vigorous circulation and chemical action.   This was clear at White Knob where a block of limestone enclosed in the granite was turned to garnet.[10]

Where shale and other rocks occur near intrusive masses or included in them, they also show changes of composition proving migration over distances of many feet.[11]

Metasomatism or Replacement. — Replacement is a term used by petrographers in a rather technical sense, but, as it is also a term used popularly in a broader sense, the technical term *metasomatism* is preferable.   Metasomatism or replacement is a practically simultaneous solution and deposition through small openings, usually submicroscopic, and mainly by hypogene water solutions, by which a new mineral of partly or wholly differing composition may grow in the body of an old mineral or mineral aggregate.   The limitation to hypogene water solutions would exclude from metasomatism some of the common pseudomorphs resulting from weathering and some rocks that a magma has replaced by assimilation.

The common examples of metasomatism in metamorphism are the recrystallization of clays to biotite schists, the contact effects, and the hydrothermal effects on the walls of veins.   There are also the replacements of limestone by iron ores, the formation of meta-

[9] Op. cit., p. 181.
[10] J. B. Umpleby: *Geology and Ore Deposits of the Mackay Region, Idaho.*   U. S. Geol. Survey, Professional Paper 97, pages 40, 44, 59, and 71 (1917).
[11] F. F. Grout: *Criteria of Origin of Inclusions in Plutonic Rocks.*   Bull. Geol. Soc. America, volume 48, page 1546, 1937.

crysts in schists, and the common silicification of both limestones and shales. Hydrothermal action typically propylitizes and sericitizes the igneous rocks. This action has been studied chemically as well as mineralogically. Potash, sulphur, and water are added; soda, lime, and others are removed. It is very remarkable that with such important changes in chemical constituents the volume may remain almost constant. Some hydrothermal carbonation commonly follows contact action in a limestone.

The Results of Metamorphism. — The results are the rocks described in the next chapter, including the minerals and structures that such rocks display.

Field and Laboratory Methods. — The description of metamorphic rocks involves little that is new in methods after the study of igneous and sedimentary rocks. Several minerals and textures that are rare in other groups are here prominent. Some of the most complex rocks known fall in this group because they have not only relics of the original complexity of the igneous or sedimentary source but the added structures and minerals of several grades of metamorphism. Field work should distinguish and map carefully not only the primary bedding or layers if recognized, but the newly developed metamorphic structures. The "linear structures" noted in some igneous rocks are even more striking in metamorphic rocks and should invariably be mapped. For research in metamorphic rocks it may be necessary to mark specimens as collected so that laboratory work can be related to the dip, strike, and pitch in the field.

CHAPTER X

THE METAMORPHIC ROCKS

THE ROCKS PRODUCED BY REGIONAL METAMORPHISM

Regional metamorphism has been briefly characterized (page 212), and the processes have been described. The results of regional metamorphism are chiefly slates, schists, gneisses, quartzites, marbles, and silicate rocks related to marbles. These groups are best learned and distinguished by a study of labelled specimens. At this point the student discovers the reason that igneous and sedimentary rocks are studied first, for the metamorphic rocks are all derived from the earlier classes, some by slight changes and others by more nearly complete change. In other words metamorphic rocks show transitions from the earlier classes, and become truly metamorphic only where the change has been so great that new minerals or textures appear. The class includes rocks of mixed origin also, in which changes in an original rock are accompanied by large additions of precipitates or magma.

Most metamorphic rocks are foliated. A *foliate* exhibits a parallelism of certain or all of its minerals. In a sense the flow structures of lavas and the lamination of sediments are foliations, but the term is much more used for the secondary structures of slates, schists and gneisses. Even the secondary foliation is of two kinds, one based largely on a parallelism of platy minerals, and the other on layers of granular material alternating with layers of different color, texture or minerals.

Slates

Definition and Origin. — A slate is a fine-grained rock with secondary cleavage independent of the bedding so that most of the cleavage pieces are like adjacent pieces. The minerals are practically all too fine-grained to be recognized even by use of the pocket lens.

Nearly all slates result from the deep-seated deformation of clays and shales, but by definition the term is purely structural and some slates are derived from basalts and other rocks. The lamination or banding of shales is commonly preserved crossing the cleavage in slates (Fig. 80). On the other hand, slates from basalts may have relics of ellipsoids, amygdules, and other igneous features. After microscopic examination, it appears that most secondary cleavage is based on the parallelism of platy mineral grains.

The processes by which clays develop parallel plates with increased grain sizes are still being discussed, and the older notions of growth along planes of shear or along planes formed by flattening under deformation are now supplemented by the ideas of rotation and internal gliding in the minerals (page 218).

Flow cleavage [1] is a rock cleavage parallel to mineral elongation and mineral cleavage. Fracture cleavage is directed by parallel fractures more or less healed. *Mineralogic Composition, Varieties.* — The cleaved surfaces of slate tend to be very smooth because of the fineness of grain, and a few which have especially good cleavages are quarried and used. Only the best are of value. Further metamorphism by recrystallization makes the surfaces rougher, and the luster of mineral cleavages more conspicuous. By this process the slates grade

FIG. 79. — Linear schistosity at right angles to "cross joints" in green schist. Saganaga Lake, Ontario.

through *phyllites,* still of very fine grain, to schists. Slates may also show cross cleavage and joints (Fig. 79), perfect

[1] As defined by C. K. Leith: *Structural Geology.* 1913, page 76.

enough so that the rock breaks in pencil shapes rather than in large slabs. Most slate quarries also show *curly slates* where an early cleavage has been deformed. Quartz veins or sandy and harder streaks in the original sediment commonly cause imperfections in the cleavage. It has been noted that in some quarries the available plates appear to become thicker in depth, as if the surface weathering had been a factor in developing the cleavages. Though commonly drab to black, slates may be red, green, or purple. Colors are most used as the basis of distinc-

FIG. 80. — Cleavage across bedding in a schist, Michigan iron ranges. About natural size.

tion of varieties. In the varieties derived from sandy clay we may still detect sand grains and call the rock a *sandy slate,* but most such rocks are gray so that *graywacke slates* are common. A few slates have so much lime as to be *calcareous slates,* and the colors indicate still other mineralogic varieties. A black slate is usually a *graphitic slate* and a red one is a *ferruginous slate.* Coarse pyrite may grow in a slate that is otherwise fine-grained, making a *pyritic slate.* Scattered crystals of silicates coarser than average grain may yield a *"knotted slate."* These are so characteristic of contact zones, that the discovery of a knotted slate should lead to the search for an igneous contact.

Common usage of the term slate is very confusing. Coal miners use the name for shales that have not been visibly altered, and have no secondary cleavage. On the other hand, geologists who find slates in a series of sediments of known origin, have a strong tendency to map the slates as sediments, ignoring their obviously metamorphic structure. Neither of these is to be recommended.

Alteration. — Slates are exceedingly resistant as is shown by their use in thin slabs for roofs, and they often crop out in prominent ledges or even peaks. They soften down to a clay in the last stages of weathering, but always on the outcrop are more tender than in depth, so that much dead work is unavoidable in opening quarries.

Distribution. — Commercial production is chiefly from Pennsylvania and Vermont, but workable deposits range from Maine to Virginia, and there are deposits farther from large markets in the Lake Superior region, in Colorado, and in the mountains west and south.

Schists

Definition and Origin. — Schist is a crystalline rock with a secondary foliation or lamination; as a rule it is finer-grained than gneiss and coarser than slate and phyllite; its foliation is based on parallelism of platy or needle-like grains; and it rarely has abundant feldspar. The name schist refers to the tendency to split along the foliation. Any one of the layers is commonly of the same sort as the layers on each side. No very sharp line can be drawn between schists and gneisses. The student who reads French or German should note that the French "schiste" and German "Schiefer" include shales, slates, and schists indiscriminately, but the English term schist is for a metamorphic rock exclusively.

The processes of formation of schists are in continuation or intensification of those forming slates (page 223). It is here in the study of schists that we find the most suggestions of zones of intensity of metamorphism. Clearly the rocks metamorphosed at great depths differ from those at shallow depths, and some may be in a doubtful intermediate position. Grubenmann listed[2] the minerals and rocks characteristic of three depth zones of metamorphism, below the belt of weathering (Fig. 81). Roughly and irregularly, the deep or kata-zone is characterized by gneisses, the meso-zone by schists, and the shallow or epi-zone by phyllites. Some metamorphic minerals range widely, but sericite, talc, and chlorite form mostly in the epi-zone; and diopside, augite, andradite, pyrrhotite, and sillimanite form mostly in the katazone. Van Hise distinguished only two zones below the belt of weathering (see page 213). Other petrographers have attempted to correlate a much larger number of facies with particular depths, temperatures and pressures, but the distinctions need further research and involve microscopic study.

Mineralogic Composition, Varieties.—The more important varieties of schist are named from the dominant ferromagnesian minerals in them, *biotite-schist, muscovite-schist, hornblende-schist, actinolite-schist, talc-schist, epidote-schist, graphite-schist, chlorite-schist,* etc. These are the constituents which give the rocks their structure, but they are by no means invariably dominant. Many schists are dominated by quartz, carbonate, or even feldspar. These are inter-leaved with the platy minerals in almost any proportions. As quartz increases the *quartzose schists* grade to *schistose quartzites.* Some less common schists high in calcite or dolomite mark transitions to crystalline limestones. They are *calcareous schists. Green schist* and *greenstone schist* are commonly colored by chlorite and epidote, but the term greenstone, when used alone, is vague, not distinguishing an igneous rock with slight alteration from a thoroughly altered schist.

The grain-size in schists ranges widely and coarse schists resemble gneisses except that they commonly show little feldspar. Fine schists grade through *phyllites* to slates. The phyllites are so fine that grains are hardly distinguishable, but the aggregate of shining scales may indicate a mica. If this is nearly white fine muscovite, the rock is commonly called a *sericite-schist.* "Hydro-

<hr>

[2] U. Grubenmann and P. Niggli: *Die Gesteinsmetamorphose.* Die kristallinen Schiefer, 3d ed., 1924, pages 398–9.

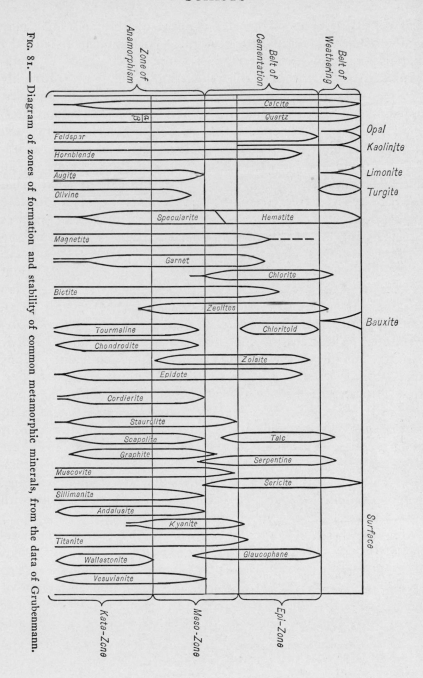

FIG. 81.—Diagram of zones of formation and stability of common metamorphic minerals, from the data of Grubenmann.

mica schist" is an old name used for such rocks in the eastern states. They may result from shales, arkose sands, or aphanitic siliceous igneous rocks.

European geologists are dividing the rocks long known as phyllites into two groups, one resulting from recrystallization of fine-grained rocks, and the other more largely from shearing, granulation, or crushing. Since the crushing is in part analogous to mylonitization (page 236), phyllites of this origin are called *phyllonites*.

Mica-schists result from the thorough metamorphism or recrystallization of sandstones, shales, and clays, and also from the crushing and excessive shearing of igneous rocks, granitoid, and porphyritic alike. A possible origin from ancient volcanic tuffs is always to be considered in the study of a district, but the origin is commonly obscure and a subject for chemical and microscopical investigation. Certain schists from igneous rocks may have feldspars in noteworthy amounts and in this respect resemble gneisses. The distinction of schist and gneiss in such cases depends on a banding or the development of layers differing mineralogically. In the absence of such layers the rock may be called schist even if feldspar remains. If the feldspar is still in phenocrysts after the groundmass is schistose such terms as *schistose rhyolite-porphyry* or *schistose basalt-porphyry* may be used (Fig. 82 (*b*)). Further deformation destroys even the phenocrysts, yielding sericite schist and phyllite.

The deformation of such rocks with original phenocrysts produces rocks called *blasto-porphyritic* (Fig. 82 (*b*)). A very different texture results from the growth in a schist of new minerals in grains notably larger than the rest; these large grains are porphyroblasts (or metacrysts as distinct from phenocrysts), and the rock is a *porphyroblastic* schist. The minerals that commonly grow large this way, in surprisingly perfect crystals unless later deformed, include garnet, staurolite (Fig. 82 (*a*)), kyanite, tourmaline, pyrite, magnetite, and ottrelite; less commonly biotite, feldspar and others. The garnet, staurolite, and aluminum silicates strongly indicate derivation from an original clay. The feldspar metacrysts may be added by magmatic emanations (Fig. 83), but some result from recrystallization without addition.

(a)

(b)

FIG. 82. — Coarse crystals in schist. About natural size. (a) Porphyroblastic garnet (and staurolite) in muscovite schist, Roxbury, Connecticut. (b) Relics of phenocrysts of plagioclase as augen in green schist, Rainy Lake.

In contrast with the mica-schists from sediments and acidic igneous rocks, hornblende-schist, chlorite-schist, and epidote-schist are mostly derived from basic igneous rocks or tuffs, or the rare sediments that are derived from basic rocks. Hornblende schists in which the hornblende needles are not well oriented are called amphibolites, a term that includes both schists and massive rocks. Some amphibolites are igneous segregations, others are metamor-

FIG. 83.—Metacrysts in schist, evidently added from the granite intruded, near by (at left of picture). Giants Range, Minnesota.

phosed igneous rocks and still others are derived from sediments, by contact or regional metamorphism. The origin in any particular exposure is determined with difficulty. The rarer *glaucophane-schist* with a bluish gray amphibole is said to be of sedimentary origin. *Talc-schists* in America are largely derived from peridotites and pyroxenites. *Eclogite,* though rare in America, is a garnet-pyroxene rock, commonly considered the metamorphic deep-seated equivalent of basalt; but the pyroxene is pale green so that it looks more like actinolite than augite.

Schists of mixed mineralogic type are common, and may be named from either prominent mineral, or from both. There are hornblende-biotite-schists, and garnetiferous chlorite-schists, etc.

Alteration. — Schists as a group result from recrystallization. Once formed they may prove to be fairly stable, but none are wholly immune from further change by several kinds of alteration. Clays which form at the surface may be altered at successively greater depths to phyllite and schist. There may finally be an alteration of a deep zone schist by deformation in a shallow zone. This is "retrograde" metamorphism, on the idea that "high grade" metamorphism results from high temperature and pressure which are characteristic of the deep zone. The retrograde changes in specific minerals are noteworthy. Augite, reaching progressively shallower zones, may yield hornblende, then biotite, and later chlorite. Garnet also yields chlorite at shallow depths. Highly magnesian silicates yield talc. Feldspars give muscovite and sericite. These all reverse the normal sequence of mineral changes that result from the deep burial of common sediments.

Most of the schists, especially those with prominent hornblende or chlorite, resist weathering very well, and form prominent outcrops. Those with abundant pyrite or iron carbonate rapidly turn soft and rusty.

Distribution. — Schists form vast areas in all the basement complex, or old Shield areas, and are even more prominent in the folded mountain regions. Chlorite-schists are quarried and crushed to supply green granules to coat tar-paper roofing, in several states in the Lake Superior region. Glaucophane-schist makes prominent formations in the Coast Range in California. Graphite-schists have enough graphite to have been commercially produced in several states, and an altered coal bed in Mexico is a large producer. Talc-schists are common along the Appalachian Mountains, and talc is produced at several places.

Gneisses

Introductory. — *Gneiss* is an old word which originated among the early German miners in the Saxon districts. It was especially applied by them to laminated rocks of the mineralogical composition of granite, and in this sense it is widely employed today.   But there are many important gneisses which correspond in mineralogy to the other plutonic rocks, and which are just as properly designated by this name.   We may therefore define gneiss as a megascopically crystalline rock with a secondary crude foliation, devel-

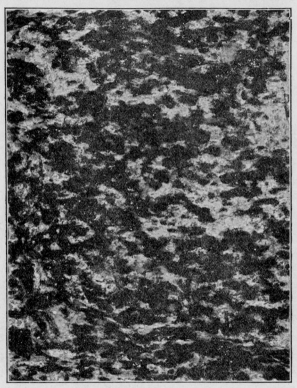

FIG. 84. — Diorite gneiss, Mt. Diablo, California.   About natural size.
Courtesy of the McGraw-Hill Book Company.

oped in bands which are commonly different from those on either side, and nearly always with a mineral composition corresponding to some granitoid igneous rock.   In most gneisses feldspar is prominent, and it is customary to let abundant megascopic feldspar distinguish gneisses from schists (Fig. 84).   Gneisses, however, grade into schists by imperceptible steps.   On the other hand, gneisses pass equally gradually into granitoid igneous rocks.   In both cases the dividing line is arbitrary.   This definition excludes the gneissoid igneous rocks sometimes called "primary gneisses,"

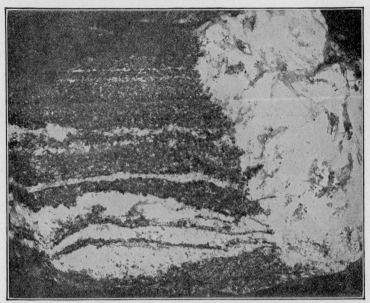

FIG. 85.— A pegmatite dike cutting biotite schist and injecting it lit-par-lit.   About natural size.   Courtesy of the McGraw-Hill Book Company.

FIG. 86. — Banded, lit-par-lit injection gneiss.   Saganaga Lake, Ontario.
Courtesy of the McGraw-Hill Book Company.

but includes those original igneous rocks which have developed foliation by shearing and those schists that have been injected in layers by igneous rock—*lit-par-lit* injection gneisses (Figs. 85 and 86).

The distinction of gneissoid igneous rocks from gneisses metamorphic by granulation or injection is complicated by the fact that some batholithic invasions are prolonged over extended periods which alternate with deformation periods. After some magma is emplaced, and only partly cooled, later supplies of magma invade and deform the first rock, which is still hot enough to yield readily, giving it a gneissic structure, or even injecting it along flow layers. The second mass may then be invaded by a third, and so on up to seven or eight invasions from the same or a closely related source of supply. Each is deformed by pressure before the next arrives or at the time the next crowds its way in, so that only the last facies, usually pegmatitic or aplitic, is free from deformation.[3] It is very difficult to tell such gneisses from those of later injection or deformation.

FIG. 87.— Conglomerate gneiss, Ensign Lake, Minnesota.

Mineralogic Composition, Varieties.—Aside from the feldspars and common minerals of granitoid rocks, the gneisses have a few metamorphic minerals including garnet, epidote, and even tourmaline, graphite, and sillimanite. Gneisses derived from igneous rocks show a succession of mafic minerals— olivine to serpentine, augite to hornblende to biotite and rarely to chlorite. This sequence is related to deformation at progressively shallower depths, and is analogous to the retrograde metamorphism noted in schists; but since this may be the first metamorphism to affect the igneous rock, it is not called retrograde; it is a metamorphism of the epizone or mesozone (Fig. 81).

[3] J. Barrell: *Relations of Igneous Invasion to Regional Metamorphism.* American Journal of Science, volume 1, pages 259–267, 1921.

Varieties of gneiss are best named by prefixing to the word gneiss the name of the granitoid igneous rock with the same minerals, thus *granite-gneiss, syenite-gneiss, gabbro-gneiss,* etc.[4] There is a strong tendency also to name such rocks from their original condition, if it can be determined, but the determination is usually a matter for microscopic study. A few gneisses can be recognized as derived from sediments, and are named from them; *quartzite-gneiss,* and *conglomerate-gneiss* (Fig. 87).

Fig. 88.— Augen gneiss, South America. About two-thirds natural size.

A further series of variety terms are based on structures. *Augen-gneisses* (Fig. 88) have resulted from partial granulation of a coarse or porphyritic igneous rock leaving some remnants of the coarse grains, commonly feldspar, only partially affected—

[4] These terms are commonly used without any implication of origin, but simply to indicate the minerals. C. H. Gordon suggested in the Bulletin of the Geological Society of America, volume VII, page 122, that these terms be restricted to rocks known to be dynamic derivatives of the corresponding massive rock, reserving granitic gneiss, syenitic gneiss, etc., for those the origin of which is unknown. The suggestion had some advocates but is not widely followed.

lenses in a matrix so far crushed as to be almost schistose. Since these lenses are shaped like eyes the German word Augen, for eyes, gives the name of the variety. Further crushing leaves little traces of the original coarse grain and the fine banded rock is a *mylonite*.[5]

Finally there are a large group of *injection gneisses*, resulting from the injection of thin dikes of igneous rocks along the cleavage planes of schist, or possibly in some cases along bedding planes of shale. These are very wide-spread and much more important than was realized in the early days of rock study. *Lit-par-lit* injection gneisses may form a high proportion of all our gneisses. They are mixed rocks, partly schists and partly igneous, but are classed as metamorphic because the cleavage which guided injection is a metamorphic structure. In the field, some of the intrusive rock, commonly granite, may be in wide dikes, but specimens for laboratory illustration are necessarily small enough to show dikes in hand specimens (Figs. 85 and 86).

Sederholm has proposed a series of terms for various mixed rocks, and the term "migmatite" for the whole group. Migmatites include gneisses, breccias, contaminated rocks, and others.

Much less satisfactory variety names for gneisses use mineralogic prefixes, *hornblende-gneiss, biotite-gneiss, chlorite-gneiss, garnet-gneiss, sillimanite-gneiss, epidote-gneiss,* etc. It is evident at once that these names are very incomplete, telling nothing of the nature of the feldspar or other minerals. It is rarely that gneisses are met in which the feldspar cannot be estimated, but when they are met, such terms may be needed. Many of the rocks in which the mafic mineral is about the only mineral that is recognized, are best classed as schists.

Two special varieties are noteworthy; the *eclogites* are garnet-pyroxene rocks which were mentioned as schists but commonly associated with gneisses; and the *granulites* may be fine-grained light-colored gneisses with garnet, feldspar, and pyroxene; but granulites

---

[5] Mylonite is a term used very differently by different students of rocks. The original suggestion referred to a banded feldspathic rock related to gneisses; but the fact that it had been granulated led to the application of the term to fault breccias or friction breccias. Mylonites are granulated at such depths that they do not lose coherence as breccias do. Shand includes under mylonites "flinty crush rocks," and some with augen.

are better described by other terms because that term has been so perverted by loose usage that it is practically valueless unless accompanied by an explanation.

Alteration. — The alteration of gneisses is similar in all respects to that of the corresponding igneous rocks. The feldspars alter to kaolinite, the micas and hornblende to chlorite and the rock softens down to loose aggregates that contribute heavily to the sedimentary rocks.

Distribution. — Gneisses are abundant in ancient, geological formations. The early Archean is their especial home, and they form the largest part of its vast areas in Canada, around the Great Lakes, along the Appalachians and in the Cordilleran region. But no single division of geological time monopolizes them. There are Cambrian and Carboniferous gneisses in New England, and dynamic metamorphism may produce them from massive rocks of almost any age. The later geological formations, however, have seldom been buried sufficiently deep to be in favorable situations. Much the same holds true of Europe and the rest of the world. The gray and red gneisses of the mining districts about Freiberg, in Saxony, those of the Highlands of Scotland, those in Scandinavia, and the wonderful exhibitions of dynamic metamorphism in the Alps are to be cited as of unusual historic and scientific interest.

Quartzites

The *quartzites* are metamorphosed sandstones, and differ from the latter principally in their greater hardness, and to a certain extent in their fairly pronounced crystalline character. These qualities result from an abundant siliceous cement which is crystalline quartz, and which is commonly deposited around the grains of the original sandstone, enlarging the quartz grains so that they are interlocked with adjoining grains. Where the original sandstone was argillaceous, the resulting quartzite contains mica, and with increase of the mica, such quartzites pass through *schistose quartzite* and quartz-schist into mica-schists. *Pebbly quartzite* and *conglomerate quartzite* result from pebbly sands and conglomerate respectively. The whole series of grain sizes in sands from very coarse to very fine (page 152) are inherited by quartzites and furnish varietal prefixes. *Slaty quartzite* and *gneissic quartzite* indicate gradations to slate and gneiss respectively. There is no sharp break between quartzites and sandstones, and whereas the extremes of soft sandstones and hard quartzites are very different, the determination of intermediate rocks is more or less arbitrary. It is customary to call a rock quartzite where the cement is so firm that the rock breaks through the sand grains instead of around them. Particular minerals may be used to name varieties. *Arkose quartzites* or *arkosites* carry notable amounts of pink or white feldspar. *Graywacke quartzite* is derived from graywacke sand.

Varieties named by color are chiefly the *red quartzites* which are *ferruginous quartzites,* and the *white quartzites* which are almost free from iron oxides. A rare quartzite with many flakes of specular hematite is called *itabirite.* Much of the ferruginous chert of the Lake Superior iron-ranges, jaspilite and taconite, is somewhat metamorphosed to quartz and specularite, but no new

Fig. 89. — Crumpled ferruginous chert, Rainy Lake.

names are commonly applied (Fig. 89). A common product is *"amphibole-magnetite rock."*

Quartzites occur in practically all extensive series of metamorphosed sediments, especially in the pre-Cambrian. They are common in the Appalachian metamorphic belt, in the region north of Lake Huron, around Lake Superior, and in many areas in western states and Alaska.

The Marbles and Dolomite Marbles

The *marbles* and *dolomite marbles* are metamorphosed equivalents of the limestones already described. The chief change is a recrystallization, making a rock more coarsely crystalline than most limestones. The dolomite marbles may be largely formed from dolomite limestones, but some magnesia may be added during metamorphism. Dolomite is more difficult to distinguish from calcite after metamorphism than before, but the test with dilute acid shows that dolomite effervesces only feebly unless the acid is hot.

The common accompaniment of deforming forces during recrystallization, is indicated by the fact that most marbles have only the crudest traces of greatly deformed organic structures. Bedding is also commonly contorted if

FIG. 90. — Highly folded marble, with more bedding than is common. Vermont.

not obliterated (Fig. 90). A secondary banding of serpentine and other minerals in streaks is common, and the rocks are said to be "marbled." There are *brecciated marbles,* but slaty and schistose varieties are very rare, in spite of the known deformation.

Carbonaceous matter in the original limy deposit affords *graphite marble* with dark grains or streaks after metamorphism. Numerous color varieties are the result of mixtures of bituminous and ferruginous material, but the common *green marble* is colored by serpentine, *"Verde antique."* *Ophicalcites* have serpentine in spots rather than streaks in the carbonate rock. If the original limestone was impure with silica, alumina, and iron oxides, various limy or magnesian silicates result from their metamorphism. In altered dolomites the magnesian silicates form before the lime combines, and we have not only serpentine marble but *tremolite marble, diopside marble, phlogopite marble, talcose marble,* and even *garnet marble.* Large marble quarries show borders and streaks rich in these minerals where the original limestone graded into shales or sandstones. For ornamental marble the occurrence of hard silicates is very injurious, making the rock difficult to cut and polish.

Most marbles form more or less extensive strata in the midst of other metamorphic rocks, commonly slates, phyllites, schists and quartzites. Thin beds of no great value may be thickened to form commercial deposits at the crests and troughs of folds.

Crystalline limestones are soluble rocks and weather with comparative facility. Where they occur in metamorphic belts, they are invariably in the valleys, and are potent factors in determining the direction of the drainage lines. Where exposed for long periods they afford a coarse, crumbling sand or gravel, that is much used for roads on the borders of the Adirondacks and in western New England. The final stage is a mantle of residual red clay from which the calcareous material has been largely leached.

The marbles are common in our metamorphic districts. In the Appalachian belt they are of great areal and economic importance and are largely quarried in Vermont, Massachusetts, New York, Pennsylvania, and Georgia. In western Colorado they are strongly developed and in the Sierras of California the same is true, Inyo County being a rather large producer of marble. The foreign mountainous and metamorphic districts exhibit enormous exposures. The great series of ranges which begin in the Pyrenees and extend through the Alps and the Carpathians to the Himalaya, have many famous quarries and ledges. The "Dolomites" in the Tyrolese Alps is a district of especial richness. The Carrara marble of the Appenines, the Pentelic of Greece, and the colored varieties from Northern Africa, are widely known.

Serpentinites, Soapstones, and Related Silicate Rocks

The marbles with silicates are transitional to silicate rocks which have too little carbonate to be classed as marble. If the original limestones had too little lime and magnesia to combine with all the silica, or if they lost the lime and magnesia during metamorphism, they might produce *serpentine rock* (*serpentinite*), *soapstone, garnet rock, amphibolite,* and others.[6] Not all of these silicate rocks are derived from impure limestone, but they may well be listed here with those that are.

The serpentinites are green to red aggregates of scales, fibers, or massive individuals of the mineral serpentine. They display considerable variety of texture according to the characters of these components. Other minerals are not especially prominent. Grains of chromite or magnetite may be detected and garnets of the variety, pyrope, are noteworthy in some of them. Veinlets of calcite or of magnesian carbonates ramify through the rock in many exposures. Remains of the original olivine, pyroxene, or hornblende from which the serpentine has been derived are abundant, and biotite or some magnesian mica is not uncommon. The varieties of the mineral serpentine are numerous, but many of them are too rare to be important rock-makers. Most serpentinites have been formed by the alteration of basic igneous rocks, among which the pyroxenites and peridotites are the chief contributors. Hornblende schists also yield them and G. F. Becker has recorded the remarkable case of sandstones that pass into them in the Coast Ranges of California.

Soapstones, called also steatites, are chiefly talc. Quartz veinlets run through many such rocks and scattered grains of quartz are common. Magnesian carbonates are likewise evident in many exposures. In the case of the Gouverneur beds of talc, C. H.

[6] Epidosite, garnetite, and jade are in this group.

Smyth has shown that the talc replaces tremolite and enstatite. The original magnesian rocks of most of the soapstones in America are probably basic intrusives low in iron oxides, but some talc rocks, especially in Europe, are formed from siliceous dolomites. The soapstones are not particularly abundant rocks but are of economic value where met. They are close relatives of the talc-schists earlier cited.

The serpentinous rocks themselves are thoroughly altered derivatives from fresher anhydrous ones and in their further decomposition simply soften to incoherent earths. The more resistant included minerals are thus set free, and in the case of platinum and garnets they may be concentrated in gravel.

The serpentinites are scattered in the Appalachian metamorphic belt and those on Staten Island are noteworthy. They are formed from basic rocks in eastern Pennsylvania, Maryland, North Carolina, and Georgia. A few are reported from the Lake Superior region and there are many in the Coast ranges along the Pacific coast. They are likewise common abroad, and in a minor capacity appear in many metamorphic districts. Soapstone is much less common, but is met in this country as a subordinate member in much the same regions as the serpentines and crystalline dolomites. Amphibolites as products of metamorphism of limestones are well-known in the Haliburton-Bancroft area of Ontario. These and garnet-rocks are prominent in contact zones.

CHAPTER XI

THE METAMORPHIC ROCKS, Continued

The Rocks Produced by Contact Metamorphism. Hydrothermally Altered Rocks

CONTACT ROCKS

Contact action results in a great variety of rocks, depending not only on the original, but on the forces and agents involved. Many of the rocks are not distinguishable from those produced by regional metamorphism, namely, slates, schists, gneisses, quartzites, and marbles. There is little doubt that these contact rocks were subject to deforming stresses as well as heat from the intruding magma. A general survey of districts in which contact rocks have been described [1] indicates that very few basaltic or gabbroic magmas are intruded with any pervasive deformation of their walls, but that probably over three-fourths of the granite batholiths deform their walls producing schists.

Since there are many more large bodies of granite than of gabbro the common contact rocks are schists and injection gneisses. The gradation or transition from igneous rock through gneisses to schists has already been described (pages 233 and 236), and the gneisses may be considered contact rocks, but here the contact effects grade into regional effects so that it is difficult to distinguish them. The schists may be derived from either clay sediments or igneous originals. The knotted slates in contact zones have been noted (pages 224 and 225).

The sandstones and limestones are changed by contact action to quartzites and marbles in most respects analogous to those resulting from regional metamorphism. Pure limestone may form

[1] F. F. Grout: *Contact Metamorphism of the Slates of Minnesota by Granite and by Gabbro Magmas.* Bulletin of the Geological Society of America, volume 44, pages 989–1040, 1933.

wide zones of marble, commonly whiter than the original gray limestone. Locally near the igneous rock, the marbles may receive abundant additions and form garnet zones and other silicate rocks (pages 218 to 220). Andradite, epidote, diopside, amphiboles, and vesuvianite are especially characteristic. Near St. John, New Brunswick, for example, granite has penetrated an ancient limestone and developed a garnet zone with some pyroxene. A series of such contacts can be found along the mountains south from New Brunswick to New Jersey or farther. In western states there are important copper ores in such contact zones. Thus in the Seven Devils district, in western Idaho, bornite occurs between diorite and white marble, and is mixed with epidote and garnet as in most contact limestones. Professor Kemp has described a similar contact at Tamaulipas, Mexico. A very carefully studied contact deposit is that at Bingham, Utah, in which a sandy limestone was the original sediment. A question arose as to whether the silicates in the metamorphic rock resulted from the reaction of original sand with the lime. Winchell by microscopic study found that the altered rock had sand grains of about the same size and abundance as the original sediment,[2] indicating that the silicates resulted from the reaction of calcite with siliceous magmatic emanations rather than with sand.

Abroad, the region around Christiania in Norway is a classic ground for these phenomena, and a great contact of diorite on Triassic limestone in the Tyrolese Alps has produced characteristic zones on a large scale. The lava flows and ejected bombs of Vesuvius include some limestone fragments from underground wall rocks, and they exhibit zones somewhat like the larger occurrences. Vesuvianite, in fact, received its name from this association.

Nearly all these contact rocks in marble are bunchy local masses not over a few hundred feet across, contrasting sharply with the extensive areas of regionally metamorphic rocks.

The effects of basic magmas on shales, lava flows, and a variety of fine-grained rocks are notably different from those of most

[2] A. N. Winchell: *Petrographic Studies of Limestone Alteration at Bingham.* American Institute of Mining and Metallurgical Engineers, Trans., volume 70, page 884, 1924.

granites, though a few granite intrusives, lacking the stresses that are involved in making schists and gneisses, give results resembling those near gabbros. The rocks in such circumstances recrystallize with a variety of minerals all tending to grow at the same time, and with no stress to orient them or give a rock cleavage. The result is a *hornfels*.

The term hornfels is used by some for a cherty-looking silicified shale produced by contact action.

Most hornfels is a contact rock with "sugary" texture, grains about the size of those in granulated sugar. More technically the texture is granulitic (or decussate or finely granoblastic) rather finer than granitoid, and without schistosity. If such contact action attacks a schist, that rock loses its schistosity.

The hornfelses are derived from a great variety of original rocks and may receive additions as emanations from a variety of magmas. They have therefore a very large number of mineralogic varieties, most of them named by prefixing some mineral term or terms to the name hornfels. The minerals, however, are so fine that few are identified without a microscope. Most hornfelses are gray, and have feldspars, biotite, and other mafic minerals along with the characteristic metamorphic minerals. Texturally most hornfels is even-grained but there are some rocks with sugary groundmass and por-

FIG. 91.—Hornfels with porphyroblasts of andalusite. Contact of Bushveld norite, South Africa.

phyroblasts of cordierite, andalusite, or others (Fig. 91). Many hornfelses are derived from clays because clays are by far the most abundant of sediments. It must therefore be expected that the hornfels minerals include aluminous silicates and even spinel and corundum.

Contact action may show a series of zones of different intensities of effect. These can be best understood by a description of certain classic localities.

At a famous American locality in the Crawford Notch of the White Mountains, on the slopes of Mt. Willard and not far from the Crawford House, the granite has penetrated an argillitic mica schist. G. W. Hawes in 1881 established the following seven zones: 1. The argillitic mica schist (chloritic); 2. Mica schist (biotitic); 3. Tourmaline hornfels; 4. Tourmaline veinstone (a small contact band, rich in tourmaline); 5. Mixed schists and granite; 6. Granite porphyry (biotitic); 7. Granite (hornblendic). This is one of the most complete and best-exposed contacts known.[3] The succession illustrates the alteration of chlorite to biotite by the granite, and then near the contact the development of tourmaline from the boracic and fluoric emanations from granite magma.

On the southeast corner of Conanicut Island, in Narragansett Bay, granite has penetrated Carboniferous shales, as described by L. V. Pirsson,[4] and has baked them to compact hornfels near the contact. The shales grade into knotted slate in which are minute porphyroblasts, but closer to the granite the rock is a hornfels.

The contact effects next to gabbros may show a similar series of spotted slates and hornfelses and mixed rocks. North of the Duluth gabbro, the first change noted in the slates is a slightly coarser grain and added tourmaline; closer to the gabbro the hornfels is recrystallized to minerals corresponding to those in the gabbro; and there is locally a zone of mixed hornfels and gabbro.

Of the remaining members of the grand division of the sedimentary rocks, the carbonaceous rocks are the principal ones deserving mention. Coal seams of the normal bituminous variety have been cut in not a few places by igneous dikes, and display in a marked degree the effects of metamorphism. The volatile hydrocarbons have been driven off and the coal has become an impure coke, where diabase dikes cut the Triassic coal basins of Virginia and North Carolina, and where basalt intrusions cut the coal beds near Puget Sound. In Colorado and New Mexico, the near approach of an igneous sheet has brought about the formation of

[3] Hawes' paper is in the American Journal of Science, volume 21, pages 21–32, 1881.

[4] L. V. Pirsson: *On the Geology and Petrography of Conanicut Island, R. I.* American Journal of Science, volume 46, page 363, 1893.

anthracite, and in fact all grades of coal can be detected from rich bituminous to hard anthracite, according to the nearness of the dike or laccolith. In Mexico coal near an igneous intrusion has been turned to commercial graphite.

Reference may also be made to the hills of soft magnetite, near Cornwall, Pa., where a great dike of diabase has apparently caused the replacement of calcareous shales with pyritous magnetite.

Where intrusions cut other igneous or metamorphic rocks the effects are much less apparent, because the walls are resistant to change, being themselves already crystalline.

Remarkable cases of contact metamorphism are, however, certainly caused by pegmatitic dikes. As rocks they are not especially abundant, although of great scientific interest. Some intrusions have emitted copious emanations of fluorine and boron in conjunction with superheated steam. These vigorous reagents have attacked the wall rocks, when originally formed of crystalline silicates, making them porous and cellular from the destruction of feldspars, and have often caused the crystallization of quartz, tourmaline, topaz, micas, fluorite, apatite, cassiterite and other characteristic minerals, some of which are of economic importance. Such metamorphic products when essentially consisting of quartz and mica are called *greisen*. *Tourmaline granites* likewise result. It is not to be overlooked, however, that mineralizers have also played a large part in the cases earlier cited, nor should the remark be omitted in conclusion that they and similar agents have been of very great importance in the formation of ores.

THE HYDROTHERMALLY ALTERED ROCKS

Mineral veins are deposited largely by hot waters and the same waters that fill fractures with minerals they carried in solution, attack the minerals of their walls producing a characteristic group of secondary minerals. These are listed in the second column of Table VIII, page 131, rather than separately here, to emphasize the fact that not all kinds of alteration are to be called weathering. The most common are chlorite, epidote, sericite, calcite, pyrite, and zeolites, with talc and serpentine fairly common. These with calcite and quartz which are almost universal, should suggest to any student of rocks that hot waters have been active. To be sure hot waters may be active and produce these minerals in regional and contact metamorphism also, but these minerals are not really characteristic of contact rocks or the deeper-seated regional metamorphic rocks. The shallow or moderate-temperature regional products are schists, and the hydrothermal rocks in the walls of veins are only rarely and accidentally schists. The hydrothermal rocks therefore constitute a distinguishable though very small group.

The chief varieties of hydrothermal rock are *propylite,* formed by hot water attack on aphanites of the andesite clan, and the similar *greenstones* derived from basalts. The mafic minerals have turned to green chlorite, serpentine, epidote and others, giving the rocks a noteworthy green color, but in the absence of deforming stress they are not green schists.

Further alteration may replace the green silicates with sericite, and sericite forms by similar action on the more acidic igneous rocks. We thus commonly consider propylitization an early stage and sericitization a more advanced stage of hydrothermal attack. A final stage may replace both by quartz or by carbonate, and sulphide ores.

Some other rocks may be attributed to similar hot water effects, but cannot be sharply distinguished from contact or autometamorphic effects; *greisen* and tourmaline granite are considered by some as hydrothermal, and by others (page 247) as contact rocks formed at temperatures supposed to be higher than those of hot waters.

The mineralogic effects have been studied by Butler,[5] who suggests an extension of Bowen's reaction series (page 38) beyond the usual igneous and deuteric reactions, without a break, into hydrothermal reactions, with possibly some overlap. Chlorite and sericite probably indicate that the really igneous stage is past and hydrothermal reaction has begun.

The chemical effects on igneous rocks have been summarized by Schwartz.[6]

[5] B. S. Butler: *Influence of Replaced Rock on Replacement Minerals Associated with Ore Deposits.* Economic Geology, volume 27, page 4, 1932.

[6] G. M. Schwartz: *Hydrothermal Alteration of Igneous Rock.* Bull. Geological Society of America, volume 50, pages 181–238, 1939.

CHAPTER XII

SUMMARIES OF METAMORPHIC ROCKS

The Determination of Metamorphic Rocks

Typical gneiss, schist, slate, quartzite, and marble are recognized at sight by those who have seen samples before. Rare and intermediate varieties, and the hornfelses and hydrothermal rocks need careful attention, and it may be necessary to refer some to workers with the microscope.

The distinction of gneissoid igneous rocks from gneisses of later deformation and from injection gneisses is very difficult. In the field the igneous rocks that are gneissoid commonly have associated late pegmatites and aplites which are not gneissic, and these serve to indicate a lack of metamorphism. In the laboratory where such associated dikes are not seen, certain differences are suggestive but not really dependable. Igneous flow may orient hornblende and other elongate minerals without in any way deforming the crystals. If on the contrary the crystals are pinched into augen or smeared into streaks it is probable that they resulted from later metamorphism. See Fig. 18. The injection gneisses commonly show almost massive bands alternating with schist.

The dividing line between schist and gneiss is arbitrary and expert students may disagree. Where feldspar is visible in hand specimens, the rocks are best classified as gneisses. The distinction of limestone and marble is equally arbitrary, but the deformation of fossils is a good guide, if they can be seen. Sandstones break around the sand grains and quartzites break as easily across the grains as around them. The magnesian rocks are characterized by a soapy feel which aids in their recognition. A spotted medium-grained ophicalcite may look in hand specimen much like a diorite, but the calcite and serpentine are softer than the plagioclase and hornblende.

To distinguish a cherty-looking hornfels from a true chert, it is likely that the hornfels will have a color banding inherited from the sedimentary lamination of the shale original.

To distinguish metamorphic from igneous textures is especially difficult where large crystals lie in a finer groundmass.

PHENOCRYSTS	METACRYSTS, OR PORPHYROBLASTS
Minerals: quartz, feldspars, hornblende, augite, olivine, biotite. May be corroded.	**Minerals:** garnet, staurolite, ottrelite, kyanite, andalusite, cordierite, pyrite; less commonly biotite, hornblende, feldspars, quartz, magnetite, tourmaline.
Groundmass: glass, felsite, basalt, or even amygdaloid.	**Groundmass:** slate, or schist.

If the groundmass has flow structure or orientation, transgressed by crystal, it is a metacryst. If the flow bends around a crystal, that is oriented in the direction of flow, the crystal is probably a phenocryst.

Quartzites may closely resemble felsites, especially if the quartzite is arkosic. Commonly the quartzite is a little harder, $H = 7$, whereas the felsite $H = 6$. There is considerable tendency for quartzite to be more vitreous in luster and felsite to be more dull. Look for bedding in quartzite, in contrast to contorted flow layers, dikes and apophyses in felsite. Most felsites have scattered grains of feldspar as phenocrysts, in contrast to small feldspars in a sand.

When dealing with complex metamorphic districts, the student must expect to find contradictory evidences, for a long series of events may have left in the rock a series of minerals and structures formed under a variety of different conditions.

Degrees and Intensities of Metamorphism

Quite aside from the grade of metamorphism (page 231) we find that the *amounts of change* in original structures, textures, and minerals are very different for different metamorphic rocks. In general we may estimate that in regional metamorphism (which produces far the largest volume of metamorphic rocks) a very large body of rocks may be slightly changed at such moderate depths that erosion may later bring them to the surface; whereas, if rocks are to be largely changed from their original condition, they would have to be moved far from their conditions of original deposition and most of them would be so deeply buried that exposure at the surface would require long erosion. We conclude that in exposed metamorphic rocks there are many which are slightly changed and only a few that are intensely changed. From this we may at times draw conclusions as to origin, and the following table may prove suggestive.

EXAMPLES OF ABUNDANT RESULTS OF METAMORPHISM

Original rock	Common slight metamorphism	Extreme change
Clay, Shale, Slate	Phyllite, Biotite-schist	Gneiss
Granite	Granite-gneiss	{ Sericite-schist Mica-schist
Basalt	Propylite, Chlorite-schist	Hornblende-schist
Limestone Dolomite limestone	Marble	{ Silicate-carbonate-rock Soapstone Serpentine

The most important point to note in the table is that biotite-schist is a common product of clays and not so common from igneous rocks, and that chlorite-schist is more commonly derived from basic igneous rocks. It should be noted also that the change from granite to gneiss and schist is largely a granulation, whereas the change from slate to schist is a recrystallization; but in each series the slight effects are more common and widely exposed than the extreme effects.

The Compositions of Metamorphic Rocks

The metamorphism of igneous rocks to gneisses and schists makes little change in composition except that water and less commonly CO_2 are added. On the other hand, in the metamorphism of clays, water is lost, and in that of limestones CO_2 is lost. In general a knowledge of these relatively slight changes from original rocks gives the student sufficient information as to the composition of metamorphic rocks, if he has in mind the compositions of igneous and sedimentary rocks.

In contact and hydrothermal metamorphism greater changes occur, but the rocks that are greatly changed are very local and of small volume.

The chemical reactions involved in replacement of one mineral by another were studied and reported in full detail by Van Hise but his estimates of volume changes are very uncertain. See Chapter XIII, Problem 12 (pages 271-2).

It is perhaps noteworthy that some altered dolomite limestones lose most of their calcium, becoming hydrous magnesian silicates, serpentine, and talc rocks. Also, that the talc with over 60% silica can be formed by adding silica to (or leaching magnesia from) serpentine with less than 45% silica.

Density

The *density* of metamorphic rocks in the deep zone tends to become greater than that of an igneous rock; as for example when a basalt (3.00) becomes an eclogite (3.50). On the other hand, rocks metamorphosed at small depths are heavier than sediments but lighter than the igneous rocks most closely related to them.

The Original of a Metamorphic Rock

In a large proportion of metamorphic rock study, it is more difficult to tell what the rock was originally than to name it in its present state. The criteria of original rock are almost as difficult in schists as in weathered residues (page 126).

The criteria of igneous or sedimentary origin are commonly the field relations. The gradation of a metamorphic rock into a sediment or igneous rock is good evidence. The preservation of original structures and textures is conclusive if they are clearly identified. Ellipsoids, diabases, amygdaloids, transgressing dikes, or pegmatites indicate igneous originals; and bedding, fossils, pebbles, and ripple marks indicate sediments. Phenocrysts are less definite signs of igneous originals because porphyroblasts of the same minerals may be added to sediments.

The rocks commonly expected from clays, granites, and basalts are listed on page 251, and furnish very suggestive ideas of origin.

Certain minerals and mineral proportions are almost equally significant. A rock almost wholly feldspar, or almost wholly olivine, is probably of igneous origin; one almost wholly quartz, or calcite, or sillimanite, or garnet is probably of sedimentary origin. Graphite is mostly derived from a sediment. The origin of a talc schist is estimated from its association—from dunite if chromite is associated, but from sediment if dolomite is associated.

The chemical criteria of sedimentary origin are (1) more magnesia than lime, (2) more potash than soda, (3) more ferric than ferrous oxide, (4) molecular ratio of alumina to the sum of soda, potash, and lime is greater than one, (5) silica in percentages greater than 80. These several criteria are dependable only in one way. If the characteristic ratios of sediments (page 193) are found in altered rocks, they indicate very strongly a derivation from original sediments; if those characters are not found, and the analysis looks like that of an igneous rock, perhaps 2/3 of the originals were igneous, but the rest were sediments which, either originally or by metamorphic alterations, have chemical ratios characteristic of igneous rocks. This criterion of igneous origin is so weak, therefore, that other evidences should be sought (see below).

None of these criteria is wholly satisfactory because the distinction of the two great classes, igneous and sedimentary, is not sharp. The tuffs are gradational to tuffaceous sediments; and igneous rocks may be half weathered to clay before metamorphism. There is need of a good deal of discretion and judgment in the study of origin and interpretation of schists. It is chiefly because the original cannot always be recognized that the metamorphic class of rocks was separated.

Economic Interest in Metamorphic Rocks.—The economic features of metamorphic rocks are less important than those of sediments and igneous rocks. As building materials quartzite, marble, serpentinite, and gneiss are harder and in several respects fully as good as the rocks before metamorphism; slates for roofing and other uses are of no value until considerably metamorphosed.

Common quartzite is more difficult to quarry and trim into blocks than sandstone, and many schists are too easily cleaved for use in buildings.

Certain minerals such as garnet for an abrasive, and talc, asbestos, corundum, magnesite, and graphite are derived chiefly from metamorphic rocks, and are products of metamorphic action. Emery is an abrasive, a mixture of corundum and magnetite, with more or less silicate and secondary minerals. Some is of igneous origin but most emery occurs in aluminous schists or crystalline limestone.

Among the ores, iron is mined largely from leached metamorphic rocks; but few ore deposits are much improved by dynamic metamorphism. Contact metamorphic ores are important in a few places but make a small proportion of metallic ores in general. Many veins of ore are associated with hydrothermally metamorphosed rocks, so that this type of metamorphism acquires a good deal of economic interest.

CHAPTER XIII

CALCULATIONS IN ROCK STUDY

The data of rock study range widely in accuracy from the crude estimates of mineral proportions in a hand specimen to the most detailed chemical and physical tests. Based on the data are a variety of calculations with which the student should be familiar. Dr. Arthur Holmes has compiled a large number of methods, with examples, in his book, *Petrographic Methods and Calculations*, published in 1921.

If a problem depends on calculations from more or less inaccurate data, the student should be careful to know the limits of accuracy expected and keep track of the percentage of error through the calculation because wholly misleading conclusions might be reached if calculated values are used without attention to the probable errors.[1]

PROBLEM 1. — To estimate the approximate chemical analyses of igneous rocks.

Method: For each mineral put down as good an estimate of an analysis as available, commonly an average, or an analysis of that mineral from a similar rock. Below these analyses make another table as follows: each item in the analysis of mineral A is multiplied by the percentage (by weight) of mineral A in this rock. Similarly each item in the analysis of mineral B is multiplied by the percentage of mineral B, and so on for each of the minerals. When all are tabulated the figures in this second table are added to give the percentages of the several oxides in the rock.

The results may be very good when the proportions of minerals and their compositions are closely determined, but even a rough estimate may have some value.

In Chapter III the phanerites of each clan were described as having certain average mineral percentages. From these and the

[1] F. F. Grout: *The Use of Calculations in Petrology.* Journal of Geology, volume 34, pages 512–558, 1926.

mineral data of Chapter I, it is possible to estimate roughly the chemical analyses of the common rocks of each clan. Making these estimates is so much easier than memorizing the range of analytical data that two examples are here given and the student should try a number of others to fix the method in mind:

(A) Given a granite with 40% orthoclase, 30% plagioclase, 20% quartz, and 10% biotite (slightly less orthoclase than indicated on page 58), what is its approximate chemical analysis?

The analyses of minerals may be roughly estimated as a rule without great errors in the final figures. Start with the data on pages 18 and 19. After recording the silica percentage characteristic of trisilicate, metasilicate or orthosilicate, the remainder of the mineral composition may be distributed among the other oxides known to be in that mineral.

CALCULATION OF APPROXIMATE ANALYSIS OF GRANITE

	SiO_2	Al_2O_3	FeO	Fe_2O_3	MgO	CaO	Na_2O	K_2O	H_2O
Orthoclase	65	17.5						17.5	
Plagioclase *	55	22.5				11.25	11.25		
Quartz	100								
Biotite	45	9.2—	9.2—	9.2—	9.2—			9.2—	9.2—

To make up the whole rock:

	SiO_2	Al_2O_3	FeO	Fe_2O_3	MgO	CaO	Na_2O	K_2O	H_2O
40% orthoclase adds	26.00	7.00						7.00	
30% plagioclase adds	16.50	6.75				3.37	3.38		
20% quartz adds	20.00								
10% biotite adds	4.50	.92	.92	.92	.92			.92	.92
Result	67.00	14.67	.92	.92	.92	3.37	3.38	7.92	.92

* Note that plagioclase is a mixture of two silicates, one of sodium and aluminum, and the other of calcium and aluminum; so that alumina is in double the amount of soda or lime.

The result differs from the average of granites on page 108 chiefly in having more potash and less soda. Many granites do contain more sodic feldspar than this one, but a few are more potassic even than this. It is true, however, that the method of distributing oxides other than silica in orthoclase assigns a little too much to potash—many of the "potash feldspars" have some soda (Fig. 2).

(B) Given an average gabbro containing 60% of plagioclase and 40% augite (see page 86); what is its approximate analysis? As compared with the analysis on page 107 this has too much silica and soda and not enough potash and water. That is partly because gabbros may contain some potash feldspar, none of which is included in the data of this problem.

CALCULATION OF APPROXIMATE ANALYSIS OF GABBRO

	SiO$_2$	Al$_2$O$_3$	FeO	Fe$_2$O$_3$	MgO	CaO	Na$_2$O	K$_2$O	H$_2$O
Plagioclase	55	22.50				11.25	11.25	+	
Augite	55	9.00	9.00	9.00	9.00	9.00	+		+

To make up the whole rock:

	SiO$_2$	Al$_2$O$_3$	FeO	Fe$_2$O$_3$	MgO	CaO	Na$_2$O	K$_2$O	H$_2$O
60% plagioclase adds	33.00	13.50				6.75	6.75	+	
40% augite adds	22.00	3.60	3.60	3.60	3.60	3.60	+		+
Total	55.00	17.10	3.60	3.60	3.60	10.35	6.75	+	+

Both of these examples give approximations well within the range of analyses in any large compilation of analyses for the clans selected. The method is useful, moreover, not only for averages given in the descriptions of clans, but even more for selected rocks the student may encounter. In a particular hand specimen he may estimate the percentages of minerals and calculate the *approximate analysis of that specimen.*

Atomic and Molecular Proportions

A general familiarity with chemical calculations serves many purposes in rock study; but many students have been assigned and actually made complex calculations according to rule, without any understanding of the process. It is well to begin with a simple example and advance to the more complex ones.

PROBLEM 2. — A chemist reports the composition of a sulphide as 47 ± 1 per cent Fe and 53 ± 1 per cent S. What is the probable formula of the mineral? The atomic weights are: Fe $=$ 55.84, and S $=$ 32.064. The errors in chemical data are about 2 per cent of the amounts reported, so that the data need not be elaborated farther than to keep three significant figures.

The algebraic rule is to let x be the number of atoms of sulphur for each iron atom. Then

$$\frac{55.8}{32.0x} = \frac{47 \pm 1}{53 \pm 1} \quad \text{and} \quad x = 1.96 \pm 4.$$

The arithmetical rule is more generally used: divide the percentage by the atomic weights, to get the atomic ratios.

$$\frac{47 \pm 1}{55.8} \text{ atoms of Fe combine with } \frac{53 \pm 1}{32.0} \text{ atoms of S}$$

.84   atoms of Fe combine with 1.65 ± 3 atoms of S.

The formula should be FeS_2, pending more accurate chemical work.

The next stage in the complexity of such calculations involves the common custom of reporting rock analyses in terms of oxides rather than elements. Instead of determining atomic ratios in a feldspar, for example, one estimates molecular ratios of K_2O, Al_2O_3, SiO_2 etc., as if feldspars were made up of oxides. The fallacy of the idea should not mislead anyone, and the convenience of the method makes it widely used.

PROBLEM 3. — Suppose a feldspar analysis is given in the usual form, stating percentages of oxides; what are the molecular proportions of the oxides in the feldspar? The rule is analogous to the preceding: divide the percentage of each oxide by the molecular weight of that oxide (page 261), and the quotients are proportional to the numbers of molecules present. Since the quotients are commonly decimal fractions, it is customary to multiply each by 1,000 to get whole numbers for discussion, the proportions not being changed by such increase. Tables have been prepared to save the work of calculating (see problem 6).

PROBLEM 4. — To find how many constituent molecules enter into an isomorphous mineral.

Given the analyses and molecular ratios of the preceding problem, how many molecules of each component are present, and what percentage of each is present? For convenience the components calculated are the pure chemical compounds, and these are given mineral names, though no one should be misled into thinking that the common specimens of natural minerals consist of a pure compound. The three main divisions of the process are: (1) calculation of molecular proportions, as in the preceding problem; (2) assignment of the molecules to simple component minerals; and (3) calculation of the ratio between them; the proportion by weight can also be calculated.

It is noteworthy that not only are the molecular ratios of oxides found in tables, but the last step in the process, that of calculating component minerals from their molecular ratios, is rapidly taken by the use of other tables (see problem 6).

An olivine with a little augite impurity, analyzed by E. S. Dana, gave the following: [2]

	Analysis	Molecular Ratio	Augite Impurity	Olivine
SiO_2	38.85%	.647	−.050	.597
FeO	28.07%	.389	−.012	.377
MnO	1.24%	.017	—	.017
MgO	30.62%	.765	−.013	.752
CaO	1.43%	.025	−.025	
Al_2O_3	Trace			
	100.21			

The remainder after deducting a little augite has the olivine ratio $2RO \cdot SiO_2$. Disregarding manganese the olivine is approximately one Fe_2SiO_4 to two Mg_2SiO_4.

PROBLEM 5.— To find the molecular ratios of oxides in a rock. Use the same method as outlined for ratios in a mineral (problem 3). The same tables save one from the detail of arithmetical work.

PROBLEM 6.— To calculate the "standard" minerals (or norm) from an analysis. This calculation and some others are complex, and perhaps better left for advanced courses, but a few references and comments are given for those who are prepared.

[2] L. V. Pirsson: *Petrography of Tripyramid Mountain.* American Journal of Science, volume 31, page 417, 1911.

For simplicity in calculation, Cross, Iddings, Pirsson and Washington,[3] in 1903 suggested some simple "standard" or "normative" minerals such that all ordinary constituents of igneous rocks could be calculated to these; and the proportions of such minerals and oxides were used to classify the rocks in a new system commonly known as the C. I. P. W. system from the initials of the names of the authors. The system of classification is not as much used as the calculation to a hypothetical mineral analysis—the "norm."

Tables for shortening the calculations are published in a number of places besides in the original C. I. P. W. report.[4]

It should be noted that in the norm and in most calculations the "molecules" chosen for albite and orthoclase are double the mineralogic formulas—$Na_2O \cdot Al_2O_3 \cdot 6SiO_2$ for albite and $K_2O \cdot Al_2O_3 \cdot 6SiO_2$ for orthoclase.

While the calculations are much shortened by the use of tables, the tables are not really necessary. A slide rule and a short table of mineral analyses may serve.[5]

Several other calculations, some with classification schemes and some with graphic representation of results, have been proposed. Johannsen has compiled them in one volume, to which the student may refer.[6]

PROBLEM 7.—To calculate from an analysis, the amounts of actual known minerals in an igneous rock, the "mode." A simplified example from the work of Pirsson[7] will serve to show the method, the accuracy of which depends on the minerals and the estimates of their composition.

    [3] W. Cross, J. P. Iddings, L. V. Pirsson, and H. S. Washington: *Quantitative Classification of Igneous Rocks.* 1903.

    [4] A. Johannsen: *A Descriptive Petrography of the Igneous Rocks;* Volume I, 1931, pages 238–253. His method of calculation is simplest. H. S. Washington: *Chemical Analyses of Igneous Rocks;* U. S. Geological Survey, Professional Paper 99, pages 1151–1180, 1917. A Holmes: *Petrographic Methods and Calculations;* 1921, pages 495–506.

    [5] W. J. Mead: *Some Geologic Short-cuts;* Economic Geology, volume 7, pp. 136–144, 1912. J. H. Hance: *Use of the Slide Rule in Computation of Rock Analyses;* Journal of Geology, volume 23, pages 560–568, 1915.

    [6] Op. cit., volume I, pages 68–158.

    [7] L. V. Pirsson: *Petrography of the Igneous Rocks of the Little Belt Mountains, Montana.* U. S. Geol. Survey, 20th Ann. Report III, pages 466–7, 1900.

TABLE XI
MOLECULAR WEIGHTS

Oxide	Formula	Molecular weight
Silica	SiO_2	60
Alumina	Al_2O_3	102
Ferric oxide	Fe_2O_3	160
Ferrous oxide	FeO	72
Magnesia	MgO	40
Lime	CaO	56
Soda	Na_2O	62
Potash	K_2O	94
Titanium dioxide	TiO_2	80
Phosphoric oxide	P_2O_5	142
Manganous oxide	MnO	71
Carbon dioxide	CO_2	44
Sulphur trioxide	SO_3	80

Mineral	Formula	Molecular weight
Quartz	SiO_2	60
* Orthoclase	$K_2O \cdot Al_2O_3 \cdot 6SiO_2$	556
* Albite	$Na_2O \cdot Al_2O_3 \cdot 6SiO_2$	524
Anorthite	$CaO \cdot Al_2O_3 \cdot 2SiO_2$	278
Nepheline	$Na_2O \cdot Al_2O_3 \cdot 2SiO_2$	284
Leucite	$K_2O \cdot Al_2O_3 \cdot 4SiO_2$	436
Wollastonite	$CaO \cdot SiO_2$	116
Enstatite	$MgO \cdot SiO_2$	100
Iron metasilicate	$FeO \cdot SiO_2$	132
Olivine		
Forsterite	$2MgO \cdot SiO_2$	140
Fayalite	$2FeO \cdot SiO_2$	204
Magnetite	$FeO \cdot Fe_2O_3$	232
Ilmenite	$FeO \cdot TiO_2$	152
Apatite	$9CaO \cdot 3P_2O_5 \cdot CaF_2$	1008
Biotite		
Mg extreme = phlogopite	$KMg_3(AlSi_3O_{10})(OH)_2$	417
Fe extreme	$KFe_3(AlSi_3O_{10})(OH)_2$	512
Muscovite	$KAl_2(AlSi_3O_{10})(OH)_2$	398
Augite	Complex, see page 15	Variable
Hornblende	Complex, see page 15	Variable

* This mineral formula is double the mineralogical formula.

Minor constituents are here omitted, but the calculation is complex enough without them, since it is based on rough estimates for several isomorphous mixtures. Following the analysis are given the molecular ratios, found as in problems 3 and 5. The following minerals were observed in thin sections, and the compositions used are simplified as shown.

Orthoclase, K_2O, Al_2O_3, $6SiO_2$

Plagioclase $\begin{cases} \text{Albite, } Na_2O, Al_2O_3, 6SiO_2 \\ \text{Anorthite, } CaO, Al_2O_3, 2SiO_2 \end{cases}$

Hornblende $\begin{cases} MgO, SiO_2 \\ CaO, SiO_2 \\ FeO, SiO_2 \end{cases}$

Magnetite, Fe_2O_3, FeO

Quartz, SiO_2

From an inspection of these formulas, it is evident that all the K_2O is in the orthoclase; all the Na_2O is in the albite; all the remaining Al_2O_3 is in the anorthite and requires an equivalent number of molecules of CaO. The remaining CaO is in the hornblende. All the MgO is in the hornblende. All the Fe_2O_3 is in the magnetite and an equivalent number of molecules of FeO are required by it. The remainder of the FeO is in the hornblende. The excess of SiO_2 then remains for the quartz.

Analysis	Per Cent	Molecular Ratio	Orth.	Albite	Anorth.	Mag.	Hornbl.	Quartz
SiO_2	64.64	1.077	.318	.426	.070		.061	.202
Al_2O_3	16.27	.159	.053	.071	.035			
Fe_2O_3	2.42	.015				.015		
FeO	1.58	.022				.015	.007	
MgO	1.27	.032					.032	
CaO	2.65	.047			.035		.022	
Na_2O	4.39	.071		.071				
K_2O	4.98	.053	.053					
Others	1.90							
	100.10							

In order to turn these results into percentages of the minerals in the rock multiply the several molecular proportions by the respective molecular weights (page 261).

Analysis in Mineral terms

.015 mol. Fe_3O_4		Magnetite =	3.48%
.007 mol. $FeSiO_3$ = .92			
.032 mol. $MgSiO_3$ = 3.20	Hornblende =	6.67%
.022 mol. $CaSiO_3$ = 2.55			
.035 mol. $CaAl_2Si_2O_8$	Anorthite =	9.73%
.071 mol. $(NaAlSi_3O_8)_2$	Albite	=	37.20%
.053 mol. $(KAlSi_3O_8)_2$	Orthoclase	=	29.47%
.202 mol. SiO_2	Quartz	=	12.12%
Others as per analysis		=	1.90%

100.57%

In the actual performance of these calculations, it is not always possible to estimate the composition of the minerals as in this simplified example. For example where biotite and orthoclase occur in a rock one cannot say how potash and alumina should be divided between them. Where iron and magnesium occur in three or four minerals the difficulty is still greater. Johannsen has shown by an example that calculation without knowledge of the actual minerals and some idea of their compositions may be misleading and not prove anything.[8] A rock supposed to have 18.52% nephelite, may have none at all. Evidently the method should be used only with caution.

Other Problems

PROBLEM 8. — Many petrologists regard granite as a differentiation product of basaltic magma, and the problem is: How much average granite can be derived from average basalt without making the differentiated fractions abnormal?

The method is to take a definite bulk of basalt of average analysis and subtract average granite noting whether the residue is similar to any rock. This involves "successive approximations."

It is evident from a simple inspection of columns I and II of Table XII, that not over three parts of basalt are needed to supply

[8] A. Johannsen: Op. cit., volume II, page 252.

enough of each constituent so that one part of granite could be produced. The calculation then is a basis for deductive reasoning. Assume that one part of granite is separated from three parts of basalt, and test, by calculation, the consequences; in other words, see if the residue, or the other differentiate, has such a composition as might be expected. Column III is the result.

To judge whether column ﹡III is a reasonable composition it may be compared with any large compilation; but perhaps as good a test as any is a calculation of the "norm" (problem 6). The norm contains over 10 per cent nepheline. Since nepheline rocks are very much more rare than granites, it is unreasonable to assume that two parts of such nepheline rock are formed every time one part of granite is formed.

By supplying successively larger amounts of basalt until the removal of granite leaves a more likely rock, it is found that nine parts of basalt cannot furnish one part granite without producing a nepheline rock as residue; but ten parts of basalt will supply all the needed elements for granite and leave a residue that is not so peculiar as to create any doubt as to the probability of the process.

TABLE XII

BASALT AND GRANITE RELATIONS

	I Average Basalt	II Average Granite	III 1/2 (3 Basalt — 1 Granite)	IV 1/8 (9 Basalt — 1 Granite)	V 1/9 (10 Basalt — 1 Granite)
SiO_2	49.06	69.92	38.63	46.45	46.74
Al_2O_3	15.70	14.78	16.16	15.82	15.80
Fe_2O_3	5.38	1.62	7.26	5.85	5.80
FeO	6.37	1.67	8.72	6.96	6.90
MgO	6.17	.97	8.77	6.82	6.75
CaO	8.95	2.15	12.35	9.80	9.70
Na_2O	3.11	3.28	3.02	3.09	3.09
K_2O	1.52	4.07	.25	1.20	1.24
H_2O	1.62	.78	2.04	1.72	1.71
TiO_2	1.36	.39	1.85	1.48	1.47
P_2O_5	.45	.24	.55	.48	.47
MnO	.31	.13	.40	.33	.33
Normative nepheline	none	none	11.50	.28	none

In this case the residue is more like basalt than any other class of rocks.   In other words, if granite is to be produced from basaltic magma, so little granite will be formed from so much basalt that the residue will be but slightly changed in character.   As a maximum, one-tenth of an average basaltic magma may become granite.

PROBLEM 9.—To discover and diagram the relations between various sets of data on rocks.

Method 1: It is simple to diagram the results on two coordinates and see whether or not a curve can be drawn that gives an approximation to the points.   In this way W. O. George found a relation between the specific gravities of natural glasses and their silica contents (Fig. 92).   The average divergence of points from the curve indicates that the silica can usually be estimated within 4 per cent.

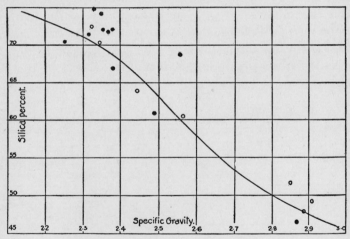

FIG. 92.— Curve relating specific gravity and silica content of natural glasses. (After W. O. George.)

Method 2: To diagram the differences in a series of igneous rocks.   The methods differ according to available data.   If the mineral proportions are known by measurement or by separations and weighings, a simple bar of definite length can be divided for each rock into a series of areas proportional to the amounts of the several minerals, not commonly too numerous; and a series of such bars shows the variety of rocks in the series (Fig. 40). The diagram is most instructive when the bars are arranged in order of field occurrence, but the data for this are not always available, and may not be easily shown in diagram.

More commonly data for the diagrams are chemical analyses. An example of the most valuable plot is Fig. 41, showing the differences in composition from a center of an intrusive at Magnet Cove, Arkansas, outward to the margin.[9]   Similar curves are shown by Broderick on the basis of distance of the specimens from the base of a thick lava flow.[10]

Where such data about locations are not available or cannot be plotted simply, the data can still be plotted and studied with productive results, by using the silica content as a base line and other oxides for the second coordinate.   This is the most common of all kinds of "variation diagram."   Fenner has given diagrams for several districts (Fig. 44), but they have been used and valued for many years (Fig. 43).

Method 3: To diagram the grade size distribution of a mechanical sediment or residue, two methods are in common use, the pyramid diagram or "histogram," and the cumulative diagram. The data needed are the weights of the several separates in a sieve analysis, or similar data from some other method of separation of grade sizes (page 268).   The student should be able to construct both kinds of diagram from a study of the following examples.   It is recommended that the standard grade sizes be plotted horizontally, the preferred scale being proportional to the logarithmic values (Figs. 93 and 94).

The common laboratory method makes use of a series of sieves and the report states the weight or per cent caught by each sieve. The "cumulative" data are derived from the weights of the sieve separates by adding to the weight of each successive separate, the sum of all those before.   In the table on page 268, for example, the cumulative value for 100-mesh is the sum of the 25 grams

[9] H. S. Washington: *The Foyaite-Ijolite Series of Magnet Cove.* Journal of Geology, volume 9, pp. 645–651, 1901.
[10] T. M. Broderick: *Differentiation in Lavas of the Michigan Keweenawan.* Bull. of the Geological Society of America, volume 46, pages 514 and 524, 1935.

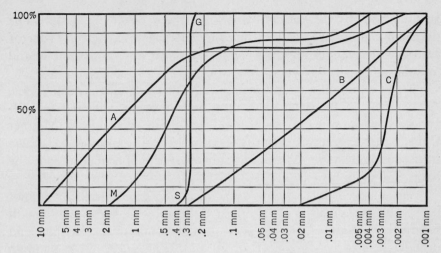

FIG. 93.—Cumulative curves of the mechanical composition of several sediments, on a semi-logarithmic scale. GS is a glass sand. MM is a foundry sand.

caught on the 100-mesh sieve and the 35, 15, 10, and 5 grams caught on coarser sieves, total 90 grams, or 90% of the original. Thus the cumulative value indicates what would be caught if only the one sieve were used.

In the cumulative curve the steeper parts indicate a considerable amount of a single size, and the horizontal parts indicate an absence of the grade corresponding to that part of the abscissa over which the horizontal part extends. Tyrrell notes that different curves indicate grade size distributions favorable for different economic purposes; such a curve as G S is favorable for glass-sand, and M M for foundry sand (Fig. 93).

DATA FOR TWO SANDS

Grade size	Sample G S	Sample M M
2—1 mm....................	—	14
1–1/2 mm....................	—	26
1/2–1/4 mm....................	100	28
1/4–1/8 mm....................		14
1/8–1/16 mm....................		4
1/16–1/32 mm....................		0
1/32–1/64 mm....................		1
1/64–1/128 mm....................		3
1/128–1/256 mm....................		9
Below 1/256 mm....................		1

Much of the work done before students of sediments generally adopted the standard scale of grade sizes (page 152) is reported by the mesh of available sieves. It is easily possible to transform the data to the standard. For example, given the following:

Data from Screen Analysis		Cumulative Percentages
10 to 20 mesh	5 grams	5
20 to 40 "	10 "	15
40 to 60 "	15 "	30
60 to 80 "	35 "	65
80 to 100 "	25 "	90
100 to 150 "	3 "	93
150 to 200 "	5 "	98
Below 200 "	2 "	100

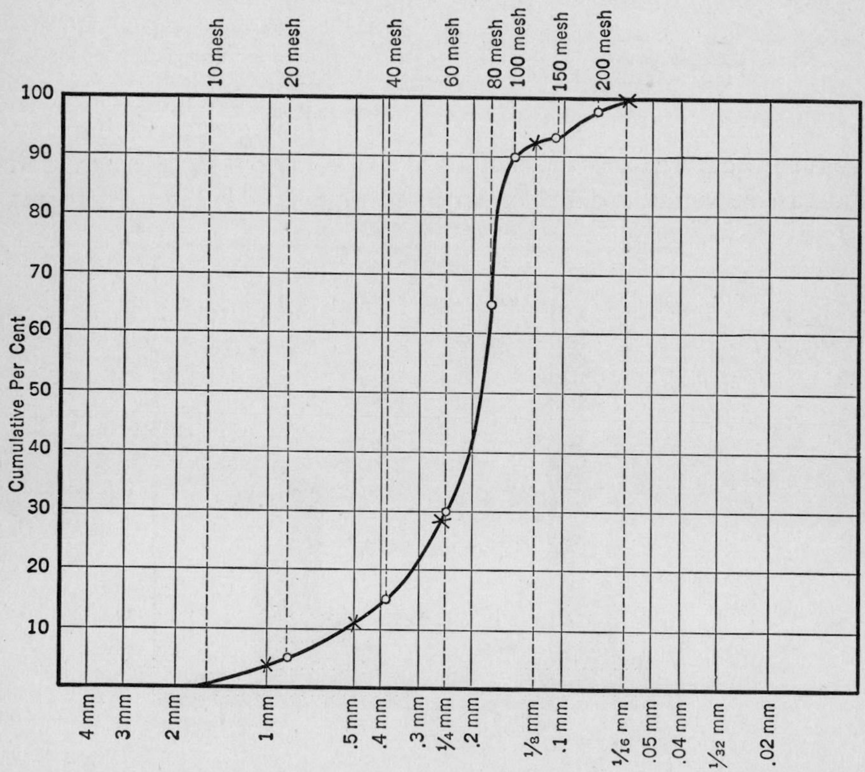

FIG. 94.— Cumulative curve of composition of a sediment, drawn from data on sieves at 20, 40, 60, 80, 100, 150 and 200-mesh. From the curve, it is possible to estimate data for a standard analysis in fractions of millimeters.

Plot on a logarithmic scale the sizes in millimeters of openings in the sieves used. Plot an ordinate at 20 mesh equal to the per cent of separate caught on 20-mesh sieve; plot at 40 mesh the "cumulative per cent" (what would be caught on 40-mesh sieve if no other sieves were used); and so on for the finer sieves. Draw a curve through such points. Then locate points on the curve (crosses in Fig. 94) which give the cumulative percentages on the approved millimeter scale, using as abscissas the division lines in the scale on page 152. In this particular problem the data become:

	Point on Cumulative Curve	Estimated Standard Screen Analysis
2 to 1 mm.	3.5%	3.5%
1 to 1/2 mm.	11. %	7.5%
1/2 to 1/4 mm.	29. %	18. %
1/4 to 1/8 mm.	92. %	63. %
1/8 to 1/16 mm.	99.+%	7. %
1/16 to 1/32 mm.	100. %	1. %

Note that the histogram based on common sieve mesh and that based on standard millimeter scale have notably different forms

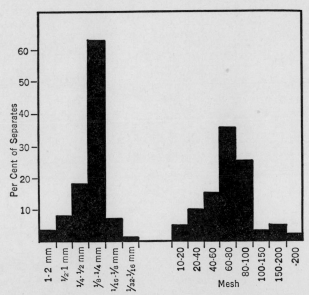

FIG. 95.—Histograms of a sand on different scales. (Compare the cumulative curve, Figure 94.)

(Fig. 95), though both give the same cumulative curve. For all reports, whether histograms or curves, it is best to base the graphic presentation on the standard grade size distribution.

PROBLEM 10.—A mineral or rock with pore spaces has a "bulk specific gravity" or "apparent specific gravity" less than it would have if there was no pore space, or if the specific gravity determination was made on a powder with pores eliminated. The relations are:

$$\text{Apparent specific gravity} = (\text{true specific gravity}) \times \frac{(100 - \% \text{ porosity})}{100}$$

$$\text{True specific gravity} = \frac{100 \text{ (apparent specific gravity)}}{(100 - \% \text{ porosity})}$$

$$\text{Per cent porosity} = 100 \frac{(\text{True specific gravity}) - (\text{apparent specific gravity})}{\text{True specific gravity}}$$

PROBLEM 11.—The "sixth power law" stated on page 133 needs mathematical expression in order to make it most serviceable. Other things being equal, the size of pebble carried is a constant times the sixth power of the velocity of the stream; $S = K(V)^6$.

If now we consider two streams with different velocities V_1 and V_2, the sizes S_1 and S_2 are proportional to the sixth powers of the two velocities, and the constant drops out.

$$\frac{S_1}{S_2} = \frac{K(V_1)^6}{K(V_2)^6} \qquad \frac{S_1}{S_2} = \frac{(V_1)^6}{(V_2)^6}$$

(A). Given a stream flowing 4 miles per hour rolling a quartz sphere 1 cubic millimeter; how large a quartz pebble will be rolled by a stream flowing 12 miles per hour?

$$\frac{S_1}{S_2} = \frac{(V_1)^6}{(V_2)^6} \qquad \frac{1 \text{ cu. mm.}}{S_2} = \frac{(4)^6}{(12)^6} = \frac{(1)^6}{(3)^6} = \frac{1}{729}$$

$$S_2 = 729 \text{ cu. mm. (Answer)}$$

(B). Given a stream flowing 6 miles per hour moving a cube ⅛ of a cubic inch; how fast a stream is needed to move a cube of 8 cubic inches?

$$\frac{S_1}{S_2} = \frac{(V_1)^6}{(V_2)^6} \qquad \frac{1/8}{8} = \frac{(6)^6}{(V_2)^6}.$$

$$1/8(V_2)^6 = 8(6)^6$$

$$(V_2)^6 = 64(6)^6 = (2)^6 \times (6)^6.$$

$$V_2 = 2 \times 6 = 12 \text{ m. p. h.} \quad \text{(Answer)}$$

The law may be stated in terms of dimensions instead of "sizes" (volumes or weights), for the sizes vary with the cubes of dimensions. In the last paragraph, for example, the size of the first pebble S_1 is a cube, the volume of which is ⅛ cubic inch. This is a cube ½ inch on each edge, and its volume S_1 is $(½)^3$. Similarly S_2 is $(2)^3$. If the ratio $(D_1)^3$ to $(D_2)^3$ is substituted for ratio S_1 to S_2, we have:

$$\frac{(D_1)^3}{(D_2)^3} = \frac{(V_1)^6}{(V_2)^6}, \quad \text{from which} \quad \frac{D_1}{D_2} = \frac{(V_1)^2}{(V_2)^2}$$

This formula serves when dimensions of the pebbles are given instead of volumes.

PROBLEM 12.—To calculate the volume change in the metamorphism of minerals.

Van Hise gives the following rule and examples.[11] *If the reaction is known in detail, the volume of the original compound is to the volume of the compound produced directly as their molecular weights and indirectly as their specific gravities.*

(A) Suppose that limestone, $2CaCO_3$, is replaced by dolomite, $CaMg(CO_3)_2$, molecule for molecule. The molecular weight of $2CaCO_3$ is 200, and its specific gravity 2.71. The molecular weight of $CaMg(CO_3)_2$ is 184.3, and its specific gravity 2.84. The formula is:

$$\frac{V_c}{V_d} = \frac{200}{184.3} \times \frac{2.84}{2.71} = \frac{100}{88},$$

or the volume of dolomite is about 88 per cent of that of calcite. Many dolomites may have 12 per cent of pore space.

The student should be warned, however, that the supposition stated in the problem is not based on any knowledge that dolomite is commonly formed by this reaction. Many replacements have material added and other materials removed without regard to

[11] C. R. Van Hise: *Treatise on Metamorphism.* U. S. Geol. Survey, Mon. 47, p. 209, 1904.

the amount of any particular element that was available to begin with.[12]

(B) Suppose calcite reacts with silica to form wollastonite, liberating CO_2 which escapes.

$$CaCO_3 + SiO_2 = CaSiO_3 + CO_2$$

The molecular weights are respectively 100, 60, and 116. Their specific gravities are respectively 2.71, 2.65, and 2.85.

$$\frac{V_c + V_s}{V_w} = \frac{\frac{100}{2.71} + \frac{60}{2.65}}{\frac{116}{2.85}} = \frac{100}{68},$$

or the volume of wollastonite is nearly 32 per cent less than that of calcite plus silica.

Barrell has shown that several such calculations are much modified by different assumptions as to the additions and losses of material.[13]

PROBLEM 13. — To calculate gains and losses in rock alteration, if analyses of the original and of the altered product are available. The problem is commonly a difficult one and has been given thorough discussion by Doctor Lindgren.[14] *The problem becomes definite only when we know that the volume has remained constant, or when we know that some constituent remains constant.*

CASE 1. *Constant Constituent.* — It has been shown in a number of examples of weathering that alumina was not appreciably dissolved.[15] A careful study of the effect of weathering on a granite gneiss from Morton, Minnesota, was made by Goldich.

[12] W. Lindgren: *Volume Changes in Metamorphism.* Journal of Geology, volume 26, page 549, 1918.

[13] J. Barrell: *Relation of Subjacent Igneous Invasion to Regional Metamorphism.* American Journal of Science, volume 1, pages 179–180, 1921.

[14] W. Lindgren: *Metasomatic Processes in Fissure Veins.* Trans. Amer. Inst. Mining Eng., volume 30, pages 579–692, 1900.

——: *Mineral Deposits.* 1913, Chapter XX.

[15] See, for example, remarks by C. K. Leith and W. J. Mead: *Metamorphic Geology.* 1915, page 83. There may be exceptions to this generalization, chiefly where soils are wet and contain abundant humus.

Method: This is shown by the following table, based on Goldich's analyses,[16] ignoring some minor constituents, and reduced to 100 per cent.

	Fresh rock. per cent	Average of 6 weathered samples. per cent	Grams per 100 grams fresh rock assuming Al_2O_3 constant	Losses and gains during weathering of 100 grams gneiss assuming Al_2O_3 constant
SiO_2	71.50	64.11	46.39	−25.11
Al_2O_3	14.61	20.19	14.61	0.00
Fe_2O_3	.69	2.72	1.97	+ 1.28
FeO	1.64	1.87	1.35	− .29
MgO	.77	.41	.30	− .47
CaO	2.08	.10	.07	− 2.01
Na_2O	3.84	.14	.10	− 3.74
K_2O	3.92	2.56	1.85	− 2.07
H_2O+	.30	6.51	4.71	+ 4.41
Others	.65	1.39	1.01	+ .36
	100.00	100.00	72.36	−27.64

The gains and losses in the last column may be further calculated to percentages of the amounts originally present, if desired. They seem to be very significant, however, in the form given.

CASE 2. *Constant Volume.* — If the change of volume during alteration is known (or known to be zero), the gains or losses per unit volume can be calculated. In metasomatic replacement, there is commonly little or no change of volume,[17] and this kind of alteration is especially important near mineral veins.

Method: When the volume can be assumed to have remained nearly constant, because of pseudomorphs, or structural features, the data required are the analyses of fresh and altered rock and their apparent (or "bulk") specific gravities; or a porosity determination and the true specific gravity of the solid (Problem 10). Calculate the weight in grams of each constituent in 100 c.c. of fresh rock, and then the same in altered rock. Comparison gives

[16] S. S. Goldich: *A Study in Rock-weathering.* Journal of Geology, volume 46, pages 17–58, 1938.

[17] W. Lindgren: *The Nature of Replacement.* Economic Geology, volume 7, pages 521–535, especially page 529, 1912.

the gains or losses per 100 c.c.; which may then be transformed into percentage of the original weight of the constituent.

Example: Field studies at Bingham, Utah, show that a limestone was converted to lime-silicate rock, without change in thickness, and hence probably without change of volume. The data and estimates are from Lindgren.[18]

| | Analyses | | Grams per 100 cc (Bulk Sp. G. ×percent) | | Change in grams |
	13 Black Yampa Limestone	3W Altered White Yampa Limestone	13	3W	3–13
SiO_2	28.90	36.66	75.33	99.72	+24.39
FeS_2	.83	1.87	2.17	5.09	+ 2.92
FeO	1.49	4.20	3.89	11.42	+ 7.53
Al_2O_3	1.23	2.69	3.21	7.32	+ 4.11
CaO	36.21	34.14	94.51	92.86	− 1.65
MgO	.67	2.86	1.75	7.78	+ 6.03
Na_2O	.31	.33	.81	.90	+ .09
K_2O	.35	.28	.91	.76	− .15
CO_2	28.56	17.35	74.54	47.19	−27.35
H_2O+	.86	.52	2.24	1.41	− .83
$H_2O−$	.04	.26	.10	.71	+ .61
C	.55	—	1.44		− 1.44
	100.00	101.16	260.90	275.16	+14.26
Sp. Gr. in bulk	2.61	2.72			

The additions are large quantities of SiO_2, FeO, MgO, and some Al_2O_3 and FeS_2. The chief constituent lost is CO_2.

CASE 3. *No Constant Assumed.* — Ransome in a study of progressive alteration used a "variation diagram" analogous to the diagram of igneous series (Fig. 41), with the curves drawn to the constituents as ordinates and to the distance from the vein as abscissas.[19] This is one of the most instructive forms of diagram. The straight-line diagram (page 129) is also instructive, in case no constant can be assumed.

[18] W. Lindgren: *Contact Metamorphism at Bingham, Utah.* Bulletin of the Geological Society of America, volume 35, pages 507–534, 1924.

[19] F. L. Ransome: *Geology and Ore Deposits of the Breckenridge District, Colorado.* U. S. Geol. Survey, Professional Paper 75, page 97.

CHAPTER XIV

ROCK DESCRIPTIONS

It cannot be expected that any scheme of nomenclature will take the place of all further description of rocks. Certainly there are many complex rocks that have such peculiarities in texture and minerals that the description of visible details proves rather lengthy. As a next step, therefore, after the distinction of the rock species and applying some prefixes indicating varietal characters (as for example in the well-logs, pages 203 to 205) the student should practice recording all the details visible by the eye and pocket lens, and the results of simple tests. A few samples selected from the literature[1] are given with slight modification in the following pages.

For commercial reports most of these might well be shortened, omitting the details that have no evident bearing on the problem, but stressing all that may have some bearing.

Sample Descriptions of Igneous Rocks

1. The *rhyolites* near Helena, Montana, are light-colored porphyries carrying phenocrysts of quartz and sanidine. The quartz phenocrysts average one-tenth of an inch in length, and the sanidine phenocrysts are perhaps twice that size; together they make up between 10 and 20 per cent of the rock. The

[1] Joseph Barrell: *Geology of the Marysville Mining District.* U. S. Geological Survey, Professional Paper No. 57, page 14, 1907.

Adolph Knopf: *Ore Deposits of the Helena Mining Region, Montana.* U. S. Geological Survey, Bulletin 527, pages 22, 26, 29, 40, 1913.

G. F. Loughlin: *The Lithology of Connecticut.* Conn. Geological & Nat. Hist. Survey, Bulletin 13, Part II, pages 162–7, 175–6, and 197–8, 1910.

A. J. Tieje: *Suggestions as to the Description and Naming of Sedimentary Rocks.* Journal of Geology, volume 29, p. 659, 1921.

A. C. Trowbridge: *Tertiary and Quaternary Rocks of the Lower Rio Grande Region, Texas.* U. S. Geological Survey, Bulletin 837, pages 61–2, 75, 76, 126, 1932.

Samuel Weidman: *The Geology of North Central Wisconsin.* Wis. Geological and Nat. Hist. Survey, Bulletin 16, pages 19, 66, and 246, 1907.

groundmass of the rhyolites ranges from material of rough fracture to that of enamel-like appearance.

2. *Stony Creek Granite,* Branford, Connecticut. This granite is a very uneven, coarse-grained, red rock. The constituent minerals visible to the naked eye are red and white feldspar, quartz, a little biotite, magnetite, and pyrite. The red feldspar is the potash variety (orthoclase or microcline), which forms the largest crystals in the rock.

The white feldspar is less abundant than the orthoclase, and forms much smaller crystals. If the white cleavage surfaces are studied with a lens, some of them will show a series of very fine parallel twinning lines or striations indicating plagioclase.

The quartz is typical, forming irregular, transparent, but rather dark and smoky-colored grains. Though a principal constituent of the rock, it is decidedly less abundant than the feldspar.

The biotite occurs in shiny flakes and crystals which may attain considerable size. The crystals usually show no definite outline, and seem to spread out into short streaky areas. Some appear ragged, as if they had been partly eaten away and encroached upon by the feldspar and quartz.

The magnetite is scattered throughout the rock in rather small grains.

The pyrite probably occurs in every specimen, but is not abundant.

The relations of the different minerals to one another may be studied with a lens. It will be seen that the magnetite and pyrite are usually enclosed by one or another of the other minerals; therefore they must have been the first minerals to crystallize from the molten mass, and the other minerals, forming later, crystallized around them. The biotite is usually enclosed in feldspar or quartz; and includes, or is attached to, a grain of magnetite. Biotite must, accordingly, have formed before the feldspar and quartz, but after the magnetite. The white soda feldspar is usually partially or completely enclosed in the red potash feldspar or in quartz; but the two latter minerals are very rarely, if ever, found enclosed in the white feldspar. The white feldspar, then, must, as a whole, have crystallized before the red feldspar and quartz. The red feldspar crystals show fairly definite boundaries, as though they had room to develop approximately a crystal outline; but the quartz grains are mostly very irregular, and appear to fill the chinks between the feldspar crystals. These facts suggest that the quartz must have followed the potash feldspar in crystallizing; but small grains of quartz are also seen enclosed in feldspar, and must have crystallized before it. In general, these two minerals crystallized almost simultaneously; but the greater part of the feldspar crystallized before the quartz, forcing the latter to fill the irregular interspaces.

3. *The Belmont porphyry* dikes of Bald Butte, Montana, hold conspicuous phenocrysts of plagioclase feldspar from one-eighth to one-fourth inch in diameter and small amounts of biotite and hornblende, the whole embedded in a dark-gray microcrystalline groundmass. The rock when fresh is of striking appearance, the white feldspar standing in contrast to the dark gray groundmass. The groundmass weathers to a light brown or gray, the feldspar phenocrysts becoming inconspicuous, and the dark minerals being more or less destroyed.

4. *Pegmatite.* The specimens were collected from a small vein one mile south of West Cornwall station, Conn. They show the feldspar and quartz in large crystals and in various amounts. The feldspar is easily distinguished by its whiteness, semi-opacity, and perfect cleavage. It generally forms well-defined, though not perfect, crystals. The quartz occurs in large irregular glassy masses, and has a gray to smoky color. As it was the last mineral to crystallize, it simply filled the interspaces among the other minerals and has no crystalline shape of its own.

The accessory minerals shown in all the specimens are muscovite and biotite. A few specimens may show tourmaline and garnet, but these minerals are not plentiful and are irregularly distributed. The muscovite occurs in distinct crystals, its shiny cleavage surface forming the base of a rudely six-sided prism. The biotite occurs in the same way, differing from muscovite only in color. The tourmaline forms black columnar crystals, generally showing longitudinal lines or striae on its prismatic faces, and a shining irregular fracture somewhat resembling coal. The garnet forms small red translucent grains which on close inspection are seen to be crystals with many faces.

5. *Nepheline syenite* of north central Wisconsin. The rock is fine to medium-grained and of grayish color. The minerals readily observed in hand specimens are feldspar, nepheline, acmite, and, in some, amphibole and brown mica. The most abundant mineral is the white or grayish feldspar, showing a tabular development, and parallel plates. The nepheline is flesh-colored and vitreous. The acmite is dark green and occurs in small to medium-sized crystals. The weathering and decomposition of the nepheline-bearing rock is a characteristic feature. Wherever this rock has been exposed, it is pitted with numerous depressions, due to the weathering and removal of the nepheline. The pitted character of the weathered rock, its brittle character, and its vitreous grayish flesh-color, allow it to be easily recognized in the field.

6. The *latite* overlying the Boulder batholith, Montana, is characterized by the occurrence of plagioclase and biotite phenocrysts in a cryptocrystalline groundmass of acidic appearance. Blue, red, and flint-gray are common colors. Streakiness and flow banding are nearly universal.

7. *Quartz monzonite.* The prevailing rock of the Boulder batholith, Montana, is a coarse granitoid rock composed in the order named essentially of plagioclase, orthoclase, quartz, biotite, and hornblende. It is remarkably homogeneous in composition over a large area. A widespread feature . . . is a rough porphyritic habit due to the development of large imperfect phenocrysts of orthoclase.

8. The Preston, Connecticut, *gabbro-diorite* is a coarse to medium-grained rock, dark green in color. Its visible components are plagioclase, pyroxene, hornblende, and magnetite. It is somewhat difficult at first glance to distinguish the different minerals, as both the feldspar and the fibrous hornblende are dark colored; but the former may be recognized by its dark purplish, and the latter by its dark green, color. A lens is indispensable for the study of this rock. Close examination shows the purple plagioclase feldspar in rectangular or lath-shaped crystals. The albite twinning is strongly developed in many

crystals and can be seen even without the aid of a lens. When the feldspar undergoes weathering, the color is whitened by kaolinite.

If the specimen be rotated, light will now and then be reflected from a considerable surface, or from several parallel surfaces in one area. These are the cleavage surfaces of large pyroxene crystals, ranging from less than an inch to two inches or more in length. Each one includes a number of small lath-shaped plagioclase crystals. The feldspar, therefore, must have crystallized before the pyroxene. The feldspar crystals are not arranged in any definite order in the pyroxene, but give it a mottled appearance, an ophitic texture.

Magnetite (or ilmenite) and pyrite form rather small grains, but these are larger and far more abundant than in granites.

Sample descriptions of sediments

1. *Micaceous, arenaceous shale,* 2 feet above granite, at Burgess Ranger station, Willow Creek, Wyoming. Granular-fragmental, thin-bedded, green when fresh, sparsely speckled with glistening mica flakes and containing lenses of whitish-green sandstone, one inch long; on weathered surface bluish-black. Hard, fracturing irregularly, fresh surface of dull luster, bedding planes slightly wavy and of sub-vitreous luster.

2. *Sandstone* below the unconformity in the Bigford formation as exposed on Concillos Creek, Texas, next below the crossing of the Bigford-Apache ranch road.

Bedding. — Bedding planes irregular with bumpy relief of 5 millimeters; are not parallel and suggest ripple marks. Fractures into irregularly rectangular blocks.

Mineralogy and Lithology. — Quartz; feldspar abundant, many altered grains; mica not abundant; heavy minerals in abundance; glauconite rare.

Size. — This sandstone is made up chiefly of fine and very fine sand, but includes a considerable percentage of silt and clay.

Shape. — All very angular. Glauconite more angular than is usual in this mineral.

Cement. — Held together by clay. Sharp edges are maintained.

Pore Space. — Uniform and filled with clay.

Color. — Buff with slight greenish cast.

Fossils. — No Foraminifera or other microfossils.

3. *Limestone;* from Bigford formation at old road a quarter of a mile east of northern house on Jones ranch, Texas.

Bedding. — No bedding planes apparent. Discontinuous slightly wavy lamination made evident by black or white lines. Black due to manganese; white to lime. Breaks with conchoidal fracture into thin chips.

Mineralogy and Lithology. — Quartz; feldspar, 8.7 per cent, more altered than fresh; muscovite, zircon, garnet, tourmaline. Soluble in 18.5 per cent HCl, 63.5 per cent. Some clay, but most of fine material is crystalline. Particles are embedded in fine matrix and are evenly spaced. Manganese dendrites are common on surface of specimen. Pyrolusite (MnO_2) is the mineral. It is soluble in HCl, hence is a part of the soluble percentage. Heavy minerals very scarce.

Size. — The mechanical analysis of the residues after solution in acid resulted as shown in Figure 96.

Shape. — Quartz predominantly angular in all grades. The grade 1/8–1/16 millimeter has a few rounded grains (2 per cent by count of 200). This is unusual, as material so fine is seldom rounded. Feldspar very angular; a larger proportion is fresh than in other samples examined. Other minerals scarce and generally in irregular fragments. Material is scattered through matrix, and grains do not touch one another.

Porosity. — Rock is fine-grained and compact.

Cement. — Cement is $CaCO_3$. Very firmly cemented. Was certainly primary.

Color. — Yellow-brown with streaks of black and white. Yellow color due to iron. Burns to a dark brick red. Residuum would doubtless be red.

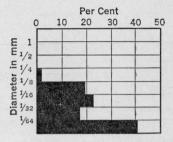

FIG. 96. — Mechanical analysis of solution residue of limestone of Bigford formation, Texas. (After Trowbridge.)

4. *Gypsum.* — Sample of white silky material in Cook Mountain formation on San Antonio road 5½ miles north of Laredo, Texas.

Bedding. — Specimen is powdery and is finely divided for the most part. Some few fragments as aggregated fine material are 8 millimeters in diameter. No bedding is evident.

Mineralogy and Lithology. — Gypsum and anhydrite abundant, quartz, feldspar, mica, clay, iron oxide, and heavy minerals scarce.

Size and Shape. — In detail as follows:

Size (millimeters)	Per cent	
2–1	0.4	Pure gypsum.
1–1/2	2.6	Pure gypsum and aggregates of finer grains.
1/2–1/4	1.8	Pure gypsum and aggregates of fine grains; also rounded quartz grains. This is notable, as rounded grains are rare, and these are extremely large for Cook Mountain. Some of the aggregates are tubular and suggest root tubes.
1/4–1/8	3.2	Chiefly sand, quartz, and feldspar. Aggregates of finer material.
1/8–1/16	8.6	Chiefly sand. Crystals of anhydrite abundant. Rod-shaped crystals both clear and milky.
1/16–1/32	13.4	Fine material, gypsum, anhydrite, quartz, and clay aggregates.
1/32–1/64	10.6	Aggregates and quartz.
Less than 1/64	59.4	

In sieving this sample no attempt was made to break up aggregates, as both gypsum and anhydrite are soft and would be crushed.

Color. — Cream-colored.

Fossils. — None were seen.

This material seems to represent a bed or lens of anhydrite changed to gypsum after original precipitation.

5. *Ferruginous Arkose-conglomerate,* west of Hunt Mountain, Wyoming. Granular-fragmental, pebbles ranging not above ⅜ inch. Prevailing color where fresh, dark brown shot with gray, the pink feldspar sharply contrasting; from the dirty grays and whites of the weathered surface, pebbles stand out in relief. Fucoid markings on bedding planes one inch apart. About 90 per cent of the pebbles quartz, faintly brownish-green, rounded to subangular, breaking with the matrix; feldspars pink, fresh cleavage fragments. Matrix; 90 per cent of the rock, sand, fine-grained, dull to earthy luster.

Sample descriptions of metamorphic rocks

1. *Quartzite* from Carrizo sandstone in bed of Neuces River, Texas, three-quarters of a mile below the Uvalde-La Pryor road crossing.

Bedding. — Specimen indicates that formation is massive. Slight hint of bedding in differential distribution of iron, but this may be due to other causes. Fractures across grains.

Minerology and Lithology. — Quartz angular for the most part; only a few rounded grains. Feldspar abundant (12.7 per cent), mostly orthoclase, fresh to weathered in about equal proportions. Other minerals in too small grains to be distinguishable. Iron oxide plentiful as coating on each grain and as crack filling. Infiltrated silica fills cracks and has to a slight extent recrystallized the quartz grains. A fragment of quartzite was strongly heated for 10 minutes in the blast-lamp flame and was immediately doused in water. The cementing silica turned milky white showing clearly the relation of the infiltrated to the original material. Another sample similarly heated and allowed to cool in air did not turn white on infiltrated material. Cement insoluble in NaOH; hence it could not be opal. Sample slightly calcareous.

Size and Shape. — Grains 15 to 20 per cent rounded. Angular but not as markedly so as the finer samples. Prevailing size ½ to 1.4 millimeter. Some grains, well rounded, with diameter of 2¼ millimeters were seen in hand specimen. Very little fine material.

Packing and Pore Space. — Rock originally had considerable pore space, but pores have been secondarily filled, so that rock is now very compact.

Color. — Brown with lighter spots due to fracture of flakes.

Weathering. — Weathered surface has hard black crust due to increased degree of oxidation of the iron. This, no doubt, makes the formation very resistant.

2. The *Quadrant quartzite* in the Helena, Montana, area ranges in thickness from 190 to 500 feet. The quartzite has a characteristic appearance that distinguishes it readily from the other quartzites of the area. It is a light

gray rock of dense, almost cherty texture, and outcrops show typical rough hackly surfaces.   As a rule the bedding is neither clearly nor positively recognizable.

3. The prevailing character of the *greenstone schists* in Central Wisconsin is uniform, . . . fine-grained, and mainly composed of feldspar, amphibole, mica, and quartz.   The weathered surface is greenish black; the fresh surface is very generally black.   On account of their fissility and the easy penetration of water into them, the greenstone schists are deeply weathered.

4. The *Graywacke-schist* in Central Wisconsin is the mashed and schistose equivalent of the graywacke.   Its most abundant constituents are granular quartz and mica.   It also contains some feldspar.   Facies of the schist along Rib River contain abundant crystals of staurolite, cordierite, and garnet. Commonly the staurolite crystals are over an inch in diameter.   On weathered surfaces of the schist, the staurolite and the cordierite, on account of their greater resistance, stand out above the other minerals having the appearance of angular and rounded fragments in the rock.   The garnet occurs in smaller crystals.   The bedding planes were cut across at various angles by the secondary cleavage of the schists.   The original beds were thus very evidently folded.

5. *Maromas Granite-gneiss,* Benvenue Quarry, Middletown, Connecticut. The rock is a medium-grained, gray granite-gneiss.   The gneissic structure is very well developed, and the rock splits very easily along the foliation planes. The chief minerals are feldspar, quartz, and biotite.

Unless carefully studied, the first two may be confused on account of their similar color and granular condition; but close inspection with a lens will show the feldspar cleavage surfaces, and the elongated, lenticular outline of the feldspar grains affords evidence of considerable compression or mashing.   The quartz also is granulated, and has consequently lost much of its glassy luster; but glassy fragments of originally larger grains are abundant.

The biotite is spread in tiny flakes, or masses of flakes, along the foliation planes and around the feldspar and quartz lenses.   Magnetite and pyrite are the only other minerals.   The magnetite is masked by the biotite, and can be detected only by aid of a lens; the pyrite occurs in small grains, and is readily recognized by its brassy yellow color.

APPENDIX

LIST OF ROCK NAMES NOT IN INDEX

The student who reads widely about rocks may find many terms applied to them which are not defined in this text or named in the index. These terms are used for varieties most of which cannot be distinguished without microscopic or chemical work. Many of the terms apply only to rocks of one locality, and many are needless. Nevertheless if one finds the terms in the literature he may lose the meaning of the context if he cannot find the general nature of the clan or family that the term indicates. The following list indicates very briefly the family to which rocks with such names belong, in terms which are defined in the text and listed in the index.

Absarokite, alkalic basalt
Adamellite, quartz-monzonite
Adinole, albite hornfels
Agpaite, nepheline-syenite
Ailsyte, granite or rhyolite
Akerite, syenite
Alaskite, granite clan
Albanite, alkalic basalt
Albertite, asphalt rock
Albitite, albite diorite
Albitophyre, porphyritic albitite
Alboranite, andesite
Aleutite, porphyritic dolerite
Algovite, gabbro clan
Allalinite, altered gabbro
Allivalite, troctolite
Allochetite, phonolite-porphyry
Alluvium, earth from streams
Alnöite, melilite basalt
Alphitite, rock-flour clay
Alsbachite, granite-porphyry
Ambonite, andesite
Amherstite, monzonite
Ampelite, carbonaceous shale
Amphibololite, igneous amphibolite
Anabohitsite, pyroxenite
Analcimite, alkalic basalt
Anamesite, coarse basalt, or fine dolerite

Anchorite, diorite
Andendiorite, augite quartz-diorite
Andengranite, biotite hornblende granite
Andesinite, diorite
Ankaramite, augitite
Ankaratrite, alkalic basalt
Anthraconite, bituminous limestone
Anthraxolite, bitumen
Apachite, phonolite
Aphrolith, aa
Aplodiorite, light biotite granodiorite
Aplogranite, light micaceous granite
Appinite, dark syenite, monzonite or diorite
Arapahite, basalt
Arenite, fragmental rock of sand size grains
Ariégite, pyroxenite
Arizonite, silexite
Arkite, porphyritic leucite rock
Aschaffite, quartz-diorite
Asperite, basalt
Assyntite, sodalite syenite
Astite, hornfels
Atatschite, trachyte vitrophyre
Ataxite, lava breccia
Auganite, augite-andesite
Augitophyre, basalt-porphyry

Australite, obsidian pebbles
Avezacite, pyroxenite breccia
Aviolite, hornfels

Bahiaite, pyroxenite
Banakite, latite-porphyry
Banatite, quartz-diorite
Bandaite, quartz basalt
Banket, conglomerate
Barolite, barite rock, etc.
Basaltite, olivine-free basalt
Basanite, alkalic basalt
Basanitoid, alkalic basalt
Batukite, alkalic basalt
Beerbachite, lamprophyre or hornfels
Bekinkinite, nepheline rock of the gabbro
  group
Belugite, dolerite
Beresite, aplite
Bergalite, alkalic basalt
Bermudite, alkalic basalt
Berondrite, nepheline diorite
Beschtauite, rhyolite-porphyry
Billitonite, glassy pebbles
Birkremite, granite
Blaes, carbonaceous shale
Blairmorite, analcime trachite
Blaviérite, contact schist
Blue ground, kimberlite
Bojite, gabbro
Bole, laterite
Boninite, andesite
Borolanite, nepheline-syenite
Bostonite, dike rock of syenite aplite, or
  trachyte
Bowenite, serpentine rock
Bowralite, syenite pegmatite
Braccianite, alkalic basalt
Bronzitite, pyroxenite
Brownstone, brown sandstone
Buchite, contact glass
Buchnerite, peridotite
Buchonite, alkalic basalt
Buhrstone, porous cherty rock suitable for
  millstones

Calc-aphanite, carbonated dolerite
Calciphyre, silicate marble
Campanite, alkalic basalt-porphyry
Canadite, nepheline-syenite
Canga, ferruginous-breccia
Cantalite, pitchstone

Carmeloïte, andesite-basalt
Cascadite, biotite lamprophyre
Catawberite, talc-magnetite rock
Catlinite, pipestone, red shale with rare
  clay minerals
Cecilite, alkalic basalt
Charnockite, hypersthene granite
Chibinite, nepheline-syenite
Chlorophyre, quartz-porphyrite
Ciminite, latite-porphyry
Cipolin, muscovite marble
Collobrierite, grünerite-magnetite rock
Comendite, rhyolite
Congressite, nepheline-syenite
Coppaelite, alkalic basalt-porphyry
Cornubianite, hornfels
Corsite, orbicular diorite
Cortlandtite, hornblende peridotite
Corundolite, emery
Covite, nepheline-syenite
Craigmontite, nepheline-syenite
Crinanite, alkalic diabase
Cromaltite, pyroxenite
Cucalite, diabase
Culm, carbonaceous shale
Cumberlandite, magnetite-rich peridotite
Cumbraite, basalt-porphyry
Cuselite, augite porphyrite

Dahamite, rhyolite-porphyry
Davainite, hornblendite
Dellenite, quartz-latite
Dermolith, pahoehoe
Desmosite, banded hornfels
Devonite, altered diabase-porphyry
Diallagite, pyroxenite
Diktyonite, migmatite
Diluvium, glacial deposits
Ditroite, sodalite nepheline-syenite
Dolerine, talc-schist
Domite, trachyte
Dumalite, latite
Dungannonite, alkalic syenite
Durbachite, dark syenite

Edolite, hornfels
Ehrwaldite, augitite
Ekerite, granite
Elaterite, bitumen
Eluvium, residual rocks
Elvan, quartz-porphyry or granite
Epidiabase, altered diabase

Epidiorite, altered diabase
Erlan, augite-schist
Espichellite, lamprophyre
Essexite, nepheline monzonite and related
    rocks
Esterellite, porphyritic quartz-diorite
Eucrite, gabbro
Euktolite, alkalic basalt-porphyry
Eulysite, peridotite
Euphotide, altered gabbro
Eurite, felsite
Evergreenite, granite

Fahlband, metamorphic ore band
Farrisite, alkalic basalt
Fasibitikite, granite
Fasinite, nepheline pyroxenite
Fergusite, leucite pyroxenite
Ferricrete, ferruginous conglomerate
Ferrolite, iron ore rocks
Forellenstein, troctolite
Fortunite, basalt vitrophyre
Fourchite, a lamprophyre
Foyaite, nepheline-syenite
Freestone, sandstone
Fruchtschiefer, spotted schist
Fulgurites, tubes of glassy rocks formed
    from others by lightning strokes

Garéwaite, peridotite-porphyry
Garganite, lamprophyre
Gauteite, latite-porphyry
Ghizite, alkalic basalt
Gibelite, trachyte
Gilsonite, bitumen
Giumarrite, limburgite
Gladkaite, lamprophyre
Gondite, altered manganese sediments
Gossan, limonitic weathered ore
Grahamite, asphalt
Granitelle, granite
Granitite, biotite granite
Granolite, granitoid rock
Granophyre, micrographic granite
Griquaite, eclogite xenoliths
Grorudite, granite-porphyry
Gumbo, clay soil

Hälleflinta, hornfels
Hard-pan, boulder clay
Harrisite, troctolite
Harzburgite, peridotite

Hatherlite, syenite
Hawaiite, basalt
Hedrumite, alkalic syenite
Heptorite, lamprophyre
Heronite, phonolite
Heumite, phonolite
Hirnandite, albitized basalt
Holyokeite, albitized diabase
Hornstone, chert
Hudsonite, peridotite
Hyalomelane, basalt-obsidian
Hyperite, gabbro
Hypersthenite, pyroxenite
Hysterobase, diabase

Ijolite, alkalic pyroxenite
Ijussite, alkalic pyroxenite
Ilmenitite, ore
Imandrite, contact rock
Impsonite, asphalt
Infusorial earth, error for diatomite
Inninmorite, basalt
Invernite, granite-porphyry
Isenite, nepheline latite
Issite, feldspathic hornblendite
Italite, granitoid leucite rock

Jacupirangite, alkalic pyroxenite
Jadeitite, metamorphic alkalic pyroxene
    rock
Jet, black lignite
Josefite, peridotite
Jumillite, leucite phonolite

Kaiwekite, trachyte-porphyry
Kakirite, intensely granulated rock
Kakortokite, nepheline-syenite
Karite, granite-porphyry
Kassaite, alkalic basalt
Katzenbuckelite, phonolite-porphyry
Kauaiite, diorite
Kedabekite, gabbro
Kentallenite, dark monzonite
Kenyte, alkalic trachyte
Keralite, hornfels
Keratophyre, sodic latite, or quartz latite
Kersantite, lamprophyre
Khagiarite, rhyolite
Kinzigite, coarse hornfels
Kodurite, spessartite syenite
Koellite, alkalic basalt
Kohalaite, andesite
Koswite, peridotite

Krablite, rhyolite tuff
Krageröite, rutile aplite
Kulaite, alkalic basalt
Kullaite, microcline-bearing diabase
Kuskite, quartz-monzonite-porphyry
Kvellite, syenite lamprophyre
Kylite, nepheline gabbro
Kyschtymite, gabbro

Laanilite, garnet pegmatite
Labradite, anorthosite
Lakarpite, sodic syenite
Lassenite, glassy trachyte
Lateritite, redeposited laterite
Laugenite, diorite
Laurdalite, nepheline-syenite
Laurvikite, alkalic syenite
Lavialite, altered basalt-porphyry
Ledmorite, nepheline-syenite
Leeuwfonteinite, alkalic syenite
Leidleite, basalt vitrophyre
Leopardite, quartz-porphyry
Leptite, schists from rhyolite, etc.
Lestiwarite, syenite aplite
Leucitite, alkalic basalt
Leucitophyre, leucite-rich phonolite porphyry
Lherzite, hornblendite
Lherzolite, peridotite
Limurite, axinite contact rock
Lindöite, trachyte dike rock
Listwänite, dolomite contact rock
Litchfieldite, albite nepheline-syenite
Lithoidite, felsitic rhyolite
Luciite, diorite
Lugarite, nepheline pyroxenite-porphyry
Lujaurite, nepheline-syenite
Lundyite, alkalic trachyte-porphyry
Luscladite, nepheline olivine-gabbro
Lusitanite, alkalic syenite
Lutite, sediment of very fine grain
Luxullianite, tourmalinized granite
Lydite = Lydian stone, silicified black shale

Macedonite, alkalic basalt
Madeirite, limburgite-porphyry
Madupite, leucite augitite
Maenaite, latite
Mafraite, alkalic diorite
Malchite, dike rock of quartz-diorite aplite
Malignite, dark nepheline-syenite

Manganolite, manganese oxide rocks
Mangerite, monzonite
Manjak, bitumen
Marekanite, perlite
Mareugite, hauynite diorite
Mariupolite, nepheline-syenite
Markfieldite, granophyre diorite
Marloesite, andesite-porphyry
Marosite, alkalic shonkinite
Marscoite, granite-gabbro hybrid
Masanite, quartz-monzonite-porphyry
Masanophyre, quartz-monzonite-porphyry
Melilitite, alkalic? basalt
Metabasite, metamorphosed dolerite
Metabolite, altered trachyte glass
Metaxite, sandstone
Miaskite, nepheline-syenite
Micropegmatite, micrographic granite
Microtinite, monzonite
Miharaite, basalt-porphyry
Mijakite, andesite or basalt-porphyry
Mililolite, limestone
Mimesite = mimosite, dolerite
Mimophyre, hornfels with coarse feldspar
Minverite, albitized diabase
Missourite, leucite pyroxenite
Moldauite = moldavite, glass pebbles
Monchiquite, alkalic lamprophyre
Mondhaldeite, andesite or alkalic basalt
Monmouthite, nepheline-syenite
Montrealite, nepheline diorite
Mugearite, latite
Muniongite, phonolite
Murasakite, piedmontite schist
Muscovadite = muscovado, hornfels

Napoleonite, diorite
Naujaite, nepheline-syenite
Navite, dolerite porphyry
Nelsonite, ilmenite-apatite rock
Nephelinite, alkalic basalt
Nevadite, granite-porphyry
Newlandite, eclogite
Nonesite, basalt-porphyry
Nordmarkite, syenite
Northfieldite, silexite
Noseanite, alkalic basalt

Obsidianites, glass pebbles
Ocher, earth rich in ferric oxides
Odinite, basalt-porphyry
Oligoclasite, diorite
Oligosite, diorite anorthosite

Olivinite, peridotite
Ollenite, amphibole-schist
Onkilonite, alkalic basalt
Ooze, soft fine deep-sea deposit
Opdalite, diorite
Ophiolite, serpentine rock
Orbite, gabbro or diorite-porphyry
Ordanchite, alkalic basalt
Orendite, leucite trachyte or syenite
Ornöite, diorite
Orthoclasite, trachyte
Orthofelsite = orthophyre, trachyte-porphyry
Orthogneiss, gneiss from igneous original
Orthophyre, trachyte porphyry
Orthosite, syenite
Ortlerite, porphyrite
Ossipite, troctolite
Ostraite, pyroxenite
Ottajanite, alkalic basalt
Ouachitite, lamprophyre
Ouénite, gabbro
Oxyphyre, leucophyre
Ozocerite, natural wax

Pacificite, basalt
Paisanite, rhyolite-porphyry
Palaeophyre, quartz-diorite-porphyry
Palagonite, basalt glass
Palatinite, dolerite
Pantellerite, alkalic latite or quartz latite
Paragneiss, gneiss from sediment
Pelagite, manganese nodule
Pele's Hair and Tears, basalt glass fragments
Pelite, fine sediments
Pencatite, brucite marble
Peperino, leucite tuff
Perknite, group of pyroxenites and hornblendites
Petrosilex, felsite
Phthanite, silicified shale, etc.
Picrite, peridotite (porphyry?)
Pienaarite, nepheline-syenite
Pilandite, syenite-porphyry
Pinolite, carbonate slate or phyllite
Piperno, trachyte
Plagiaplite, diorite aplite
Plagioclasite, anorthosite
Plagiophyre, andesite-porphyry
Plauenite, syenite
Plumasite, corundum diorite
Pollenite, alkalic trachyte

Polzenite, melilite basalt
Ponzite, trachyte
Porcellanite, fused shale
Porphyroid, porphyroblastic hornfels, or schist
Prasinite, green schist
Predazzite, periclase marble
Proteolite, hornfels
Proterobase, altered dolerite
Protogine, gneiss
Protomylonite, mylonite at intrusive contact
Prowersite, lamprophyre
Psammite, sandstone
Psephite, conglomerate or breccia
Pseudotachlyte, intrusive crush rock
Puddingstone, conglomerate
Puglianite, gabbro
Pulaskite, nepheline-syenite
Pyromeride, spherulitic rhyolite
Pyroxenolite, pyroxenite

Queluzite, garnet rock

Raglanite, nepheline-syenite
Rapakiwi, granite with orthoclase phenocrysts mantled with oligoclase
Regolith, weathered mantle
Rhomben-porphyry, syenite-porphyry
Rhyobasalt, quartz-latite
Rizzonite, limburgite
Rockallite, sodic granite
Rock-flour, silt sized sediment
Rodingite, garnet pyroxenite
Rougemontite, gabbro
Routivarite, quartz-monzonite
Rouvillite, nepheline gabbro
Rubble, coarse detritus
Rudite, coarse sediments

Saernaite, alkalic syenite-porphyry
Sagvandite, pyroxene-carbonate rock
Sanidinite, trachyte or syenite
Santorinite, quartz gabbro
Sanukite, andesite
Sarnaite, alkalic syenite
Saxonite, peridotite
Schalstein, sheared basalt
Schoenfelsite, basalt-porphyry
Schriesheimite, peridotite
Scyelite, peridotite
Sebastianite, gabbro
Seebenite, hornfels

Selagite, trachyte
Shackanite, analcime syenite-porphyry
Shastaite, dacite
Shastalite, andesite glass
Shonkinite, dark syenite
Shoshonite, olivine trachydolerite
Sideromelane, basalt glass
Silcrete, conglomerate with silica cement
Sinaite, syenite
Sismondinite, sismondine schist
Skarn, silicate contact gangue
Skleropelite, argillite
Skomerite, andesite
Sodalitite, sodalite-rich syenite
Soggendalite, diabase
Sölvsbergite, syenite
Sommaite, alkalic monzonite
Sondalite, hornfels
Sordawalite, basalt glass selvage
Sparagmite, sandstones
Sperone, alkalic basalt
Spessartite, lamprophyre
Spilite, albitized basalt
Spilosite, spotted contact slate
Stronalite, gneiss
Stubachite, peridotite
Sudburite, basalt
Suldenite, andesite
Sussexite, alkalic basalt-porphyry
Sviatonossite, syenite
Syenodiorite, monzonite
Syenogabbro, orthoclase gabbro

Tactite, silicate contact rocks from limestone, as gangue of ores
Tahitite, hauyne latite-porphyry
Taimyrite, trachyte
Tamaräite, lamprophyre
Taraspite, dolomite limestone
Taspinite, granite
Taurite, rhyolite
Tavolatite, alkalic basalt-porphyry
Tawite, sodalite-rich syenite
Taxite, apparently clastic lava
Tectonite, recrystallized mylonite
Tektites, glass pebbles
Tephrite, alkalic basalt
Teschenite, alkalic dolerite
Theralite, dark nepheline gabbro
Tholeiite, olivine-free basalt
Tilaite, olivine-gabbro
Timazite, andesite
Tinguaite, phonolite

Tjosite, lamprophyre
Toadstone, basalt
Toellite, porphyrite
Toensbergite, syenite
Tonalite, quartz-diorite
Topsailite, lamprophyre
Torbanite, oil shale
Tordrillite, rhyolite-porphyry
Toscanite, quartz-latite
Trachyandesite, latite
Trachydolerite, trachyte-basalt
Trap, any dark fine, igneous rocks
Trass, pumice tuff
Trondjemite, quartz-diorite
Trowlesworthite, altered granite
Tsingtauite, granite-porphyry
Tusculite, alkalic basalt

Uintaite, bitumen
Ulrichite, phonolite-porphyry
Ultra-mylonite, flinty crush rock
Umptekite, alkalic syenite
Unakite, granite
Uncampahgrite, melilite-rich pyroxenite
Ungaite, dacite
Urbainite, titaniferous iron segregation
Urtite, light, granitoid, nepheline acmite rock

Valbellite, peridotite
Vallevarite, monzonite
Variolite, spherulitic basalt glass
Värnsingite, sodic syenite pegmatite
Vaugnérite, quartz-monzonite
Venanzite, alkalic basalt-porphyry
Verite, lamprophyre
Vesbite, alkalic basalt
Vesuvite, alkalic basalt
Vicoite, alkalic basalt
Vintlite, quartz-porphyrite
Viterbite, leucite trachyte-porphyry
Vitrophyre, porphyry with glassy groundmass
Vogesite, lamprophyre
Volcanite, dacite
Volhynite, lamprophyre
Vulsinite, latite

Websterite, pyroxenite
Wehrlite, peridotite
Weiselbergite, basalt
Wennebergite, trachyte (porphyry)

Whinstone, dolerite
Wichtisite, basalt glass
Wilsonite, rhyolite-andesite tuff
Windsorite, quartz-monzonite
Woodendite, basalt
Wurtzilite, bitumen
Wyomingite, phlogopite-leucite porphyry

Yamaskite, pyroxenite
Yatalite, pyroxenite pegmatite
Yentnite, scapolite diorite
Yogoite, syenite

Zobtenite, gabbro gneiss
Zwitter, greisen

INDEX

Aa, 91
Accessory minerals, 18
Acidic, 13, 46
Adobe, 156
Age of rocks in classification, 22
Agglomerate, 34
Alkalic rocks, 49
Allen, V. T., 166
Alling, A. L., 12
Allogenic minerals, 143
Alluvial rocks, 156
Alteration gains and losses, 272–274
   of rocks, 125–133, 208
Amphiboles reviewed, 15, 16
Amphibole-magnetite rock, 239
Amphibolite, 241
Amygdaloid, 50, 90
   conglomerate, 92, 93
Amygdaloidal structure, 37
Analyses, see Chemical Composition
   proximate, of coal, 181
Anamorphism, 213
Andesite, distinction from basalt, 47, 48, 94
Andesite-diorite clan, 46, 78–83
Anemoclastic, 152
Anhydrite rock, 183
Anogene, 28
Anorthosite, 84, 87
Anthracite, 180
Aphanite defined, 31
Aplite, 29, 32–33, 52
Apobsidian, 102
Apophyses, 28
Aqueous rocks, 22
Arenaceous, 151
Argillaceous, 151
Argillite, 156
Arkose, 165
Arkosite, 238
Aschistic rocks, 29
Ash, volcanic, 111
Asphalt, 182

Assimilation by magma, 37
Association of minerals, igneous, 19
   sedimentary, 190
Athy, L. F., 192
Augen gneiss, 60, 87, 162, 235
Augitite, 46, 91, 97
Authigenic minerals, 143
Autoclastic breccias, 159
Autometamorphism, 38

Bailey, J. P., 150
Balk, Robert, 5, 6
Barrell, J., 190, 215, 272, 275
Basalt, 46
   distinction from andesite, 47, 48, 94
Basalt-gabbro clan, 46, 84–100
Basic, 13, 46
   segregation, 40, 46
Bastin, E. S., 183
Batholith, 27, 28
Bauxite, 132, 157
Becker, G. F., 241
Bedded rocks, 23
Bedding, 137
Belt of weathering, 226
Bentonite, 155
Berkey, Charles P., III, IV, V
Billings, M. H., 199
Binary granite, 52
Bioclastic, 152
Biogenic, 152
Bituminous clay, 154
   coal, 179
Black band iron ore, 174, 177, 188
Black sand, 165
Blackwelder, Eliot, 128
Blasto-porphyritic schist, 228, 229
Bog ores of iron, 177
Bombs, 111
Bone coal, 181
Bosses, 26
Boulders, 152
Bowen, N. L., 38, 55

291